£1·50

O

Colin
Campbell
5 Burn R.D
Inverness
Scotland

PENGUIN BOOKS

# The Book of COMPARISONS

The Diagram Group is a London-based team of researchers, writers, editors, designers and artists. Over the past seven years, their books have been translated into seventeen languages and have sold over five million copies in twenty countries. Their previous books include *Rules of the Game, Man's Body, Woman's Body, Musical Instruments of the World,* and for children, *Earth* and *Junior Book of the Road.*

D1347870

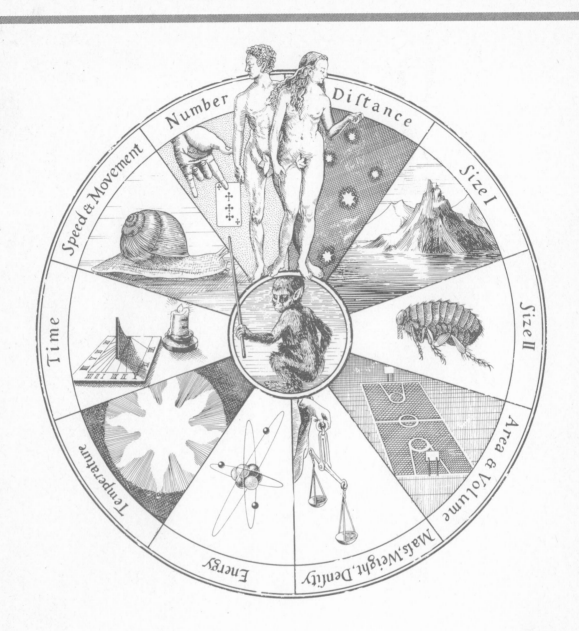

# The Book of COMPARISONS

of distance, size, area, volume, mass, weight, density, energy, temperature, time, speed and number throughout the universe

## by the Diagram Group

PENGUIN BOOKS
in association with
SIDGWICK & JACKSON

Penguin Books Ltd, Harmondsworth, Middlesex, England
Penguin Books, 625 Madison Avenue, New York, New York 10022, U.S.A.
Penguin Books Australia Ltd, Ringwood, Victoria, Australia
Penguin Books Canada Ltd, 2801 John Street, Markham, Ontario, Canada L3R 1B4
Penguin Books (N.Z.) Ltd, 182-190 Wairau Road, Auckland 10, New Zealand

First published in hardback by Sidgwick & Jackson and Penguin Books 1980
This paperback edition published by Penguin Books and Sidgwick & Jackson 1981

Copyright © Diagram Visual Information Limited, 1980
All rights reserved

Made and printed in Great Britain by
Morrison and Gibb Ltd, London and Edinburgh

Except in the United States of America, this book is sold subject
to the condition that it shall not, by way of trade or otherwise, be lent,
re-sold, hired out, or otherwise circulated without the
publisher's prior consent in any form of binding or cover other than
that in which it is published and without a similar condition
including this condition being imposed on the subsequent purchaser

# FOREWORD

**"Comparisons"** is an exciting visual guide to how man measures—and measures up to—his universe. By making comparisons between like and like and between like and unlike we can evaluate the different properties of the known world.

Man has devised many units and scales of measurement, and **"Comparisons"** brings these together in one handy reference volume, pointing out differences from system to system and providing methods of conversion.

Most readers are familiar with the excellent "Guinness Book of Records," which has for many years recorded the extremes of the human and physical worlds. **"Comparisons"** displays and relates not only extremes, but also presents what we encounter in everyday experience.

To make this wealth of information easier to understand and remember, the artists and editors have created hundreds of illustrations and diagrams, all accompanied by concise, explanatory captions. This technique makes it possible to see at a glance and to appreciate fully comparisons that are not readily grasped from photographs or prose alone.

The originality of **"Comparisons"** will, we hope, both fascinate and inform, and also stimulate every reader to make further comparisons of his own.

**The Diagram Group**

| | |
|---|---|
| **Managing editor** | Ruth Midgley |
| **Research editors** | Hope Cohen; Norma Jack |
| **Contributors** | Jeff Cann; Cornelius Cardew; Michael Carter; Maureen Cartwright; Marion Casey; Sam Elder; David Lambert; Gail Lawther; Linda Proud; Bernard Moore; Angela Royston; Marita Westberg |
| **Art editor** | Richard Hummerstone |
| **Artists** | Steven Clark; Mark Evans; Brian Hewson; Susan Kinsey; Janos Marffy; Graham Rosewarne, Kathleen McDougall |
| **Art assistants** | Steve Clifton; Richard Colville; Neil Connell; Steve Hollingshead; Richard Prideaux; Ray Stevens |
| **Picture researcher** | Enid Moore |
| **Indexer** | Mary Ling |

**Acknowledgments**
The authors and publishers wish to extend their warmest thanks to the many individuals, institutions and companies who have responded with great patience and generosity to numerous research enquiries. Special thanks are due to the following:

Amateur Athletic Association; American Embassy, London; Australia House, London; Robert Barry; Damaris Batchelor; British Airways; British Museum; British Olympic Association; British Petroleum Co. Ltd; British Rail; Cottie G. Burland; Cunard Steamship Co. Ltd; Department of Energy, UK; Ford Motor Co. Ltd; Greater London Council; Guinness Superlatives Ltd; Christopher Hand; Hovercraft Developments Ltd; Institute of Geological Sciences, London; International Glaciological Society; Intourist; Library of the Zoological Society of London; Lloyds Register of Shipping; London Transport; Military Archive and Research Services; Museum of Mankind, London; National Maritime Museum, London; National Motor Museum, Beaulieu, Hants; Natural History Museum, London; Railway Magazine; Royal Geographical Society, London; Royal Greenwich Observatory; School of Oriental and African Studies, London; Science Museum, London; Martin Suggett; United Nations London Information Centre; Claudio Vita-Finzi

**Dedication**
This book is dedicated to: Tom McCormack, who thought of the idea; Len and Elkie Shatzkin, who introduced Tom to the Diagram Group; Ruth Midgley, who had to work harder than she had ever done before; and Patricia Robertson, who brought up four children single-handed while Bruce Robertson was too busy to come home

# CONTENTS

# CHAPTER 1

Confirming the length of the rood, an old linear measure, by lining up and measuring the feet of the first 16 men out of church—from Jacob Köbel's *Geometrey von künstlichen Feldtmessen* of 1598 (Science Museum, London).

# DISTANCE

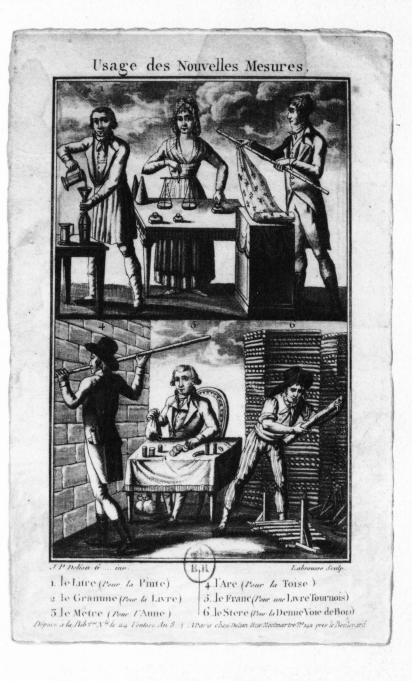

A contemporary French
print illustrating the use of
the new metric measures
introduced in the wake of
the French Revolution of
1789 (Photo: Bulloz).

# MEASURING DISTANCE

The width of a finger, the length of a foot, the distance covered in a stride, and the length of a furrow ploughed by a horse are ingenious linear measurements from earlier times. Today, demands for greater precision and standardization are resulting in a much wider acceptance of the scientifically based metric system.

| US customary/imperial units of linear measurement | | |
|---|---|---|
| 12 inches (in) | = | 1 foot (ft) |
| 3 feet | = | 1 yard (yd) |
| 1760 yards | = | 1 mile (mi) |
| **Metric units of linear measurement** | | |
| 10 millimeters (mm) | = | 1 centimeter (cm) |
| 100 centimeters | = | 1 meter (m) |
| 1000 meters | = | 1 kilometer (km) |

**The body rules** *below*
Illustrated are two ancient measuring systems based on the human body.
**Egyptian measurements**
**A** Digit, one finger width
**B** Palm (= four digits)
**C** Hand (= five digits)
**D** Cubit, elbow to finger tips (= 28 digits, 20.6in)

**Roman measurements**
**E** Foot, length of one foot (subdivided into 12 *unciae*, hence our inches)
**F** Pace (= 5 feet), of which 1000 made up the Roman mile (*mille passus*)

**Basic units** *above*
Included here are the most commonly used units of linear measurement, both US/imperial and metric. Given in brackets are the standard abbreviations used in this book. (For additional tables, see pp. 14, 16, 18.)

**Ready measures** *below*
These common objects can be used as convenient measures for US/imperial and metric distances. They are shown here real size together with a US/imperial and metric scale.
**a** Key 2in
**b** Cent ¾in
**c** Paper clip 1¼in
**d** Shirt button 1cm
**e** Paper match 4cm

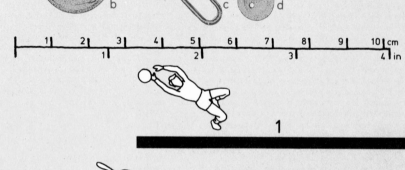

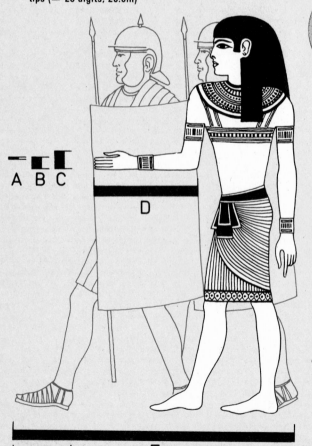

It's a good thing that some of our great poets of former days used the league as a unit of measurement. Imagine Tennyson's famous poem beginning "A mile and a half, a mile and a half, a mile and a half onwards," instead of "Half a league, half a league . . ."

The ell was once widely used for measuring cloth, but lengths varied: the French ell was 54in, the English 45in and the Flemish only 27in.

12 douzièmes = 1 line
4 lines = 1 barleycorn
3 barleycorns = 1 inch

5½ yards = 1 rod
4 rods = 1 chain
10 chains = 1 furlong
8 furlongs = 1 mile
3 miles = 1 league

**Unusual US/imperial units** *left* Originating in a largely agricultural society, most of the imperial units of length given in this table have now virtually died out.

**Conversion tables** *below* These tables can be used to convert US/imperial distances (inches, feet, yards and miles) into metric (centimeters, meters and kilometers), and vice versa. For example, to convert 5in into centimeters, find 5 in the center column of the first table and then read the figure opposite it in the right-hand column (12.700cm). To find the inch equivalent of 5cm, find 5 in the center column and then read the corresponding left-hand column figure (1.9685in).

| in | | cm | ft | | m | yd | | m | mi | | km |
|---|---|---|---|---|---|---|---|---|---|---|---|
| 0.3937 | 1 | 2.5400 | 3.2808 | 1 | 0.3048 | 1.0936 | 1 | 0.9144 | 0.6214 | 1 | 1.6093 |
| 0.7874 | 2 | 5.0800 | 6.5617 | 2 | 0.6096 | 2.1872 | 2 | 1.8288 | 1.2427 | 2 | 3.2187 |
| 1.1811 | 3 | 7.6200 | 9.8425 | 3 | 0.9144 | 3.2808 | 3 | 2.7432 | 1.8641 | 3 | 4.8280 |
| 1.5748 | 4 | 10.160 | 13.123 | 4 | 1.2192 | 4.3744 | 4 | 3.6576 | 2.4855 | 4 | 6.4374 |
| 1.9685 | 5 | 12.700 | 16.404 | 5 | 1.5240 | 5.4680 | 5 | 4.5720 | 3.1069 | 5 | 8.0467 |
| 2.3622 | 6 | 15.240 | 19.685 | 6 | 1.8288 | 6.5617 | 6 | 5.4864 | 3.7282 | 6 | 9.6560 |
| 2.7559 | 7 | 17.780 | 22.966 | 7 | 2.1336 | 7.6553 | 7 | 6.4008 | 4.3496 | 7 | 11.265 |
| 3.1496 | 8 | 20.320 | 26.247 | 8 | 2.4384 | 8.7489 | 8 | 7.3152 | 4.9710 | 8 | 12.875 |
| 3.5433 | 9 | 22.860 | 29.528 | 9 | 2.7432 | 9.8425 | 9 | 8.2296 | 5.5923 | 9 | 14.484 |
| 5.9055 | 15 | 38.100 | 49.213 | 15 | 4.5720 | 16.404 | 15 | 13.716 | 9.3206 | 15 | 24.140 |
| 9.8425 | 25 | 63.500 | 82.021 | 25 | 7.6200 | 27.340 | 25 | 22.860 | 15.534 | 25 | 40.233 |
| 13.779 | 35 | 88.900 | 114.83 | 35 | 10.668 | 38.276 | 35 | 32.004 | 21.748 | 35 | 56.327 |
| 17.716 | 45 | 114.30 | 147.64 | 45 | 13.716 | 49.212 | 45 | 41.148 | 27.962 | 45 | 72.420 |
| 21.654 | 55 | 139.70 | 180.45 | 55 | 16.764 | 60.149 | 55 | 50.292 | 34.175 | 55 | 88.514 |
| 25.591 | 65 | 165.10 | 213.25 | 65 | 19.812 | 71.085 | 65 | 59.436 | 40.389 | 65 | 104.61 |
| 29.528 | 75 | 190.50 | 246.06 | 75 | 22.860 | 82.021 | 75 | 68.580 | 46.603 | 75 | 120.70 |
| 33.465 | 85 | 215.90 | 278.87 | 85 | 25.908 | 92.957 | 85 | 77.724 | 52.817 | 85 | 136.79 |
| 37.402 | 95 | 241.30 | 311.68 | 95 | 28.956 | 103.89 | 95 | 86.868 | 59.030 | 95 | 152.89 |

**Critical distances** *left, below* Some examples from the world of sport:
**1** Soccer penalty spot to goal mouth center, 12yd
**2** Bowling lane, 60ft long
**3** Pitcher to batter at baseball, 60ft 6in
**4** Cricket pitch, distance between wickets, 22yd

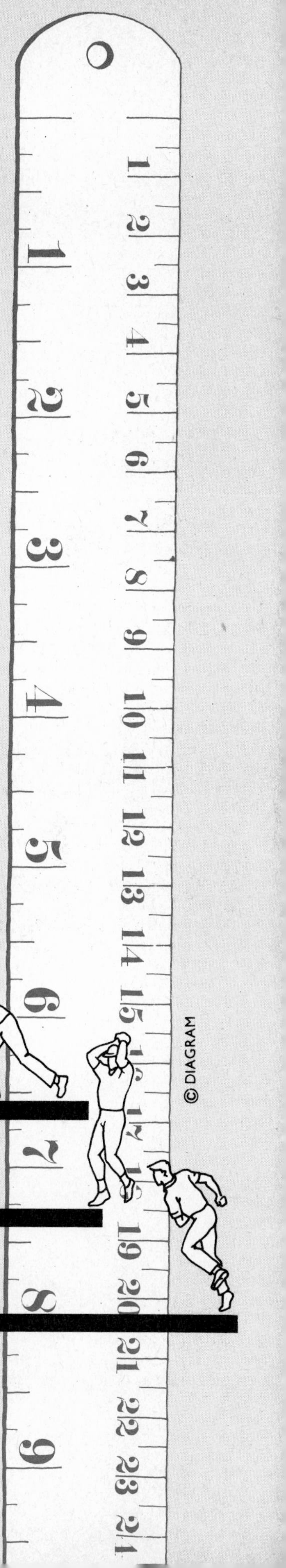

© DIAGRAM

"Full fathom five thy father lies," sings Ariel in Shakespeare's *Tempest*. He meant that Ferdinand's father had been drowned and was lying at a depth of 30ft; a fathom is a mainly nautical unit equal to 6ft.

**Common rule** *right* Shown real size is part of a rule with both US/imperial and metric divisions.

# THE MICROSCOPIC WORLD

Our vision of the world is literally restricted, for with our eyes alone we can see only objects that are above a certain size. We can, for instance, see the dot above an "i" but without a microscope a single grain of most types of pollen is invisible. Here we look at measurements in the microscopic world.

**Explanation of scales**
*below* Starting with a real-size illustration of a section of a rule marked with both inches and centimeters, we have drawn a series of scales, each of which represents a 10-fold magnification of a tenth of the previous one.

Measurements here—and on other pages where we have similar scales—are expressed in metric units, since the decimal character of the metric system makes it ideal when using factors of 10. On each scale we state the distance that 1cm represents.

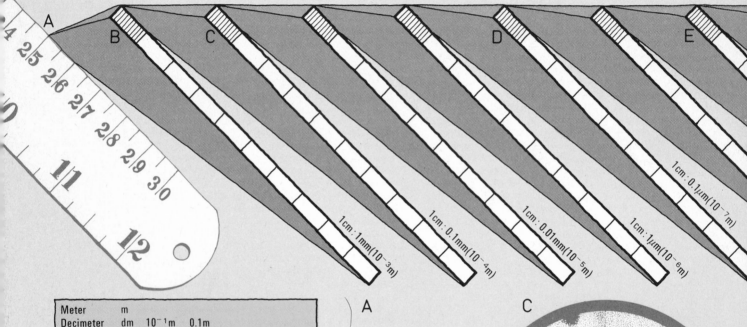

A

B 1cm : 1mm($10^{-3}$m)

C 1cm : 0.1mm($10^{-4}$m)

1cm : 0.01mm($10^{-5}$m)

D 1cm : 1$\mu$m($10^{-6}$m)

1cm : 0.1$\mu$m($10^{-7}$m)

E

| Meter | m | | |
|---|---|---|---|
| Decimeter | dm | $10^{-1}$m | 0.1m |
| Centimeter | cm | $10^{-2}$m | 0.01m |
| Millimeter | mm | $10^{-3}$m | 0.001m |
| Micrometer | $\mu$m | $10^{-6}$m | 0.000 001m |
| Nanometer | nm | $10^{-9}$m | 0.000 000 001m |
| Picometer | pm | $10^{-12}$m | 0.000 000 000 001m |
| Femtometer | fm | $10^{-15}$m | 0.000 000 000 000 001m |
| Attometer | am | $10^{-18}$m | 0.000 000 000 000 000 001m |

**Small metric units**
*above* The table lists metric units for measuring small and microscopic distances. We start with the meter, the base unit of the International System of Units (SI), defined as 1,650,763.73 wavelengths in vacuum of the orange-red line of the spectrum of krypton-86. This is followed by the names of smaller units, together with their abbreviations, and meter equivalents expressed first as powers of 10 and then as decimals.

A

1cm
$10^{-2}$m

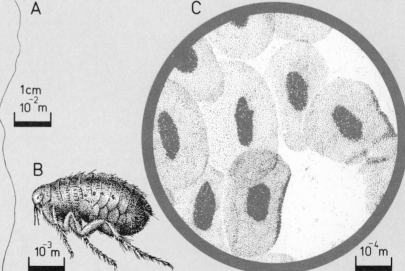

B
$10^{-3}$m

C

$10^{-4}$m

An attometer, the smallest unit of linear measurement, is to a shirt button what a shirt button is to a planetary system with a diameter 8.6 times that of the solar system.

If each page in a 1000 page book were only 1 micrometer (micron) thick, then all the pages together would measure only 1 millimeter, half the thickness of the gray line below.

If magnified according to a scale where 1 centimeter represents 1 picometer ($10^{-12}$ cm), a small raindrop (diameter 1.4 millimeters) would be as large as the Sun (diameter approximately 1,400,000 kilometers).

# Distance

**Small made large**
*bottom* Each illustration has been drawn to a different one of our scales, shown by a letter. In this way we are able to see how the application of progressively larger scales brings smaller and smaller objects into view.

**A** The first illustration in our sequence is of a human hair, real size.
**B** Next we have a flea, which has been drawn to scale B, i.e. magnified 10 times. Each centimeter of our flea is equivalent to one millimeter in real life.

**C** The red blood cells of a frog are drawn to scale C, appearing in our illustration as they would when seen under a microscope magnifying them 100 times. Each centimeter of the enlarged image is equivalent to one tenth of a millimeter in real life.

**D** Next we have a selection of viruses drawn to scale D. They appear in our illustration as they would under an electron microscope magnifying them 100,000 times. Each centimeter represents one tenth of a micrometer.

**E** Here we see iron atoms (large dots) and sulfur atoms (small dots) as they appear in a crystal of marcasite (iron sulphide) that has been magnified 10 million times (scale E). Each centimeter is equivalent to one nanometer.

**F** At the right edge of the page we show part of a sodium atom that has been drawn to scale F. This represents a magnification of 1000 million. On this scale, one centimeter of our drawing is equivalent to one hundreth of a nanometer.

F     G

1cm : 0.01μm ($10^{-8}$m)

1cm : 1nm ($10^{-9}$m)

1cm : 0.1nm ($10^{-10}$m)

1cm : 0.01nm ($10^{-11}$m)

1cm : 1pm ($10^{-12}$m)

1cm : 0.1pm ($10^{-13}$m)

D    E    F

$10^{-7}$ m

$10^{-9}$ m

$10^{-11}$ m

*If we were to draw our solar system to a scale where one femtometer of our illustration represented one centimeter in reality, it would be possible to fit more than 400 such illustrations on a single page of this book.*

**G** The dot in the box represents the nucleus of a hydrogen atom drawn to scale G, i.e. magnified 100,000 million times. One centimeter in the box is equivalent to one tenth of a picometer.

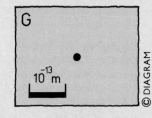

G

$10^{-13}$ m

© DIAGRAM

# OUR WORLD AND BEYOND 1

On the preceding two pages we used progressively larger scales to look down into the microscopic world. Here and on the next two pages we use progressively smaller scales to allow us to visualize distances in the world and out into space. In doing so, detail is lost, but bigger and bigger distances are brought into view.

**Explanation of scales**
*below* As on the previous two pages, we start with part of a centimeter/inch rule and then follow this with a series of scales. But here our scales become smaller, each new scale reducing the preceding scale to one tenth.

**Large made small**
*bottom* Our sequence of drawings shows how by using progressively smaller scales we encompass bigger and bigger distances.
**A** We start with a picture of a junction in New York, drawn to scale A where 1cm is equivalent to 10m.

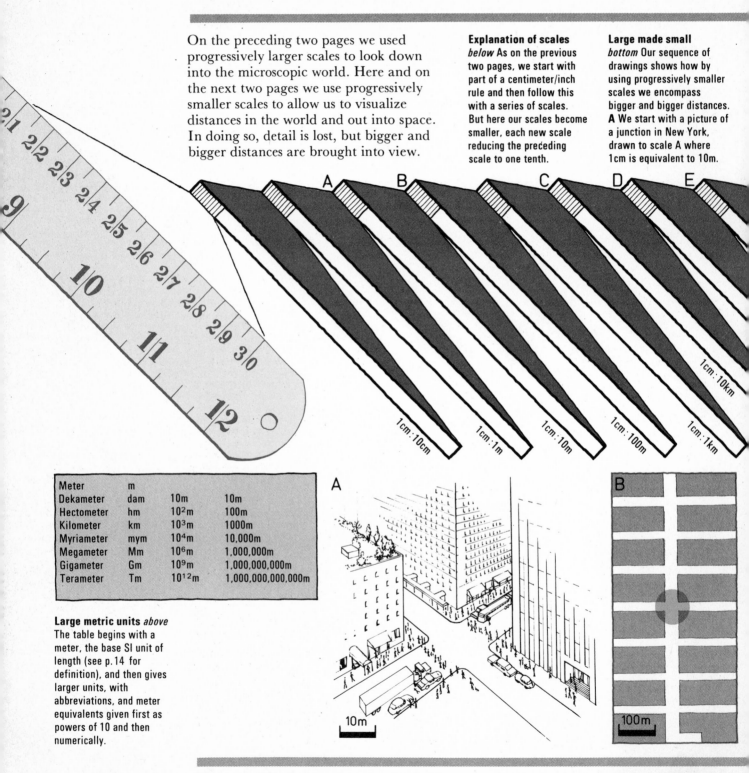

A · B · C · D · E

1cm:10cm · 1cm:1m · 1cm:10m · 1cm:100m · 1cm:1km · 1cm:10km

| Meter | m | | |
|---|---|---|---|
| Dekameter | dam | 10m | 10m |
| Hectometer | hm | $10^2$m | 100m |
| Kilometer | km | $10^3$m | 1000m |
| Myriameter | mym | $10^4$m | 10,000m |
| Megameter | Mm | $10^6$m | 1,000,000m |
| Gigameter | Gm | $10^9$m | 1,000,000,000m |
| Terameter | Tm | $10^{12}$m | 1,000,000,000,000m |

**Large metric units** *above*
The table begins with a meter, the base SI unit of length (see p.14 for definition), and then gives larger units, with abbreviations, and meter equivalents given first as powers of 10 and then numerically.

A

10m

B

100m

*The world's longest river, the Nile, would be the length of an average shoelace (66.7cm) if drawn to our scale D (1cm:100km).*

If drawn to a scale where 1cm is equivalent to 10m (our scale A) this book would be no bigger than the dot on this i.

If drawn to our scale D, where 1cm represents 100km, an average raindrop (diameter 2mm) would have the dimensions of a smallish atom (diameter 0.000 000 2mm).

**B** Our New York junction is here drawn to scale B, where 1cm is equivalent to 100m in reality. We now see the junction in the context of the streets around it, as though looking at it from above, or locating it on a city street plan.

**C** This map is drawn to scale C, where 1cm is equivalent to 10km. We can no longer see the junction or the pattern of the city streets. Instead we have a detailed view of the geographical location of New York City and its neighbors.

**D** Long Island appears as a prominent feature on this map where 1cm represents 100km (scale D). The area shown on map C is on this map indicated by a box. Around it we see parts of New York State, Philadelphia, Massachusetts and Connecticut.

**E** Our drawing of part of a globe has been made to scale E, where 1cm is equivalent to 1000km. We can no longer identify Long Island, but can now see the whole of the East coast of North America, Central America and much of South America as well.

**F** When drawn to scale F, where 1cm is equivalent to 100,000km, Earth and Moon appear as tiny dots. Our scale diagram does, however, allow us to visualize the distance between them—3.8cm as drawn, or approximately 380,000km in reality.

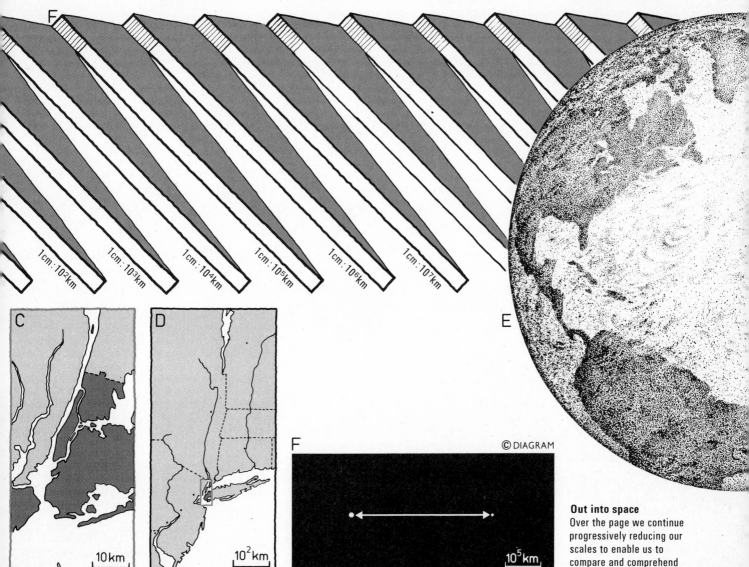

1cm:10²km  1cm:10³km  1cm:10⁴km  1cm:10⁵km  1cm:10⁶km  1cm:10⁷km

10km  10²km  10⁵km

© DIAGRAM

**Out into space**
Over the page we continue progressively reducing our scales to enable us to compare and comprehend the vast distances of space.

Distances at sea are measured in nautical miles. The international nautical mile is equal to 1852m (6076ft); the UK nautical mile, based on the original definition, is equal to the mean length of one minute of longitude (6080ft or 1.152 statute miles).

# OUR WORLD AND BEYOND 2

### Out into space
Here we continue the series of scales begun on the previous two pages. As before, each scale reduces the preceding scale to one tenth. Colored bars are used to show the change over to light years as our unit of measurement.

**G** This diagram of part of the solar system is drawn to scale G, with 1cm equivalent to $10^8$km. Shown are the orbits of the inner planets, the distance between Sun and Earth(**1**), the asteroid belt (**2**), the orbit of Jupiter (**3**) and of Halley's comet (**4**).

**H** Scale H is 100 times smaller than scale G; 1cm now represents $10^{10}$km. On this scale the solar system appears quite insignificant. Shown are the orbits of the outer planets around the Sun (with Pluto a mean 5900 million km away), and the orbit of Halley's comet.

**I** On scale I, 1cm represents $10^{12}$km. The long scale bar on our diagram shows 1 ly drawn to this scale. Also shown is the distance between the Sun and its nearest stellar neighbor, Proxima Centauri, some 40,207,125 million km or 4.25 ly away.

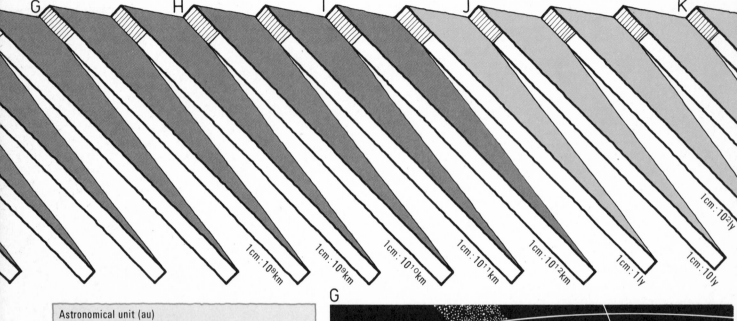

G · 1cm : $10^8$km  H · 1cm : $10^9$km · 1cm : $10^{10}$km · 1cm : $10^{11}$km  J · 1cm : $10^{12}$km · 1cm : 1 ly  K · 1cm : 10 ly · 1cm : $10^2$ ly

Astronomical unit (au)
1 au = 149,600,000km = 93,000,000mi
Light year (ly)
1 ly = 9,460,500,000,000km = 5,878,000,000,000mi
Parsec (pc)
1 pc = 30,857,200,000,000km = 19,174,000,000,000mi
63,240au = 1 ly
206,265au = 1 pc
3.262 ly = 1 pc

### Units for space *above*
The table lists standard abbreviations and equivalents of units used in the measurement of astronomical distances. These units are further defined as follows.
An astronomical unit is the mean distance between the Earth and the Sun.
A light year is the distance traveled in one year by electro-magnetic waves in vacuo.
A parsec is the distance at which a base line of 1 astronomical unit in length subtends an angle of 1 second.

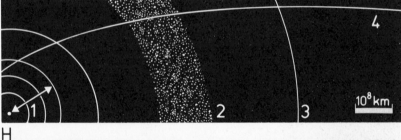

G

H

Using light years as a unit may save us from writing a long string of zeros but it is not always easy to appreciate the great distances involved. For example, the radio galaxy 3C–295 is over 26,000,000,000,000,000,000,000 miles away!

**J** When drawn to scale J where 1cm represents 10 ly, the Sun and Proxima Centauri, here indicated by arrows, appear very close together, as indeed they are in galactic terms.

**K** Here the central part of our galaxy is drawn to scale K, where 1cm is equivalent to $10^4$ly. The diameter of the entire galaxy is about 100,000ly, or 10cm on this scale.

**L** Our galaxy, indicated by an arrow, is shown with other galaxies in our local group in this illustration to scale L, where 1cm is equivalent to $10^6$ly.

**M** This illustration of M104 (popularly called the Sombrero galaxy, in the Virgo cluster of galaxies) has not been drawn to scale, but the distance between M104 and Earth, some 41 million ly, occurs within scale M, where 1cm is equivalent to $10^7$ly.

**N** Indicated on the illustration by an arrow is the radio galaxy 3C-295, one of the most distant galaxies ever photographed. Its distance from Earth, some 5000 million ly, occurs within scale N, where 1cm is equivalent to $10^9$ly.

**Toward infinity**
Our scales continue off the page toward infinity. As yet, however, the greatest distance claimed for an object detected in space is 15,600 million ly, which could be measured on the scale where 1cm represents $10^{10}$ly.

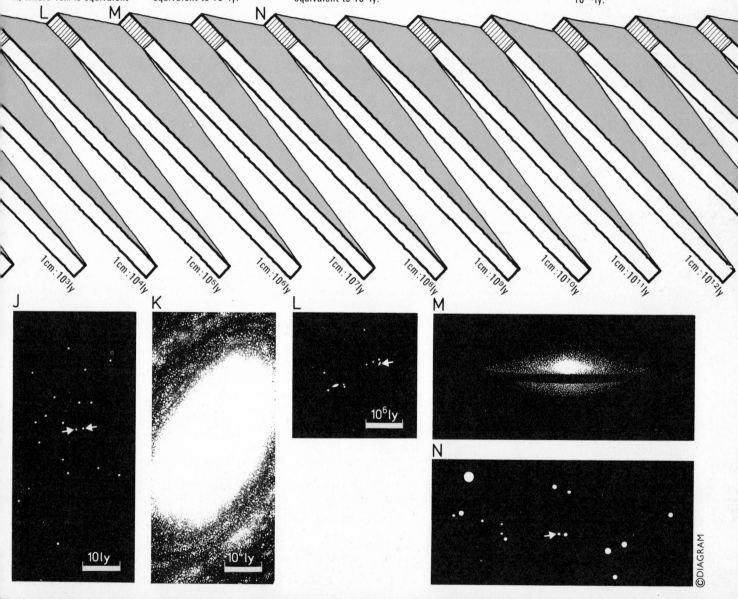

1cm:$10^3$ly  1cm:$10^4$ly  1cm:$10^5$ly  1cm:$10^6$ly  1cm:$10^7$ly  1cm:$10^8$ly  1cm:$10^9$ly  1cm:$10^{10}$ly  1cm:$10^{11}$ly  1cm:$10^{12}$ly

J — 10ly

K — $10^4$ly

L — $10^6$ly

M

N

©DIAGRAM

1ly

# DISTANCES RUN AND WALKED

Distance presents man with a variety of sporting challenges. Here we compare the distances run and walked in Olympic events, where the object is to cover a prescribed distance as fast as possible. Also compared are distance endurance records, where the aim is to travel as far as possible in a particular manner.

**Around the world** *right* Some of man's more unusual distance endurance records are here shown to scale as if they had been achieved along the Equator, 40,075km (24,900mi) long.

**1** Walking on hands, 1400km (871mi), equal to one twenty–ninth of the length of the Equator.
**2** Swimming, 2938km (1826mi), one fourteenth of the length of the Equator.
**3** Running, 8,224km (5,110mi), equal to one fifth of the Equator.
**4** Backward walking, 12,875km (8000mi), one third of the Equator.
**5** Walking, 48,000km (29,825mi), equal to one and a fifth times the length of the Equator.
**6** Cycling, 160,934km (100,000mi) in one tour, just over four times the length of the Equator.

**Olympic distances** *right* Listed are running/walking distances, given in meters in keeping with International Olympic Committee practice, plus approximate US/imperial distance equivalents, and whether there is an event for men, women or both.

**a** 100m (110yd) men/women
**b** 100m (110yd) hurdles women
**c** 110m (120yd) hurdles men
**d** 200m (220yd) men/women
**e** 400m (440yd) men/women
**f** 400m (440yd) hurdles men
**g** 4 x 100m (110yd) relay men/women
**h** 800m (880yd) men/women
**i** 1500m (1640yd) men/women
**j** 4 x 400m (440yd) relay men/women
**k** 3000m (3280yd) steeplechase men
**l** 5000m (3.1mi) men
**m** 10,000m (6.2mi) men
**n** 20km (12.4mi) walk men
**o** 42.195km (26mi 385yd) marathon men
**p** 50km (31mi) walk men

**Running for a train** *right* The diagram shows the Olympic sprint and hurdle race distances to scale with a passenger train whose cars are a typical 30m (100ft) long. The longest sprint race, the 400m, is slightly longer than 13 such cars.

**Racing through New York** *right* Middle and long distance Olympic running and walking events are here shown to scale with a map of Manhattan Island, New York. The 10,000m would take you from Battery Park (**A**) at the southern tip of the island as far as the middle of Central Park (**B**). The longest Olympic road walk, the 50km (31mi) walk is approximately equal to walking from Battery Park (**A**) to Inwood Hill Park (**C**) and back again.

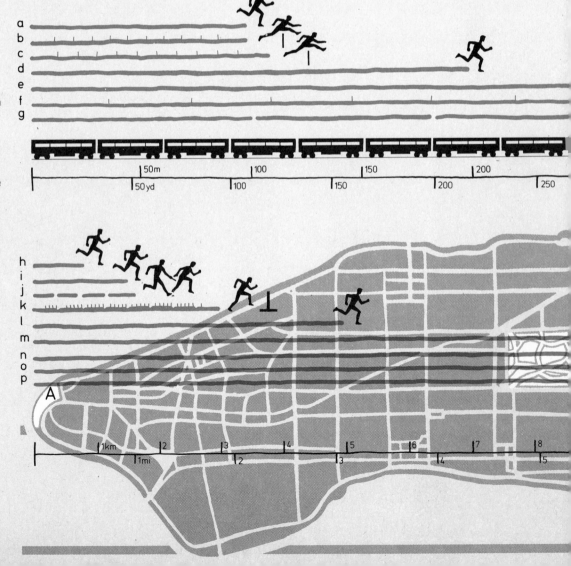

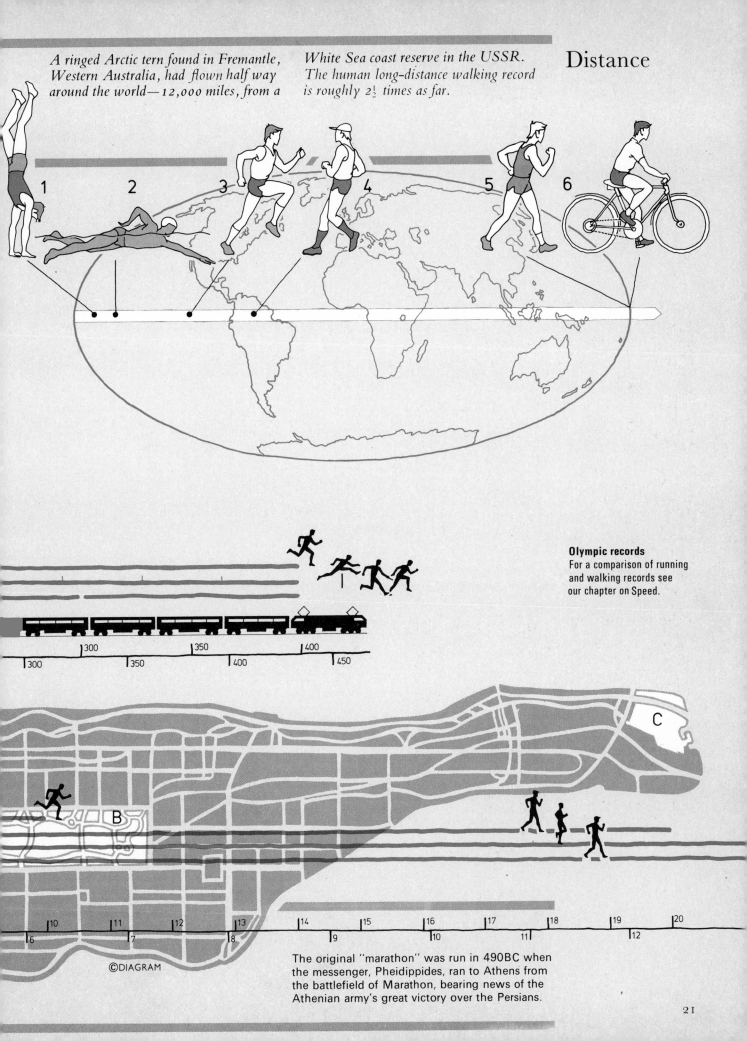

# Distance

A ringed Arctic tern found in Fremantle, Western Australia, had flown half way around the world—12,000 miles, from a White Sea coast reserve in the USSR. The human long-distance walking record is roughly 2½ times as far.

**Olympic records**
For a comparison of running and walking records see our chapter on Speed.

©DIAGRAM

The original "marathon" was run in 490BC when the messenger, Pheidippides, ran to Athens from the battlefield of Marathon, bearing news of the Athenian army's great victory over the Persians.

21

# DISTANCES JUMPED

The competitive urge in man compels him to extend himself and to push his body to the limit. Here we compare the achievements of man with woman, and of humans with animals in performing different types of jump. We give world records as in 1979 and compare the results of Olympic jumping events since the revival of the Games in 1896.

**How far can we jump?** *below* Human long jump performances are here compared with those of three animals known for their jumping ability— the flea, the frog and the kangaroo. An average man is about 9in taller than a red kangaroo, but the world long jump record is less than three-fourths of the distance that the kangaroo can cover with ease. Relative to its size, the performance of the flea is even more impressive: to equal its achievement man would have to leap about 400yd!

A

B

15  16  17  18  19
5
1948

**Jumping Jacks** *right*
**1** Amateur standing long jump record, 11ft 11¾in, clearing two average men lying head to foot.
**2** World long jump record, clearing 5 men.
**3** World triple jump record, 58ft 8½in, clearing 10 men with ease.

1

2

3

**High divers** *left*
Professional divers at Acapulco, Mexico dive into water from rocks 118ft high, equal to a dive from the roof of an 11-story building!

*The world long jump record for men is equal to the length of two Ford Mustangs or two Jaguar E-types parked fender to fender.*

To better the world pole vault record it will be necessary to exceed the height of three average men and a 5-year-old boy standing one on top of another's shoulders.

©DIAGRAM

**Long jump results**
**A** Flea 13in
**B** Frog 17ft 6¾in
**C** Women's world record, Vilma Bardauskiene (USSR) 23ft 3¼in
**D** Men's world record, Robert Beamon (USA) 29ft 2½in
**E** Red kangaroo 40+ft

C          D          E

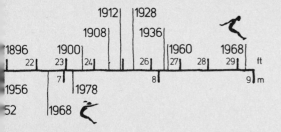

**How high can we jump?**
*above* Shown are the heights reached by the women's and men's world high jump records, the world pole vault record (men), and the official high jump record for horses. Kangaroos have cleared an unofficial 10½ft.

**Heights cleared**
**1** Women's world high jump record, Sara Simeoni (Italy) 6ft 7in
**2** Men's world high jump record, Vladimir Yashchenko (USSR) 7ft 8in
**3** Horse, official FEI high jump record 8ft 1¾in
**4** World pole vault record. David Roberts (USA) 18ft 8¼in

**Farther and farther**
*above* The diagram allows us to compare record long jump performances from 1896 to the present. Dates when records were set are shown here on a distance scale. In 1896 E. Clark (USA) jumped 20ft 10in— a distance equaled by the women's Olympic record in 1956 (E. Krzesinska, Poland). In 1968, R. Beamon (USA) increased the men's Olympic record by an amazing 2ft 7in. This is, however, 1¾in less than the amount by which the 1896 record was bettered in 1900.

**Higher and higher**
*left* This diagram allows us to compare current world high jump records with the heights attained when the high jump became a modern Olympic event for men and for women. Also in scale are a man and woman of average height.

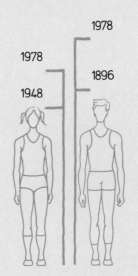

If the holder of the men's world high jump record had made his jump on Mercury where gravity is weaker, he would have cleared 20ft 8in, exceeding the world pole vault record by almost 2ft.

23

# HEIGHTS AND DEPTHS REACHED

Man has achieved truly amazing feats of vertical mobility. He has climbed to the top of Earth's highest mountain, even without the use of breathing equipment; in a spacecraft he has orbited the Moon. Without breathing equipment he has dived down 282ft; in a bathyscaphe he has been to the bottom of the deepest ocean trench.

## Reaching the heights

Plotted here against a logarithmic scale and listed in the table *right* are details of altitude records achieved since the first successful balloon trials in 1783. Within the first year the record was boosted from only 80ft to an incredible 9000ft. In 1923 the general altitude record was for the first time taken by an aircraft. From 1933 until 1951 this record was again held by balloons, but since then first a rocket and rocket planes and then spacecraft have been highest of all.

### Heights achieved by man

| | | |
|---|---|---:|
| 1 | Hot air balloon, tethered (1783) | 80ft |
| 2 | Hot air balloon, tethered (1783) | 324ft |
| 3 | Hot air balloon (1783) | 3000ft |
| 4 | Hydrogen balloon (1783) | 9000ft |
| 5 | Hydrogen balloon (1803) | 20,000ft |
| 6 | Coal gas balloon (1837) | 25,000ft |
| 7 | Coal gas balloon (1875) | 27,950ft |
| 8 | Aircraft (1923) | 36,565ft |
| 9 | Aircraft (1930) | 43,166ft |
| 10 | Hydrogen balloon (1933) | 61,237ft |
| 11 | Helium balloon (1935) | 72,395ft |
| 12 | Skyrocket (1951) | 79,600ft |
| 13 | Rocket plane (1954) | 93,000ft |
| 14 | Rocket plane (1956) | 23.9mi |
| 15 | Rocket plane (1961) | 203.2mi |
| 16 | Spacecraft (1966) | 850.7mi |
| 17 | Spacecraft (1968) | 234,473mi |
| 18 | Spacecraft (1970) | 248,655mi |

## Life at high altitudes

Also included on our graph *below* are the height of Mount Everest, and the highest recorded altitudes for various forms of life.

**a** Mount Everest 29,002ft
**b** Alpine chough, highest recorded bird, 26,900ft
**c** Non-flowering plant 20,833ft
**d** Flowering plant 20,130ft
**e** Yak 20,000ft
**f** Highest inhabited human dwelling 19,700ft
**g** Bacteria 135,000ft

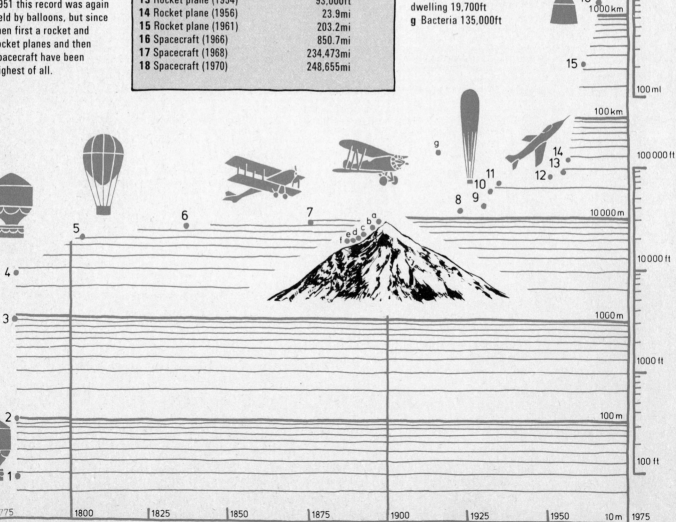

## Depths achieved by man

*Women's record
**Died in the attempt
***Simulated dive
†First scuba record

### A) Breath-held dives
1 Georghios (1913) c200ft
2 Mayol (1966) 198ft
3 Croft (1967) 212ft 6in
4 Treleani (1967) 147ft 6in*
5 Croft (1967) 217ft 6in
6 Mayol (1968) 231ft
7 Croft (1968) 240ft
8 Maiorca (1971) 250ft
9 Mayol (1973) 282ft

### B) Dives using air
1 Lambert (1885) 162ft
2 Greek and Swedish divers (1904) 190ft
3 Damant (1906) 210ft
4 Drellifsak (1914) 274ft
5 Crilley/Nielson/Loughman (1915) 304ft
6 Hilton (1932) 344ft
7 Dumas (1947) 307ft†
8 Farques (1947) 396ft**
9 Root (1947) 400ft**
10 Clarke-Samazen (1954) 350ft
11 Troutt (1964) 320ft*
12 Watts/Johnson (1966) 355ft
13 Watts/Munns (1967) 380ft
14 Giesler (1967) 325ft*
15 Gruener/Watson (1968) 437ft

### C) Dives using gas mixtures
1 Nohl (1937) 420ft
2 Metzger/Conger (1941) 440ft
3 Zetterstrom (1945) 528ft**
4 Bollard/Soper (1948) 450ft
5 Johnson (1949) 550ft
6 Wookey (1956) 600ft
7 Keller/Macleish (1961) 728ft
8 Keller/**Small (1962) 1000ft
9 USN Aquanauts (1968) 1025ft***
10 Deckman (1968) 1100ft***
11 Brauer/Veyrunes (1968) 1197ft***
12 Bevan/Sharphouse (1970) 1500ft***
13 Chemin/Gauret (1972) 2001ft***

### D) Dives in machines
1 Steel sphere (1865) c245ft
2 Diving bell (1889) c830ft
3 Hydrostat (1911) c1650ft
4 Bathysphere (1930) 1426ft
5 Bathysphere (1932) 2200ft
6 Bathysphere (1934) 2510ft
7 Bathysphere (1934) 3028ft
8 Benthoscope (1949) 4500ft
9 Bathyscaphe (1953) 5085ft
10 Bathyscaphe (1953) 6890ft
11 Bathyscaphe (1953) 10,335ft
12 Bathyscaphe (1954) 13,287ft
13 Bathyscaphe (1959) 18,600ft
14 Bathyscaphe (1960) 24,000ft
15 Bathyscaphe (1960) 35,802ft

### A) Breath-held dives
Dives of around 120ft have long been made by divers collecting oysters and sponges. Georghios' 1913 record for a dive without breathing equipment lasted until the challenges of Mayol and Croft in the late 1960s.

### B) Dives using air
The development of scuba (self-contained underwater breathing apparatus) has led to the establishment of impressive new underwater diving records. The record scuba dive using air is 437ft—over 150ft deeper than the breath-held record.

### C) Dives using gas mixtures
Breathing gas mixtures allows divers to go even deeper than when air is breathed. In 1962 divers established a record of 1000ft after release from a diving bell; since then simulated dives have doubled the record.

### D) Dives in machines
Man's deepest dives have been made in a variety of machines developed for the purpose. The latest of these, the bathyscaphe, has taken the record dive in a machine down from 4500ft to 35,802ft, on the seabed in the Marianas Trench.

### Deep-sea life *right*
Also listed and shown here are the greatest depths at which various animals have been recorded. Divers at 35,802ft saw what may have been a fish.

### Deep-sea life
a Seal 1968ft
b Sperm whale 3720ft
c Sponge 18,500ft
d *Bassogigas profundissimus* 23,230ft
e Amphipod 32,119ft

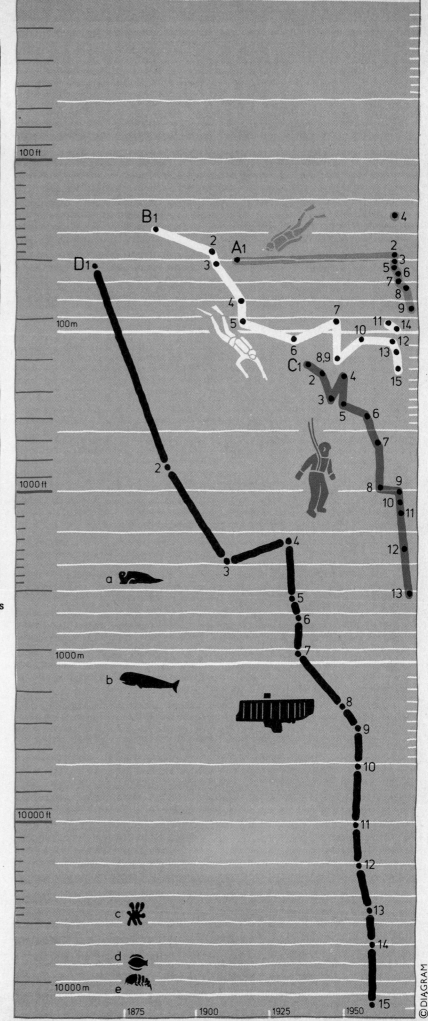

©DIAGRAM

# DISTANCES FROM PLACE TO PLACE

The shortest theoretical surface route between two places on Earth can never exceed 12,451 miles, that is one half of Earth's circumference. Among major cities, Wellington/Paris (11,791 miles), Wellington/London (11,682 miles), and Rio de Janeiro/Tokyo (11,535 miles) most nearly approach this maximum.

**Shortest distances** *below*
The table gives the shortest distances between selected cities around the world. These "great circle" distances (see explanation *right*) are given here in miles (colored band) and kilometers.

| | Berlin, Germany | Bombay, India | Cape Town, South Africa | Darwin, Australia | London, England | Los Angeles, USA | Mexico City, Mexico | Moscow, USSR | New York, USA | Paris, France | Peking, China | Port Said, Egypt | Quebec, Canada |
|---|---|---|---|---|---|---|---|---|---|---|---|---|---|
| Berlin, Germany | | 3910 / 6292 | 5977 / 9619 | 8036 / 12,932 | 574 / 924 | 5782 / 9305 | 6037 / 9715 | 996 / 1603 | 3961 / 6374 | 542 / 872 | 4567 / 7350 | 1747 / 2811 | 358 / 576 |
| Bombay, India | 3910 / 6292 | | 5134 / 8262 | 4503 / 7247 | 4462 / 7181 | 8701 / 14,003 | 9722 / 15,646 | 3131 / 5039 | 7794 / 12,543 | 4359 / 7015 | 2964 / 4770 | 2659 / 4279 | 737 / 11,86 |
| Cape Town, South Africa | 5977 / 9619 | 5134 / 8262 | | 6947 / 11,180 | 6005 / 9664 | 9969 / 16,043 | 8511 / 13,697 | 6294 / 10,129 | 7801 / 12,554 | 5841 / 9400 | 8045 / 12,947 | 4590 / 7387 | 785 / 12,64 |
| Darwin, Australia | 8036 / 12,932 | 4503 / 7247 | 6947 / 11,180 | | 8598 / 13,837 | 7835 / 12,609 | 9081 / 14,614 | 7046 / 11,339 | 9959 / 16,027 | 8575 / 13,800 | 3728 / 5999 | 7159 / 11,521 | 972 / 15,64 |
| London, England | 574 / 924 | 4462 / 7181 | 6005 / 9664 | 8598 / 13,837 | | 5439 / 8753 | 5541 / 8917 | 1549 / 2493 | 3459 / 5567 | 213 / 343 | 5054 / 8133 | 2154 / 3466 | 310 / 499 |
| Los Angeles, USA | 5782 / 9305 | 8701 / 14,003 | 9969 / 16,043 | 7835 / 12,609 | 5439 / 8753 | | 1542 / 2482 | 6068 / 9765 | 2451 / 3944 | 5601 / 9014 | 6250 / 10,058 | 7528 / 12,115 | 257 / 415 |
| Mexico City, Mexico | 6037 / 9715 | 9722 / 15,646 | 8511 / 13,697 | 9081 / 14,614 | 5541 / 8917 | 1542 / 2482 | | 6688 / 10,763 | 2085 / 3355 | 5706 / 9183 | 7733 / 12,445 | 7671 / 12,345 | 24 / 39 |
| Moscow, USSR | 996 / 1603 | 3131 / 5039 | 6294 / 10,129 | 7046 / 11,339 | 1549 / 2493 | 6068 / 9765 | 6688 / 10,763 | | 4662 / 7503 | 1541 / 2480 | 3597 / 5789 | 1710 / 2752 | 42 / 68 |
| New York, USA | 3961 / 6374 | 7794 / 12,543 | 7801 / 12,554 | 9959 / 16,027 | 3459 / 5567 | 2451 / 3944 | 2085 / 3355 | 4662 / 7503 | | 3622 / 5829 | 6823 / 10,980 | 5590 / 8996 | 43 / 7 |
| Paris, France | 542 / 872 | 4359 / 7015 | 5841 / 9400 | 8575 / 13,800 | 213 / 343 | 5601 / 9014 | 5706 / 9183 | 1541 / 2480 | 3622 / 5829 | | 5101 / 8209 | 1975 / 3178 | 32 / 52 |
| Peking, China | 4567 / 7350 | 2964 / 4770 | 8045 / 12,947 | 3728 / 5999 | 5054 / 8133 | 6250 / 10,058 | 7733 / 12,445 | 3597 / 5789 | 6823 / 10,980 | 5101 / 8209 | | 4584 / 7377 | 64 / 10,3 |
| Port Said, Egypt | 1747 / 2811 | 2659 / 4279 | 4590 / 7387 | 7159 / 11,521 | 2154 / 3466 | 7528 / 12,115 | 7671 / 12,345 | 1710 / 2752 | 5590 / 8996 | 1975 / 3178 | 4584 / 7377 | | 52 / 84 |
| Quebec, Canada | 3583 / 5766 | 7371 / 11,862 | 7857 / 12,644 | 9724 / 15,649 | 3101 / 4990 | 2579 / 4150 | 2454 / 3949 | 4242 / 6827 | 439 / 706 | 3235 / 5206 | 6423 / 10,337 | 5250 / 8449 | |
| Rio de Janeiro, Brazil | 6144 / 9888 | 8257 / 13,288 | 3769 / 6065 | 9960 / 16,029 | 5772 / 9289 | 6296 / 10,132 | 4770 / 7676 | 7179 / 11,553 | 4820 / 7757 | 5703 / 9178 | 10,768 / 17,329 | 6244 / 10,048 | 51 / 82 |
| Rome, Italy | 734 / 1181 | 3843 / 6185 | 5249 / 8447 | 8190 / 13,180 | 887 / 1427 | 6326 / 10,180 | 6353 / 10,224 | 1474 / 2372 | 4273 / 6877 | 682 / 1098 | 5047 / 8122 | 1317 / 2119 | 39 / 63 |
| Tokyo, Japan | 5538 / 8912 | 4188 / 6740 | 9071 / 14,598 | 3367 / 5419 | 5938 / 9556 | 5470 / 8803 | 7035 / 11,321 | 4650 / 7483 | 6735 / 10,839 | 6033 / 9709 | 1307 / 2103 | 5842 / 9402 | 64 / 10,3 |
| Wellington, New Zealand | 11,265 / 18,129 | 7677 / 12,355 | 7019 / 11,296 | 3310 / 5327 | 11,682 / 18,800 | 6714 / 10,805 | 6899 / 11,103 | 10,279 / 16,542 | 8946 / 14,397 | 11,791 / 18,975 | 6698 / 10,779 | 10,249 / 16,494 | 92 / 14,8 |

**Long and winding roads**
*right* Great circle distances are of only limited use when planning a journey by car. Natural features and cities make routes far from direct.

| | | 1 Great circle distance | 2 Extra distance by road | % extra |
|---|---|---|---|---|
| a | Berlin/Paris | 542mi (872km) | 124mi (200km) | 23% |
| b | Berlin/Rome | 734mi (1181km) | 224mi (360km) | 31% |
| c | London/Rome | 887mi (1427km) | 292mi (470km) | 33% |
| d | London/Moscow | 1549mi (2493km) | 294mi (473km) | 19% |
| e | Los Angeles/Mexico City | 1542mi (2482km) | 475mi (764km) | 31% |
| f | Los Angeles/New York | 2451mi (3944km) | 464mi (747km) | 19% |

a
b
c
d
e
f

The world's longest continuous frontier, between the USA and Canada, is 3987 miles long—more than 500 miles longer than the great circle distance between New York and London.

The world's shortest frontier, between Spain and Gibraltar, is only 1672 yards long—less than half the width, at 42nd Street, of Manhattan Island, New York.

**A great circle** *right*
Any two points on the Earth's surface can be connected by a great circle line, which traces the shortest surface route between them. Great circle lines are formed by slicing a globe in half through its center.

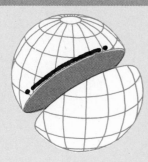

**Getting it straight** *right*
The use of a map "projection" allows us to transfer the curved surface of the Earth onto a flat map. This process inevitably causes some distortion, different projections distorting different features while keeping others reasonably accurate. Included here for comparison are maps drawn to three different projections. Marked on each of them is the great circle line between New York and Moscow; although this line represents the shortest actual distance between these cities, it appears as an arc not as a straight line even on map C, where the distortion of this area of the globe is fairly slight. Our maps are details from the following projections:
**A** Mercator
**B** Polyconic
**C** Polar azimuthal equidistant

A
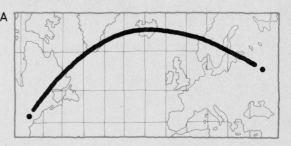

B
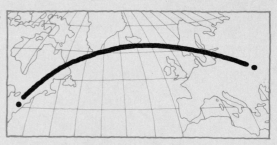

C

**Antipodal points** *left*
A city's "antipodal point" is the place on Earth most distant from it. On a globe this can be found by projecting a line through the center and out the other side. In practice, however, "antipodes" are found by calculation.

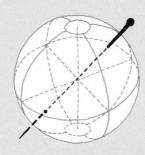

**A world apart** *below*
Shown on this Mercator map are six cities and their antipodal points.
**1** Los Angeles
**2** New York
**3** Rio de Janeiro
**4** London
**5** Moscow
**6** Tokyo

| Rio de Janeiro, Brazil | Rome, Italy | Tokyo, Japan | Wellington, New Zealand | |
|---|---|---|---|---|
| 6144 | 734 | 5538 | 11,265 | Berlin, Germany |
| 9888 | 1181 | 8912 | 18,129 | |
| 8257 | 3843 | 4188 | 7677 | Bombay, India |
| 3,288 | 6185 | 6740 | 12,355 | |
| 3769 | 5249 | 9071 | 7019 | Cape Town, South Africa |
| 6065 | 8447 | 14,598 | 11,296 | |
| 9960 | 8190 | 3367 | 3310 | Darwin, Australia |
| 6,029 | 13,180 | 5419 | 5327 | |
| 5772 | 887 | 5938 | 11,682 | London, England |
| 9289 | 1427 | 9556 | 18,800 | |
| 6296 | 6326 | 5470 | 6714 | Los Angeles, USA |
| ),132 | 10,180 | 8803 | 10,805 | |
| 4770 | 6353 | 7035 | 6899 | Mexico City, Mexico |
| 7676 | 10,224 | 11,321 | 11,103 | |
| 7179 | 1474 | 4650 | 10,279 | Moscow, USSR |
| ,553 | 2372 | 7483 | 16,542 | |
| 4820 | 4273 | 6735 | 8946 | New York, USA |
| 7757 | 6877 | 10,839 | 14,397 | |
| 5703 | 682 | 6033 | 11,791 | Paris, France |
| 9178 | 1098 | 9709 | 18,975 | |
| ),768 | 5047 | 1307 | 6698 | Peking, China |
| ,329 | 8122 | 2103 | 10,779 | |
| 6244 | 1317 | 5842 | 10,249 | Port Said, Egypt |
| ),048 | 2119 | 9402 | 16,494 | |
| 5125 | 3943 | 6417 | 9228 | Quebec, Canada |
| 3248 | 6345 | 10,327 | 14,851 | |
| | 5684 | 11,535 | 7349 | Rio de Janeiro, Brazil |
| | 9147 | 18,563 | 11,827 | |
| 5684 | | 6124 | 11,524 | Rome, Italy |
| 9147 | | 9855 | 18,546 | |
| ,535 | 6124 | | 5760 | Tokyo, Japan |
| 3,563 | 9855 | | 9270 | |
| 7349 | 11,524 | 5760 | | Wellington, New Zealand |
| ,827 | 18,546 | 9270 | | |

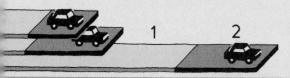

1    2

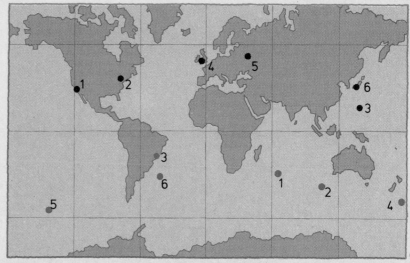

©DIAGRAM

# THE SOLAR SYSTEM

Perpetual movement of objects in the solar system means that distances between them are always changing. As we show here, differences in relative positions can be immense. For example, the difference between Pluto's maximum and minimum distances from the Sun is almost 20 times the mean distance from Earth to Sun.

**Earth's atmosphere** *left*
This scale illustration allows us to compare the extent of the various layers occurring within Earth's atmosphere.
**A** Troposphere, upper limit about 5mi (8km) above ground at the Poles, 8mi (13km) at the Equator.

**B** Stratosphere, up to a limit of about 30mi (50km).
**C** Mesosphere, to about 50mi (80km) above ground.
**D** Thermosphere, up to an average in the region of 220mi (350km).
**E** Exosphere, with traces of hydrogen up to about 5000mi (8000km).

**Worlds away** *above*
The mean distance from Earth to Moon (center to center) is 238,840mi (384,365km). This is 30.1 times the diameter of Earth and 110.7 times that of the Moon. Minimum (**A**) and maximum (**B**) distances are also shown.

**A down to Earth scale**
*below* Mean distances of the planets from the Sun are compared here with relative distances across the USA. If the Sun were at New York, Pluto (**9**) would be at Los Angeles, and Jupiter (**5**) near Pittsburgh.

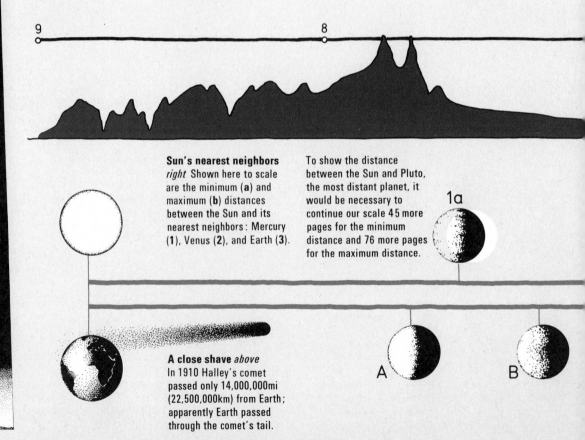

**Sun's nearest neighbors**
*right* Shown here to scale are the minimum (**a**) and maximum (**b**) distances between the Sun and its nearest neighbors : Mercury (**1**), Venus (**2**), and Earth (**3**).

To show the distance between the Sun and Pluto, the most distant planet, it would be necessary to continue our scale 45 more pages for the minimum distance and 76 more pages for the maximum distance.

**A close shave** *above*
In 1910 Halley's comet passed only 14,000,000mi (22,500,000km) from Earth ; apparently Earth passed through the comet's tail.

When closest to us, Venus, our nearest planetary neighbor, is 105 times more distant than our Moon. Neptune, however, never comes nearer than 11,208 times the distance from Earth to Moon.

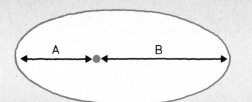

**Planetary orbits** *right*
Since their orbits around the Sun are elliptical, planets have a minimum or "perihelion" (**A**) and a maximum or "aphelion" (**B**) distance from the Sun.

©DIAGRAM

**Planetary distances** *right*
The table lists minimum, maximum and mean distances of each planet from the Sun. Although the mean distance of Pluto is nearly 900 million miles more than that of Neptune, its minimum distance is 4 million miles less.

| | | Minimum distance from Sun | | Maximum distance from Sun | | Mean distance from Sun | |
|---|---|---|---|---|---|---|---|
| 1 | Mercury | 28,600,000mi | 46,000,000km | 43,400,000mi | 69,800,000km | 36,000,000mi | 57,900,000km |
| 2 | Venus | 66,800,000mi | 108,000,000km | 67,700,000mi | 109,000,000km | 67,200,000mi | 108,000,000km |
| 3 | Earth | 91,400,000mi | 147,000,000km | 94,500,000mi | 152,000,000km | 93,000,000mi | 150,000,000km |
| 4 | Mars | 128,000,000mi | 206,000,000km | 155,000,000mi | 249,000,000km | 142,000,000mi | 229,000,000km |
| 5 | Jupiter | 460,000,000mi | 740,000,000km | 507,000,000mi | 816,000,000km | 484,000,000mi | 779,000,000km |
| 6 | Saturn | 837,000,000mi | 1,347,000,000km | 936,000,000mi | 1,506,000,000km | 887,000,000mi | 1,427,000,000km |
| 7 | Uranus | 1,702,000,000mi | 2,739,000,000km | 1,866,000,000mi | 3,003,000,000km | 1,784,000,000mi | 2,871,000,000km |
| 8 | Neptune | 2,766,000,000mi | 4,451,000,000km | 2,822,000,000mi | 4,541,000,000km | 2,794,000,000mi | 4,496,000,000km |
| 9 | Pluto | 2,762,000,000mi | 4,445,000,000km | 4,587,000,000mi | 7,382,000,000km | 3,674,000,000mi | 5,913,000,000km |

**Halley's comet** *below*
Indicated on our scale is the minimum distance of Halley's comet from the Sun: 55,000,000mi (89,000,000km).

**Orbit of Halley's comet**
Our scale would have to extend another 54 pages to show this comet's greatest distance from the Sun: 3,281,400,000mi (5,280,800,000km).

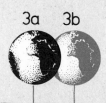

**Earth's nearest neighbors**
*left* Shown to the same scale as the distances between the Sun and its neighbors (*above*) are the shortest distances between Earth and its nearest neighbors: Venus (**A**), Mars (**B**), and Mercury (**C**).

| | | Mean distance from Earth | |
|---|---|---|---|
| A | Venus | 25,000,000mi | 40,200,000km |
| B | Mars | 35,000,000mi | 56,300,000km |
| C | Mercury | 50,000,000mi | 80,500,000km |
| D | Jupiter | 367,000,000mi | 591,000,000km |
| E | Saturn | 744,000,000mi | 1,197,000,000km |
| F | Uranus | 1,606,000,000mi | 2,585,000,000km |
| G | Pluto | 2,670,000,000mi | 4,297,000,000km |
| H | Neptune | 2,677,000,000mi | 4,308,000,000km |

**Distances from Earth**
*left* The table shows how close the other planets come to Earth. If we were to continue the scale showing the distances of Earth's nearest neighbors, we would find both Pluto and Neptune after 44 pages.

The mean distance from the Sun to Pluto, the outermost planet, is over 100 times greater than the mean distance between the Sun and Mercury, the innermost planet.

# CHAPTER 2

A 19th-century depiction of the Tower of Babel. Excavations and written sources suggest that the tower of the Bible story was the ziggurat of the temple of Marduk at Babylon, believed to have stood 300ft tall on a square base with sides 300ft long (Mansell Collection).

God using dividers to measure the Universe, which is depicted as a series of concentric cir in this 17th-century engraving.

# SIZE: NATURAL FEATURES AND MAN'S CONSTRUCTIONS

The Flatiron Building, New York City. At the time of its construction, in 1902, it was the tallest building in the world (Museum of the City of New York).

# NATURAL FEATURES 1

We are often impressed by great heights in nature, but from our own relatively diminutive standpoint it is often difficult to appreciate the true scale involved. By comparing natural features with each other and also with possibly more familiar manmade objects it is possible to bring even Mt Everest into closer perspective.

**Angel over the Empire State** *below*
The world's highest waterfall, the Angel in Venezuela, is over twice the height of the Empire State Building (1472ft with mast). Shown here to scale with the Empire State are the heights of the world's 10 highest waterfalls; in each case the height is that of the total drop, which in some instances is made up of several smaller falls.

3212ft Angel, Venezuela
3110ft Tugela, S Africa

2625ft Utigård, Norway
2540ft Mongefossen, Norway
2425ft Yosemite, USA

2154ft Østre Mardøla Foss, Norway
2120ft Tyssestrengane, Norway
2000ft Kukenaom, Venezuela
1904ft Sutherland, NZ
1841ft Kjellfossen, Norway

**Himalayan giants** *right*
Some 25 peaks in the Himalayas exceed 20,000ft. We show the eight highest.
**A** Everest 29,002ft
**B** Godwin Austen 28,250ft
**C** Kanchenjunga 28,208ft
**D** Makalu 27,824ft
**E** Dhaulagiri 26,810ft
**F** Nanga Parbat 26,660ft
**G** Annapurna 26,505ft
**H** Gasherbrum I 26,470ft
**Highest volcanoes**
Of these, Cotopaxi is active, Llullaillaco is quiescent, the others are believed extinct. All are in S America except for Kilimanjaro and Elbrus.
**I** Aconcagua 22,834ft
**J** Llullaillaco 22,057ft
**K** Chimborazo 20,560ft
**M** Cotopaxi 19,344ft
**N** Kilimanjaro 19,340ft
**O** Antisana 18,713ft
**P** Citlaltepetl 18,700ft
**Q** Elbrus 18,480ft
**Top peaks by continent**
**A** Everest (Asia) 29,002ft
**I** Aconcagua (S Am) 22,834ft
**L** McKinley (N Am) 20,320ft
**N** Kilimanjaro (Afr) 19,340ft
**Q** Elbrus (Eur) 18,480ft
**R** Vinson Massif (Antarctica) 16,863ft
**S** Wilhelm (Oceania) 15,400ft
**Other high spots**
**T** Cook (NZ) 12,349ft
**U** Kosciusko (Australia) 7316ft
**V** Ben Nevis (UK) 4406ft
**W** Highest point in the Netherlands 321ft

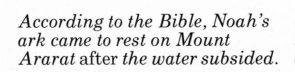

*According to the Bible, Noah's ark came to rest on Mount Ararat after the water subsided.*

*Since this mountain is 16,946ft high, it really must have been quite some flood!*

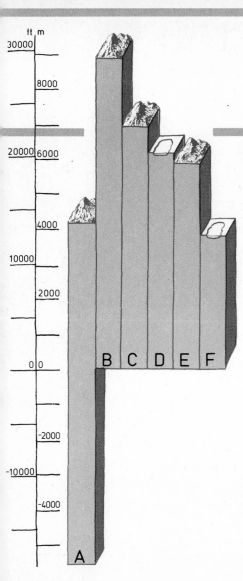

## Wavepower *right*

The heights of different types of wave are shown in scale with Columbus' ship, *Santa Maria* (95ft).
**a** Waves in a fjord-like bay in Alaska, caused by an avalanche, 1740ft high.
**b** Highest recorded tsunami wave 220ft. (Estimated highest tsunami 278ft.)
**c** Highest calculated ocean wave 112ft.
**d** Highest instrumentally measured ocean wave 86ft.
**e** Flood wave on the R Mekong (SE Asia) 46ft.
**f** Hang-chou-fe (China) tidal bore 25ft.
**g** Flood wave at Lava Falls, R Colorado (USA) 12ft.

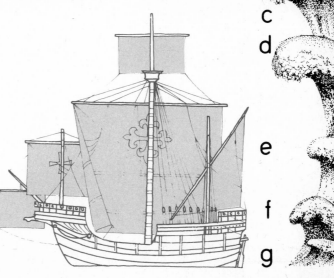

## High features *above*

**A** Mauna Kea (Hawaii) is 4448ft taller than Mt Everest, but only 13,796ft of its total 33,476ft are above sea level.
**B** Everest, the world's highest peak, 29,002ft
**C** Aconcagua, highest extinct volcano, 22,834ft.
**D** World's highest lake, un-named (Tibet), 20,230ft.
**E** Cotopaxi, highest active volcano, 19,344ft.
**F** Titicaca (Peru/Bolivia), world's highest steam-navigated lake, 12,506ft.

## State of elevation *right*

The highest point in the Netherlands is only 321ft above sea level, less than one-quarter the height of the Empire State Building (1472ft with mast).

## Skyscraper rock *left*

Balls Pyramid, a rock pinnacle near Lord Howe Island, off the E coast of Australia, is 1843ft tall, making it 371ft taller than the Empire State Building (1472ft with mast).

©DIAGRAM

# NATURAL FEATURES 2

The deepest land depression, below the ice in Marie Byrd Land, Antarctica, dips 8100ft below sea level. The deepest known point in the ocean, in the Marianas Trench in the Pacific Ocean, is over four times as deep—36,198ft below sea level, or over 7000ft deeper than Mount Everest is high.

**A) Deepest caves by country** Shown to scale *left* and listed *right* are some of the world's deepest caves. Deepest of all known caves is Pierre St-Martin in the Pyrenees—almost three times as deep as the Empire State is high (1472ft).

**B) Land depressions** *right* Listed in the table and indicated on column B are the depths below sea level of some of the world's lowest areas. Depths for **2, 3, 9** are at surface level. Depths for **8, 10** are for land lying under many thousands of feet of ice.

**C) Sea depths** *right* Column C is drawn to a smaller scale than column B, so allowing us to compare the maximum known depths of the world's oceans and seas. Although smaller than the Arctic Ocean, the Malay and Caribbean Seas are deeper.

**D) Below sea level** *right* Column D is drawn to the same scale as column C. **a** Lake Baykal, the world's deepest lake, is 6365ft deep, taking it some 4872ft below sea level. **b** The Dead Sea has the lowest surface of any lake or sea, at −1296ft.

**c** Under the ice, the land depression in Marie Byrd Land, Antarctica dips 8100ft below sea level. **d** The tallest submarine mountain, off the Tonga Trench, is 28,500ft tall. Its peak is at −1200ft. **e** The average depth of the ocean floor is more than 12,000ft below sea level. **f** The deepest known point in any ocean is the Pacific's Marianas Trench, 36,198ft below sea level. **g** If its base were at the bottom of the Marianas Trench, Mount Everest's peak would be 7196ft below sea level.

| A) | Caves | | |
|----|-------|--|--|
| 1 | Ghar Parau | Iran | 2464ft |
| 2 | Snieznej | Poland | 2569ft |
| 3 | Holloch | Switzerland | 2713ft |
| 4 | San Augustin | Mexico | 2819ft |
| 5 | Kacherlschact | Austria | 2996ft |
| 6 | Kievskaya | USSR | 3118ft |
| 7 | Corchia | Italy | 3118ft |
| 8 | Cellagua | Spain | 3182ft |
| 9 | Jean Bernard | France | 4258ft |
| 10 | Pierre St-Martin | France/Spain | 4370ft |

| B) | Land depressions | | |
|----|------------------|--|--|
| 1 | (Coastal areas) | Netherlands | 15ft |
| 2 | Lake Eyre | Australia | 39ft |
| 3 | Caspian Sea | USSR | 92ft |
| 4 | Death Valley | USA | 282ft |
| 5 | Danakil | Ethiopia | 383ft |
| 6 | Qattara | Egypt | 436ft |
| 7 | Turfan | China | 505ft |
| 8 | (Central area) | Greenland | 1200ft |
| 9 | Dead Sea | Israel/Jordan | 1296ft |
| 10 | Marie Byrd Land | Antarctica | 8100ft |

| C) | Sea depths | | |
|----|-----------|--|--|
| 1 | Baltic | | c.1300ft |
| 2 | North | Skagarrak | 1998ft |
| 3 | Red | 20°N 38°E | 7254ft |
| 4 | Japan | | c.10,200ft |
| 5 | East China | | c.10,500ft |
| 6 | Andaman | | c.11,000ft |
| 7 | Okhotsk | Kuril Trench | 11,154ft |
| 8 | Bering | Buldir Trench | 13,422ft |
| 9 | Mediterranean | Matapan | 14,435ft |
| 10 | Arctic Ocean | | 17,850ft |
| 11 | Malay | Kei Trench | 21,342ft |
| 12 | Caribbean | Cayman Trench | 23,000ft |
| 13 | Indian Ocean | Diamantina | 26,400ft |
| 14 | Atlantic Ocean | Puerto Rico Trench | 27,498ft |
| 15 | Pacific Ocean | Marianas Trench | 36,198ft |

Traveling at the speed of the fastest elevator in the Empire State Building it would take just over 30 minutes to reach the bottom of the Marianas Trench.

**Under-statement** *right*
The Empire State (1472ft with mast) is shown on the land mass below the ice in Marie Byrd Land. 4½ more Empire States are needed to reach sea level.

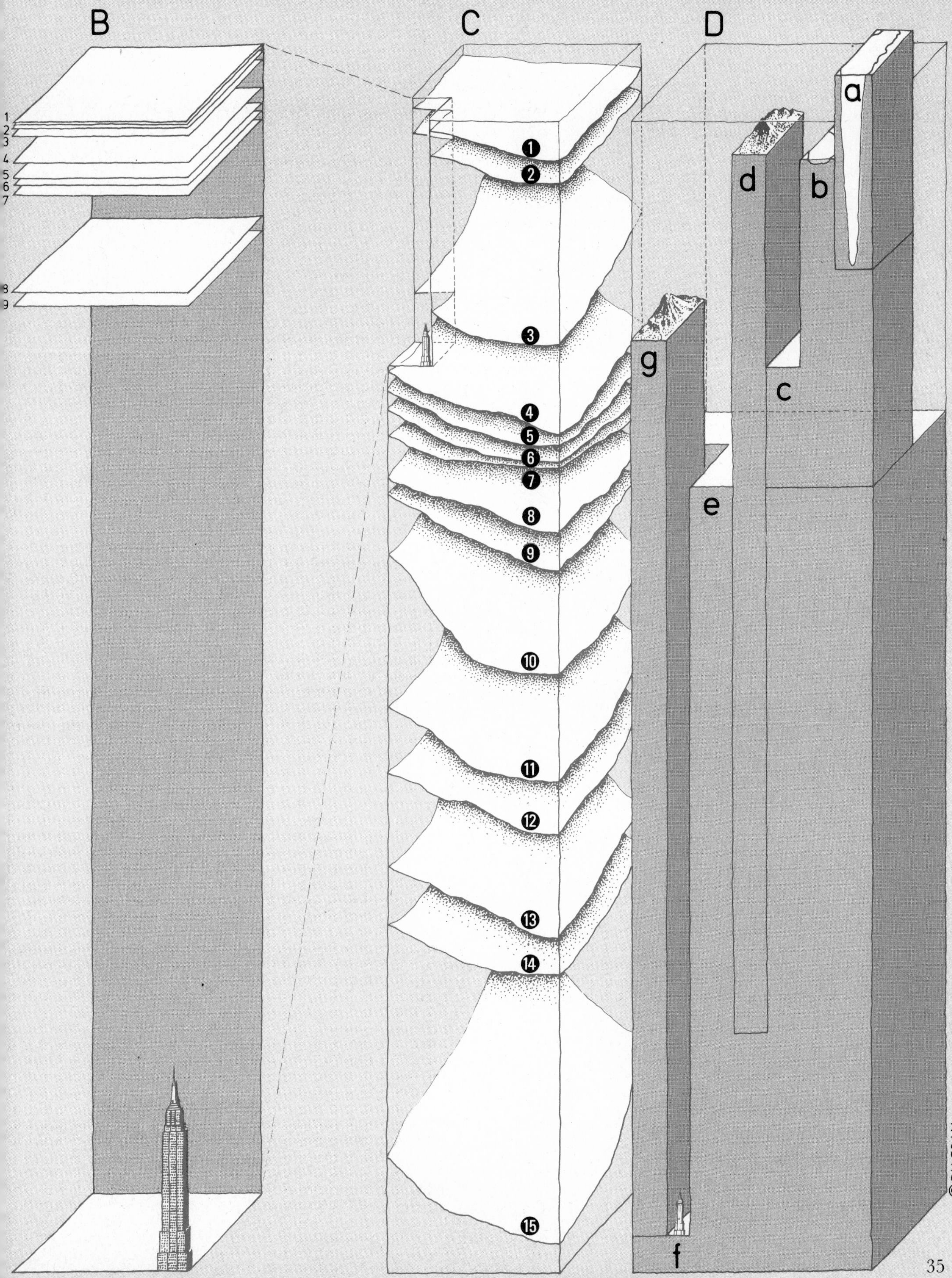

B

C

D

1
2
3
4
5
6
7

8
9

a

d    b

c

g

e

① ② ③ ④ ⑤ ⑥ ⑦ ⑧ ⑨ ⑩ ⑪ ⑫ ⑬ ⑭ ⑮

f

© DIAGRAM

# NATURAL FEATURES 3

Counted among nature's longest features are mountain ranges and rivers longer than the width of North America, a glacier that stretches farther than the width of Switzerland, and a cave system that exceeds the length of Long Island, NY. Compared here are the world's longest rivers and mountain ranges, drawn to scale across North America to illustrate their enormous length; also shown is a selection of glaciers and cave systems. The longest mountain range (4500mi) is over 14 times the length of the longest glacier (Lambert-Fisher, 320mi) and more than 24 times the length of the longest cave system (Flint Ridge, 181.4mi).

**Longest mountain ranges**
Listed in the table *right* and drawn to scale *far right* are the world's longest mountain ranges. Although the Himalayas boast the world's highest mountains, this range ranks only third in the world in terms of length.

**Longest rivers**
*right, far right* Here we compare the world's longest rivers. Of the top 10, five are in Asia, two in Africa, two in N America and one in S America. Europe's longest river, the Volga, ranks only 16th.

**Equator to Arctic** *left*
The world's longest river, the Nile (4132mi), begins at the Equator and flows North to the Nile delta. If it began at the delta and flowed North along a Great Circle line, it would reach to within 100 miles of the North Pole.

**Rivers of ice**
Listed *right* and shown to scale with a map of Switzerland *left* are the world's longest glaciers. All but two of those listed are in Antarctica. Novaya Zemlya is much the longest glacier in the Northern Hemisphere.

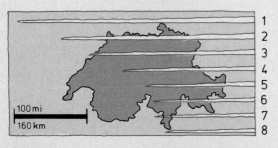

100 mi
160 km

| Mountain ranges | | | |
|---|---|---|---|
| 1 | Cordillera de Los Andes | S America | 4500mi |
| 2 | Rocky Mountains | N America | 3750mi |
| 3 | Himalayas–Karakoram–Hindu Kush | Asia | 2400mi |
| 4 | Great Dividing Range | Oceania | 2250mi |
| 5 | Trans-Antarctic Mountains | Antarctica | 2200mi |
| 6 | Brazilian East-Coast Range | S America | 1900mi |
| 7 | Sumatran-Javan Range | Asia | 1800mi |
| 8 | Aleutian Range | N America | 1650mi |

| Rivers | | | |
|---|---|---|---|
| 1 | Nile | Africa | 4132mi |
| 2 | Amazon | S America | 3900mi |
| 3 | Mississippi–Missouri–Red Rock | N America | 3860mi |
| 4 | Ob-Irtysh | Asia | 3461mi |
| 5 | Yangtze | Asia | 3430mi |
| 6 | Hwang Ho | Asia | 2903mi |
| 7 | Congo (Zaire) | Africa | 2900mi |
| 8 | Amur | Asia | 2802mi |
| 9 | Lena | Asia | 2653mi |
| 10 | Mackenzie | N America | 2635mi |
| 11 | Mekong | Asia | 2600mi |
| 12 | Niger | Africa | 2590mi |
| 13 | Yenisey | Asia | 2566mi |
| 14 | Paraná | S America | 2450mi |
| 15 | Plata-Paraguay | S America | 2300mi |
| 16 | Volga | Europe | 2293mi |
| 17 | Madeira | S America | 2060mi |
| 18 | Indus | Asia | 1980mi |

| Glaciers | | | |
|---|---|---|---|
| 1 | Lambert-Fisher | Antarctica | 320mi |
| 2 | Novaya Zemlya | USSR | 260mi |
| 3 | Arctic Institute | Antarctica | 225mi |
| 4 | Nimrod-Lennox-King | Antarctica | 180mi |
| 5 | Denman | Antarctica | 150mi |
| 6 | Beardmore | Antarctica | 140mi |
| 7 | Recovery | Antarctica | 140mi |
| 8 | Petermanns | Greenland | 124mi |

"In the space of one hundred and seventy-six years the Lower Mississippi has shortened itself two hundred and forty-two miles. That is an average of a trifle over one mile and a third per year. Therefore . . . just over a million years ago next November, the Lower Mississippi River was upward of one million three hundred thousand miles long, and stuck out over the Gulf of Mexico like a fishing-rod. And by the same token . . . seven hundred and forty-two years from now the Lower Mississippi will be only a mile and three-quarters long, and Cairo and New Orleans will have joined their streets together. . . . There is something fascinating about science. One gets

Although Europe is the second smallest continent in terms of area, it has the second longest coastline (37,887 miles).

Size 1

**Global girdle** *right*
The world's longest natural feature is the submarine mountain range that runs down the Atlantic, through the Antarctic. and on to end in the NE Pacific. If straightened, its 40,000mi would go more than 1½ times around the Equator.

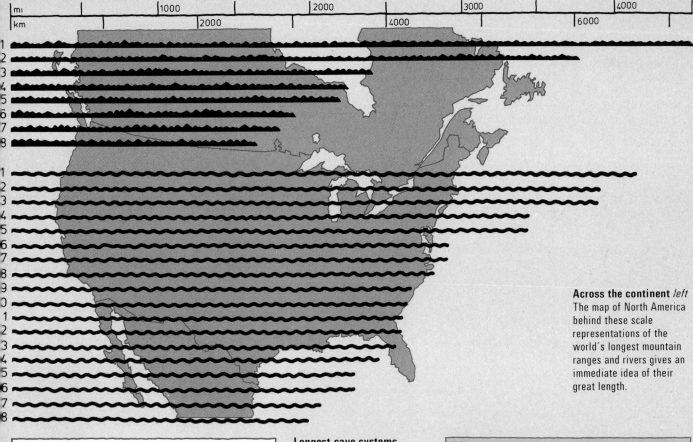

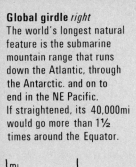

**Across the continent** *left*
The map of North America behind these scale representations of the world's longest mountain ranges and rivers gives an immediate idea of their great length.

**Cave systems**

| | | | |
|---|---|---|---|
| 1 | Flint Ridge | USA | 181.4mi |
| 2 | Holloch | Switzerland | 72mi |
| 3 | Cuyaguatega | Cuba | 32.7mi |
| 4 | Werfen | Austria | 26.1mi |
| 5 | Peschtschera | USSR | 22.7mi |
| 6 | Palomera | Spain | 22.5mi |
| 7 | Ogof Ffynnon | UK | 20.3mi |
| 8 | Postojnska | Yugoslavia | 17mi |

**Longest cave systems**
Listed *left* and shown to scale with Long Island, New York *right* are the longest cave systems of eight countries. Linking the Mammoth Cave System to the Flint Ridge System, Kentucky in 1972 made this the world's longest.

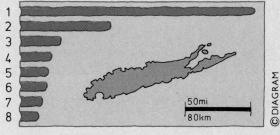

© DIAGRAM

such wholesome returns of conjecture out of such a trifling investment of fact.''
(Extract from *Life on the Mississippi* by Mark Twain.)

The longest cave system in the world, Flint Ridge, USA, is some 80 miles longer than the tunnels of the world's longest subway system, in London, England (101 miles).

37

# BUILDINGS AND MONUMENTS

The United States boasts the world's tallest apartment block, tallest hotel, tallest office block, and several of the world's tallest monuments. It is, however, to Europe that we must turn for the tallest of all manmade structures—the Warsaw Radio mast, some 57ft taller than the KTHI-TV mast in Fargo, N Dakota.

**Tall stories** *right*
**A** Ulm cathedral, W Germany, the world's tallest cathedral, 528ft.
**B** World's largest cooling tower, at Uentrop, W Germany, 590ft.
**C** Lake Point Towers, Chicago, tallest apartment block, 645ft.
**D** Peachtree Center Plaza, Atlanta, tallest hotel, 723ft.
**E** Chrysler Building, New York, 1046ft.
**F** Tallest chimney, International Nickel Co, Sudbury, Ontario, 1245ft.
**G** Empire State Building, New York, 1250ft without mast, 1472ft with mast.
**H** World Trade Center, New York, 1353ft.
**I** Sears Tower, Chicago, since 1973 the tallest office building in the world, 1454ft without mast, 1559ft with mast.
**J** CN Tower, Toronto, the tallest self-supporting tower, 1815ft.
**K** Warsaw Radio mast, near Płock, Poland, the tallest structure in the world, 2120ft 8in.

*When building the Tower of Babel, the descendants of Noah sought to build a tower "whose top may reach unto heaven." To reach only as high as Mount Everest (29,002ft), a tower would have to be 20 times the height of Sears Tower (1454ft without mast).*

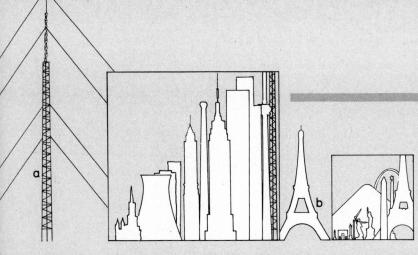

**All to scale** *left*
Shown here to a common scale are the various man-made structures included on these two pages. The Warsaw Radio mast (**a**) and the Eiffel Tower (**b**) have been drawn outside the boxes to give a view of their full heights.

**Mighty monuments** *left*
**1** Cleopatra's Needle, now in London, 68ft.
**2** Arch of Septimus Severus, Rome, 68ft.
**3** Trajan's Column, Rome, 115ft.
**4** Tallest totem pole, at Alert Bay, Canada, 173ft.
**5** Motherland sculpture, Volgograd, USSR, world's tallest free-standing statue, 270ft.
**6** Statue of Liberty, New York, height from sandals to top of torch 151ft, height with pedestal 305ft.
**7** Great Pyramid of Cheops, Giza, Egypt, original height 480ft 11in.
**8** Washington Memorial, Washington DC, 555ft.
**9** San Jacinto Column, Texas, world's tallest monumental column, 570ft.
**10** Gateway to the West Arch, St Louis, Missouri, 630ft.
**11** Eiffel Tower, Paris, original height 985ft 11in, since addition of TV mast 1052ft 4in.

©DIAGRAM

**The Statue of Liberty, New York, is approximately 20 times life size; the Motherland sculpture, Volgograd, is more than 30 times life size.**

The top platform of the Eiffel Tower is the same height as the 73rd floor of the Empire State Building; the Empire State's own observatories are on the 86th and 102nd floors.

# DRILLING AND MINING

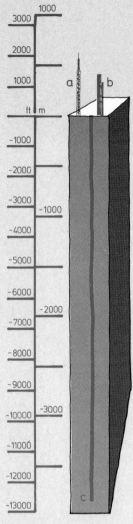

Man's search for clean water, coal, precious metals and stones, gas and oil has led him to delve deep into the Earth's crust. Here we compare some of the depths to which he has gone—down some 12,600ft (or over 2 miles) in the deepest mine, and down some 31,911ft (or just over 6 miles) with the deepest drilling.

| A) | Deep mining | | |
|---|---|---|---|
| 1 | Kolar (1919) | India | 5419ft |
| 2 | Witwatersrand (1931) | S Africa | 7640ft |
| 3 | Nova Lima (1933) | Brazil | 8051ft |
| 4 | Witwatersrand (1933) | S Africa | 8198ft |
| 5 | Witwatersrand (1934) | S Africa | 8400ft |
| 6 | Johannesburg (1938) | S Africa | 8527ft |
| 7 | Kolar (1939) | India | 8604ft |
| 8 | Johannesburg (1949) | S Africa | 9071ft |
| 9 | Boksburg (1953) | S Africa | 9288ft |
| 10 | Boksburg (1958) | S Africa | 11,000ft |
| 11 | Boksburg (1959) | S Africa | 11,246ft |
| 12 | Western Deep (1975) | S Africa | 12,600ft |

| B) | Deep drilling | | |
|---|---|---|---|
| 1 | Szechwan (c150BC) | China | 2000ft |
| 2 | Olinda (1927) | California | 8046ft |
| 3 | Vera Cruz (1931) | Mexico | 10,585ft |
| 4 | Belridge (1934) | California | 11,377ft |
| 5 | Pecos County (1944) | Texas | 15,279ft |
| 6 | Caddo County (1947) | Oklahoma | 17,823ft |
| 7 | Sublette County (1949) | Wyoming | 20,521ft |
| 8 | Bakersfield (1953) | California | 21,482ft |
| 9 | Plaquemines (1956) | Louisiana | 22,570ft |
| 10 | Pecos County (1958) | Texas | 25,340ft |
| 11 | St Bernard Parish (1970) | Louisiana | 25,600ft |
| 12 | Pecos County (1972) | Texas | 28,500ft |
| 13 | Beckham County (1972) | Oklahoma | 30,050ft |
| 14 | Washita County (1974) | Oklahoma | 31,441ft |
| 15 | Kola peninsula (1979) | USSR | 31,911ft |

**Highest and lowest** *above*
The highest man-made structure is the Warsaw Radio mast (**a**), at 2120ft 8in; the tallest office building is the Sears Tower, Chicago (**b**), at 1454ft without mast. The lowest at which men work is 12,600ft, in the world's deepest mine (**c**).

**Deep mining and drilling**
Listed in the table *above* and drawn to scale *far right* are some of the depths that man has reached by mining (**A**) and drilling (**B**). The date of the achievement is given in brackets after the name of the mine or drilling site.

**Digging deep** *right*
This diagram shows to scale some of man's excursions into the Earth's crust. The greatest depth at which a man has worked is 12,600ft, but drilling machinery has been operated at more than 2½ times this depth, at 31,911ft.

*The world's deepest mine is nearly three times as deep as the world's deepest known cave.*

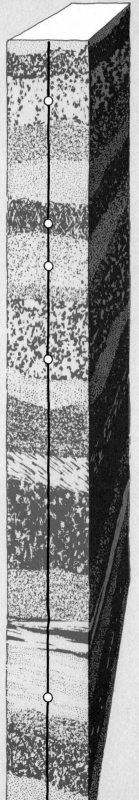

−2540ft the world's deepest open mine

−7320ft the deepest water well in the world, in Montana, USA

−9029ft the world's deepest steam well, in California, USA

−12,600ft the deepest mine in the world, Western Deep, S Africa

−26,192ft the greatest depth reached during the Moho project (5709ft into the seabed)

31,911ft the world's deepest drilling (July 1979), on the Kola peninsular, USSR

**If made from the top of Mount Everest, the world's deepest drilling would extend some 2909ft below sea level.**

**A Deep mining** *left*
Shown here to scale are some of man's deepest mines, all of which are gold mines. The deepest (12,600ft) is nearly six times the height of the world's tallest structure—the Warsaw Radio mast.

**B Deep drilling** *left*
Shown to a smaller scale are various depths achieved by drilling into the ground. The deepest drilling (31,911ft) exceeds the depth of the deepest mine by 19,311ft – over 13 times the height of Sears Tower (1454ft without mast) or 9 times the height of the Warsaw Radio mast (2120ft 8in).

**Structures to scale** *left*
Included on our mining and drilling diagrams to illustrate the scales are:
**a** Warsaw Radio mast (2120ft 8in)
**b** Sears Tower (1454ft without mast, 1559ft with mast)
**c** Empire State Building (1250ft without mast, 1472ft with mast)

41

©DIAGRAM

# BRIDGES, TUNNELS AND CANALS

A suspension bridge with a single span some seven-eighths of a mile wide, a ship canal deep enough to take sea-going vessels for a distance in excess of 140 miles, and a 17-mile-long tunnel in the London underground railway system are among the greatest feats of engineering devised in the face of daunting obstacles to efficient transportation.

**Lengths of bridge spans**
*right* Listed are the five longest examples of three types of bridge span—suspension, cantilever, and steel arch. The longest span for a suspension bridge is over 2½ times that for any other type of bridge.

| Bridge spans | | |
| --- | --- | --- |
| **Suspension** | | |
| 1  Humber Estuary* | Humberside, UK | 4626ft |
| 2  Verrazano Narrows | New York, USA | 4260ft |
| 3  Golden Gate | San Francisco, USA | 4200ft |
| 4  Mackinac Straits | Michigan, USA | 3800ft |
| 5  Atatürk | Istanbul, Turkey | 3524ft |
| **Cantilever** | | |
| 1  Quebec | Quebec, Canada | 1800ft |
| 2  Firth of Forth | Midlothian/Fife, UK | 1710ft |
| 3  Delaware River | Pennsylvania, USA | 1644ft |
| 4  Greater New Orleans | Louisiana, USA | 1575ft |
| 5  Howrah | Calcutta, India | 1500ft |
| **Steel arch** | | |
| 1  New River Gorge | W Virginia, USA | 1700ft |
| 2  Bayonne | New Jersey/ | |
| | New York | 1652ft |
| 3  Sydney Harbour | Sydney, Australia | 1650ft |
| 4  Fremont | Oregon, USA | 1255ft |
| 5  Port Mann | Vancouver, Canada | 1200ft |
| *Due for completion 1980 | | |

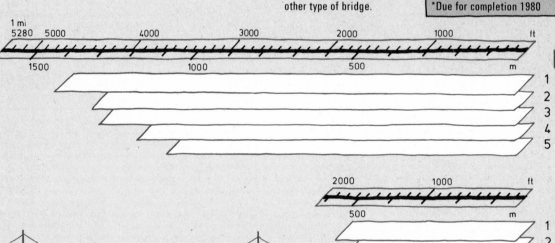

**Suspension spans** *left*
Shown to scale are the five longest single spans. The span of the new Humber Bridge will be longest by 366ft.

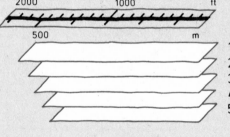

**Cantilever spans** *left*
The five longest are shown to the same scale as the suspension spans. The Forth (**2**), of 1889, is the oldest of our 15 examples.

**Royal span** *above*
The center span of the Verrazano Narrows Bridge (4260ft) is over 35 times the width of the largest passenger liner ever, the *Queen Elizabeth* (118.6ft).

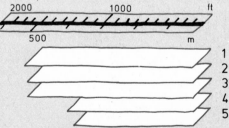
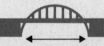

**Steel arch span** *left*
Also to the same scale are the five longest steel arch spans. The theoretical limit for a span of this type is about 3280ft.

A bridge 21 miles long would be needed to traverse the English Channel between Dover and Calais; the world's longest bridging to date is the 23.8–mile–long Second Lake Pontchartrain Causeway in Louisiana.

*The world's longest vehicular tunnel, London Transport's Northern Line, would stretch under the Mediterranean Sea from the Rock of Gibraltar to a point in Morocco some 3 miles from the coast.*

Size 1

**Tunnels**

| | | | |
|---|---|---|---|
| 1 | Northern Line (subway) | London, UK | 17.3mi |
| 2 | Simplon I, II (rail) | Switzerland/Italy | 12.3mi |
| 3 | Shin Kanmon (rail) | Japan | 11.6mi |
| 4 | Gt Apennine (rail) | Italy | 11.5mi |
| 5 | St Gotthard (road)* | Switzerland | 10.1mi |
| 6 | Rokko (rail) | Japan | 10.0mi |
| 7 | Henderson (rail) | USA | 9.8mi |
| 8 | Lötschberg (rail) | Switzerland | 9.0mi |

**Canals**

| | | | |
|---|---|---|---|
| 1 | White Sea—Baltic | USSR | 141mi |
| 2 | Suez | Egypt | 100.6mi |
| 3 | Volga—Don | USSR | 62.2mi |
| 4 | North Sea | Germany/Denmark | 60.9mi |
| 5 | Houston | USA | 56.7mi |
| 6 | Panama | Panama | 50.7mi |
| 7 | Manchester Ship | UK | 39.7mi |
| 8 | Welland | Canada | 28.0mi |

*Due for completion 1980

**Lengths of tunnels**
The table *left* and the diagram *below* show the eight longest vehicle-carrying tunnels in the world. The longest non-vehicular tunnel, the Delaware Aqueduct in New York State, is 105 miles in length.

**Largest diameter tunnel**
*right* The tunnel through Yerba Buena Island in San Francisco is 76ft wide and 58ft tall (or over 11 typical cars wide and 12 typical cars high).

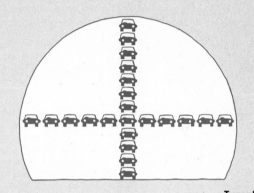

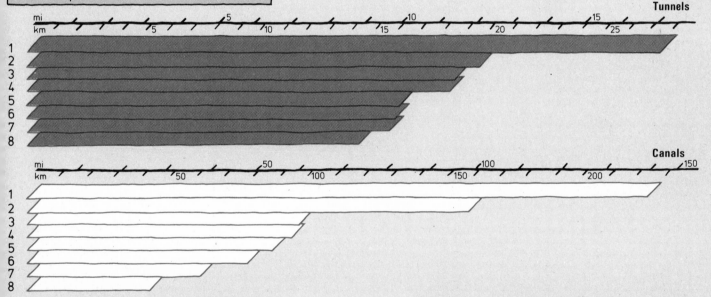

**Lengths of ship canals**
Listed in the table *top* and shown to scale in the diagram *above* are the world's eight longest deep-draft ship canals (minimum depth 16.4ft).
Suez, the oldest major ship canal (1869), is still the second longest.

**Longest canal system**
*right* The longest canal system in the world is the Volga-Baltic Canal, from Astrakhan on the Caspian Sea (**A**) to Leningrad (**B**)— a distance of 1850mi, equal to the road distance from Leningrad to the edge of Paris (**C**).

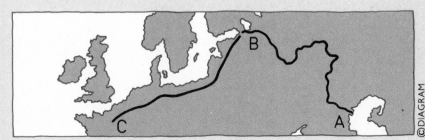

©DIAGRAM

**If the canals of the Netherlands (2182 miles in all) had been dug end to end along a Great Circle from New Amsterdam (or, as it is now known, New York), they would extend 97 miles beyond Mexico City.**

# SHIPS AND BOATS

Throughout history man has designed ships to transport passengers and cargo and to serve as weapons of war. Shown below to a common scale are civil and military ships from different periods. Vessels of the new generation of supertankers, represented here by the *Bellamya*, are longer than the world's longest aircraft carrier.

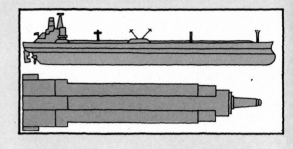

**Lengths of merchant and passenger ships** *below*
**A** *Bellamya*, French oil tanker, 1312ft. (The largest ship afloat is another tanker, the *Pierre Guillaumat*, 1359ft.)
**B** 19th-century whaling ship, 107ft.

**C** RMS *Queen Elizabeth*, launched 1938, the largest liner ever, 1031ft. (Today's largest, the QE2, is 963ft.)
**D** SS *Great Eastern*, 1858, passenger ship, largest vessel until 1899, 692ft.
**E** *Natchez*, 1869, Mississippi packet, 307ft.

**F** Egyptian merchant ship, c.1500 BC, 90ft.
**G** Soling class yacht, 26ft 9in.

**Long and tall**
*above* The supertanker *Bellamya* (1312ft) is 62ft longer than the Empire State Building is tall (1250ft without mast).

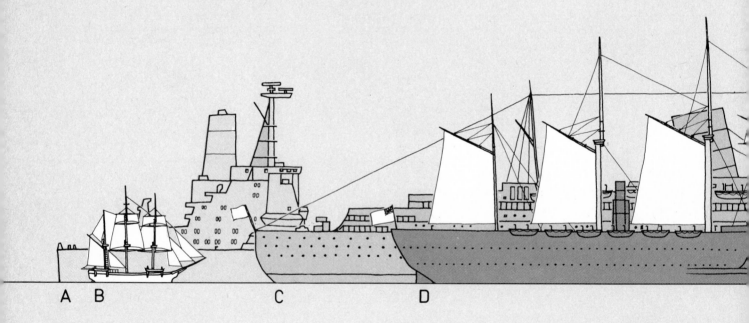

A  B          C          D

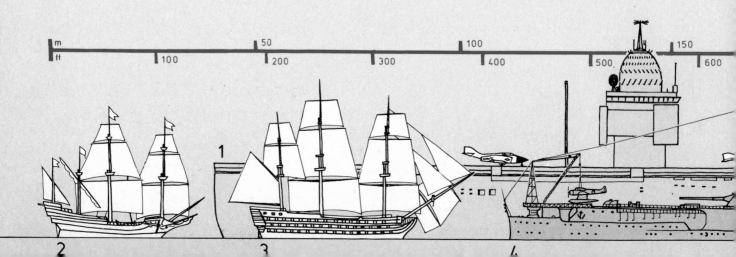

2          3          4

Noah was a remarkable man according to the Bible, for with his three sons he built the 450ft-long ark—twice as long as Nelson's *Victory*.

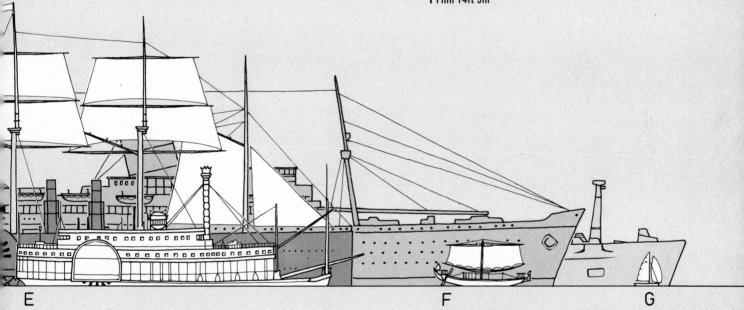

**Lengths of warships**
See illustrations *below*.
**1** USS *Enterprise*, 1960, nuclear-powered aircraft carrier, the longest warship ever, 1123ft.
**2** English warship of the 17th century, 142ft.

**3** HMS *Victory*, Nelson's flagship at Trafalgar in 1805, 226ft.
**4** *Yamato*, Japanese WW2 battleship. With its sister *Musashi*, the largest but not the longest battleship ever, 863ft.

**5** USS *Monitor*, 1862, ironclad warship of the American Civil War, 172ft.
**6** Roman galley, 235ft.

**Olympic yachts**
*above* Lengths for yachts in the six Olympic classes for 1980 are:
**a** Soling 26ft 9in
**b** Star 22ft 8in
**c** Tornado 20ft
**d** Flying dutchman 19ft 10in
**e** "470" 15ft 4¾in
**f** Finn 14ft 9in

E      F      G

| 200 | | 250 | | 300 | | 350 m |
|---|---|---|---|---|---|---|
| 700 | 800 | 900 | 1000 | 1100 | 1200 | 1300ft |

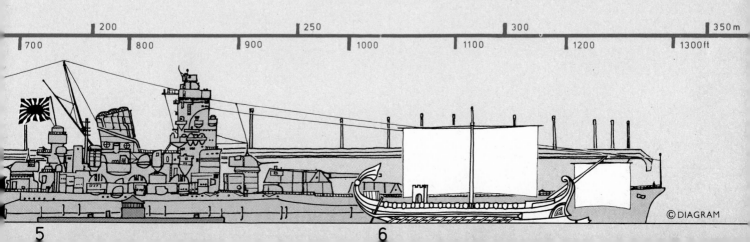

5         6

© DIAGRAM

# LAND VEHICLES

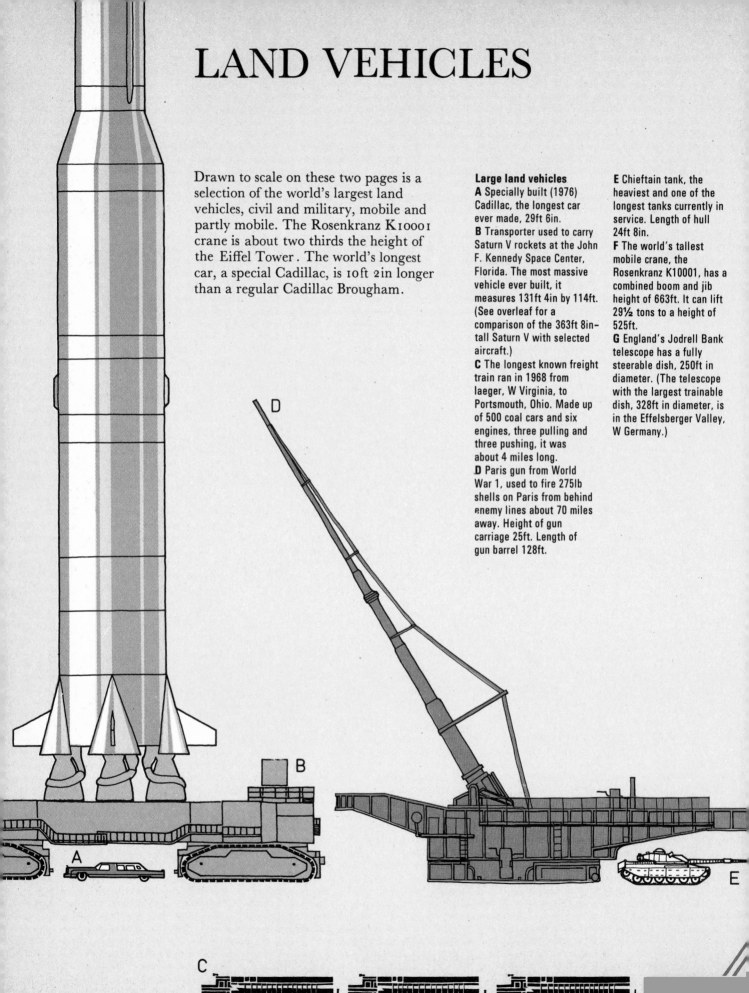

Drawn to scale on these two pages is a selection of the world's largest land vehicles, civil and military, mobile and partly mobile. The Rosenkranz K10001 crane is about two thirds the height of the Eiffel Tower. The world's longest car, a special Cadillac, is 10ft 2in longer than a regular Cadillac Brougham.

**Large land vehicles**

**A** Specially built (1976) Cadillac, the longest car ever made, 29ft 6in.

**B** Transporter used to carry Saturn V rockets at the John F. Kennedy Space Center, Florida. The most massive vehicle ever built, it measures 131ft 4in by 114ft. (See overleaf for a comparison of the 363ft 8in-tall Saturn V with selected aircraft.)

**C** The longest known freight train ran in 1968 from Iaeger, W Virginia, to Portsmouth, Ohio. Made up of 500 coal cars and six engines, three pulling and three pushing, it was about 4 miles long.

**D** Paris gun from World War 1, used to fire 275lb shells on Paris from behind enemy lines about 70 miles away. Height of gun carriage 25ft. Length of gun barrel 128ft.

**E** Chieftain tank, the heaviest and one of the longest tanks currently in service. Length of hull 24ft 8in.

**F** The world's tallest mobile crane, the Rosenkranz K10001, has a combined boom and jib height of 663ft. It can lift 29½ tons to a height of 525ft.

**G** England's Jodrell Bank telescope has a fully steerable dish, 250ft in diameter. (The telescope with the largest trainable dish, 328ft in diameter, is in the Effelsberger Valley, W Germany.)

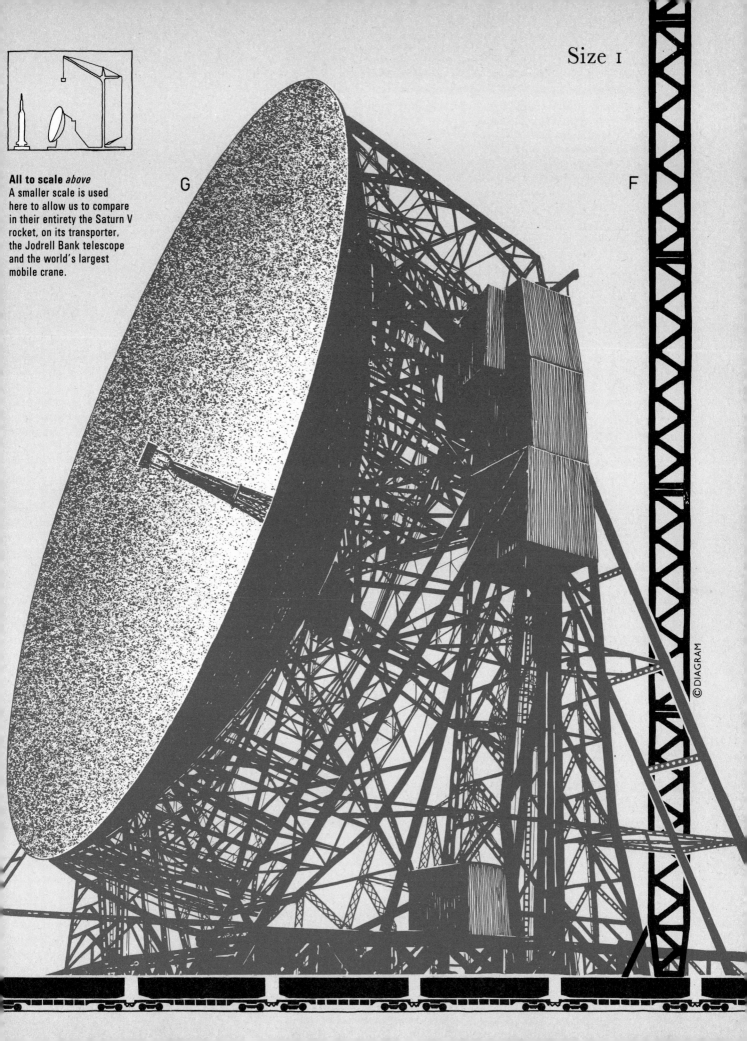

G

F

**All to scale** *above*
A smaller scale is used
here to allow us to compare
in their entirety the Saturn V
rocket, on its transporter,
the Jodrell Bank telescope
and the world's largest
mobile crane.

©DIAGRAM

# AIRCRAFT

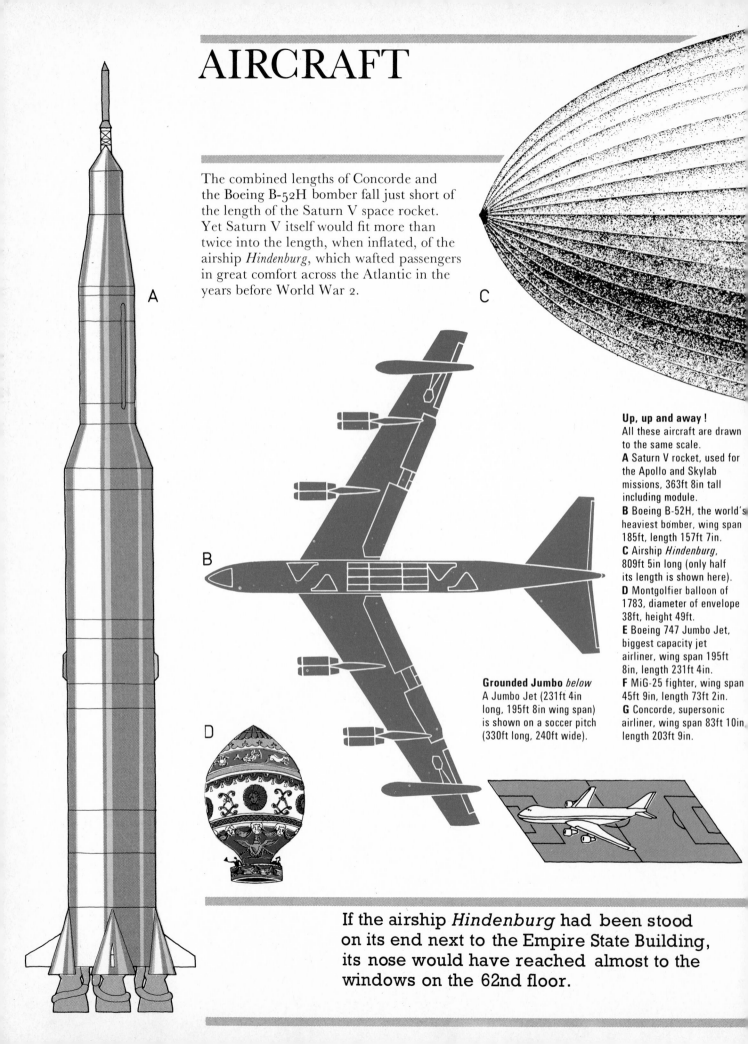

The combined lengths of Concorde and the Boeing B-52H bomber fall just short of the length of the Saturn V space rocket. Yet Saturn V itself would fit more than twice into the length, when inflated, of the airship *Hindenburg*, which wafted passengers in great comfort across the Atlantic in the years before World War 2.

**Up, up and away !**
All these aircraft are drawn to the same scale.
**A** Saturn V rocket, used for the Apollo and Skylab missions, 363ft 8in tall including module.
**B** Boeing B-52H, the world's heaviest bomber, wing span 185ft, length 157ft 7in.
**C** Airship *Hindenburg*, 809ft 5in long (only half its length is shown here).
**D** Montgolfier balloon of 1783, diameter of envelope 38ft, height 49ft.
**E** Boeing 747 Jumbo Jet, biggest capacity jet airliner, wing span 195ft 8in, length 231ft 4in.
**F** MiG-25 fighter, wing span 45ft 9in, length 73ft 2in.
**G** Concorde, supersonic airliner, wing span 83ft 10in, length 203ft 9in.

**Grounded Jumbo** *below*
A Jumbo Jet (231ft 4in long, 195ft 8in wing span) is shown on a soccer pitch (330ft long, 240ft wide).

If the airship *Hindenburg* had been stood on its end next to the Empire State Building, its nose would have reached almost to the windows on the 62nd floor.

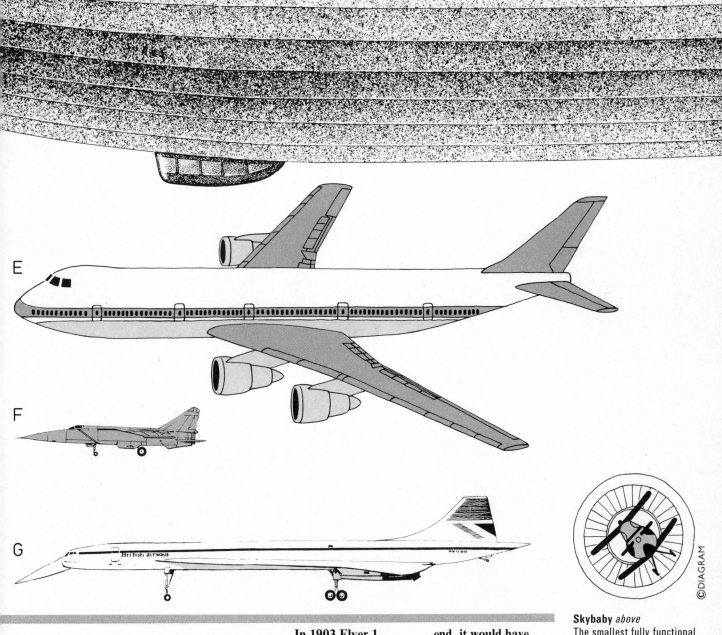

**Hindenburg**

E

F

G

**Skybaby** *above*
The smallest fully functional airplane, the Stits Skybaby (wing span 7ft 2in, length 9ft 10in) is shown here with a Pratt & Witney JT90 engine (intake diameter 8ft) used to power a Boeing 747.

In 1903 Flyer 1, the Wright brothers' biplane, traveled for 120ft through the air. If it had taken off inside a Boeing 747 Jumbo Jet at the tail end, it would have touched down 111ft from the nose—still inside the plane!

©DIAGRAM

49

# THE SOLAR SYSTEM

The Sun is much larger than any of the planets in orbit around it. Even Jupiter, the largest planet, has an equatorial diameter only about one tenth that of the Sun. Earth, which ranks fifth among the planets in terms of size, has an equatorial diameter less than one tenth that of Jupiter and one hundredth that of the Sun.

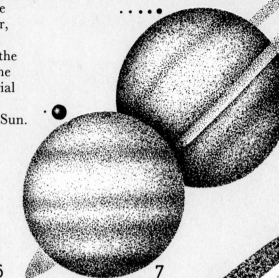

. . . . .

8

2  3  4  5  6  7

| | | | |
|---|---|---|---|
| Sun | 865,500mi | 1,392,900km | |
| Mercury | 3032mi | 4880km | 0 |
| Pluto | 3700mi | 6000km | 0 |
| Mars | 4217mi | 6787km | 2 |
| Venus | 7521mi | 12,104km | 0 |
| Earth | 7926mi | 12,756km | 1 |
| Neptune | 30,800mi | 49,500km | 2 |
| Uranus | 32,200mi | 51,800km | 5 |
| Saturn | 74,600mi | 120,000km | 10 |
| Jupiter | 88,700mi | 142,800km | 13 |

**Solar sisters** *above*
The scale drawings across the top of these pages and the tabular material on equatorial diameters allow us to compare the sizes of the Sun and its planets. We have included both imperial and metric measurements on these pages because scientific data is now more usually expressed in metric units. The most up-to-date information available has been used, but figures are subject to frequent revision. Also shown here are the known number of satellites for each planet.

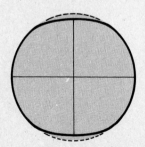

**Imperfect world** *left*
Like other planets the Earth is not a perfect sphere, being flattened slightly at the top and bottom. Measured at the Equator, its diameter is 7926mi (12,755km); at the Poles the diameter is only 7900mi (12,713km).

**On a human scale** *above*
If we suppose that the Sun's diameter is equal to the height of an average man, then Jupiter, the largest planet, would be slightly smaller than the man's head, while Earth would be slightly bigger than the iris of his eye.

**Size of asteroids** *right*
Asteroids are rocky bodies with diameters ranging from a few feet to several hundred miles. Examples are shown in scale with California.
a Ceres 429mi (690km)
b Vesta 244mi (393km)
c Fortuna 100mi (161km)
d Eros 11mi (18km)

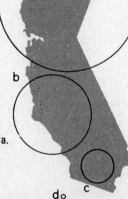

a
b
c
d

Measuring only 6 miles by 7½ miles by 10 miles, Deimos, the smaller of Mars's tiny rocky moons, would fit onto the John F. Kennedy Space Center, Cape Canaveral, Florida.

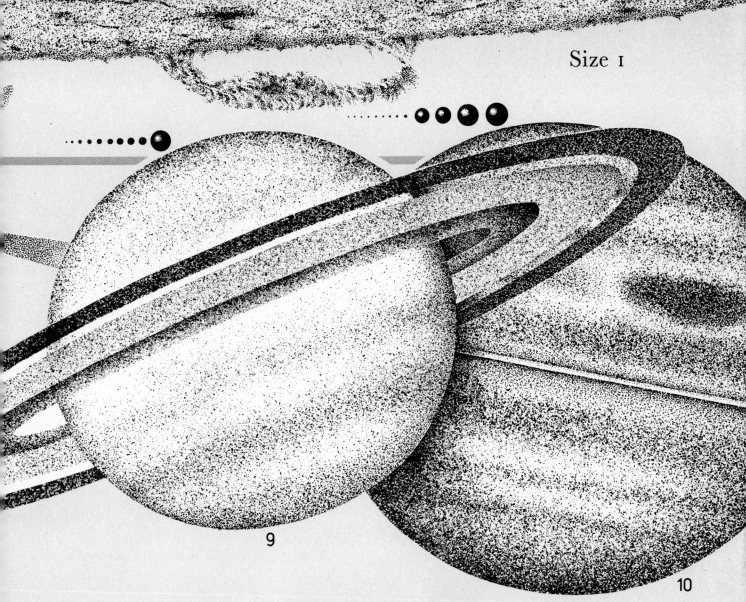

9

10

**Earth and Moon** *below*
For its size, Earth (**1**) has a larger satellite, or "moon" (**2**), than any other planet in our solar system. Earth's equatorial diameter is 7926mi (12,755km), while the Moon's diameter is just over one quarter of that, 2158mi (3473km).

**Large moons** *below*
Though much smaller than their own planets, these are bigger than Mercury:
**a** Titan, a moon of Saturn, 3600mi (5800km)
**b** Ganymede, a moon of Jupiter, 3275mi (5270km)
**c** Triton, a moon of Neptune, roughly 3000mi (4800km)

**Mighty meteorite** *below*
Meteorites—pieces of rock drawn into Earth's atmosphere from space— usually burn up before landing. The largest known to have landed, drawn here with a man of average size, is 9ft (2.74m) long by 8ft (2.44m) wide.

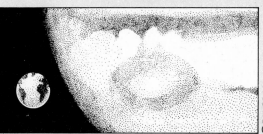

©DIAGRAM

**Great Red Spot** *above*
Often visible in Jupiter's atmosphere is the Great Red Spot, thought to be an anticyclone with a difference, for this one is some 8000mi (13,000km) wide and 25,000mi (40,000km) long—more than three times the diameter of Earth.

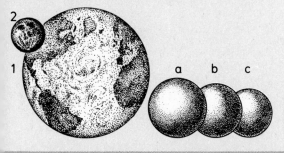

At a steady jogger's pace of 6mph it would take 173 days to go around the equatorial circumference of Earth, and more than 5 years (some 1935 days) to go around the circumference of the largest planet, Jupiter.

# SUN AND STARS

The Sun is over 100 times bigger than Earth, and in Earth terms solar features like flares and sunspots are of truly gigantic proportions. In galactic terms, however, our Sun is only one of perhaps 100,000 million stars, which range in size from half as big as our Moon to over 10,000 times larger than Earth.

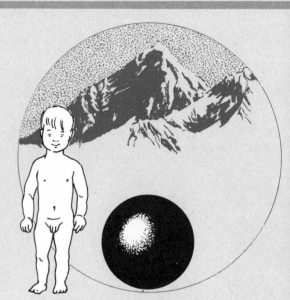

**Relative sizes** *right*
If the diameter of the largest known star, IRS5, were the height of Mount Everest, our Sun's diameter would be the height of an 18-month-old child, and Sirius B, one of the smallest known stars, would be only 1in in diameter.

1

**Solar flares** *above*
Violent eruptions of incandescent gases, solar flares are an impressive feature of the Sun's atmosphere. Huge arcs of gas disintegrate and stream out into space (**1**), to distances greater than that from Earth to Moon.

**Sunspots** *left*
Groups of sunspots are a common feature of the Sun's surface, sometimes visible to the naked eye. A single spot may measure as much as 8 times the Earth's diameter. Groups are typically 100,000mi (160,000km) across.

**Star story** *right*
At its birth the Sun was a small red star, formed by the contraction of interstellar material. It is now in the second stage of its development, a fairly small brilliant star, represented here by the small sphere in the center. Over a period of perhaps 10,000 million years it is expected to expand, as shown here, until its diameter is 50 times its present size. It will then become unstable, eject matter and collapse into a small dense white dwarf, smaller than it is now.

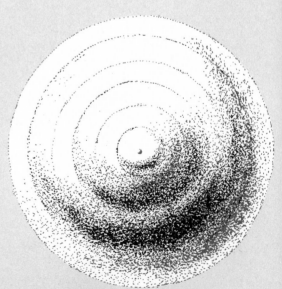

**Little star** *left*
The smallest known star is the white dwarf LP 327–186. As shown here, its estimated diameter, approximately 1000mi (1600km), is only one-half that of our Moon.

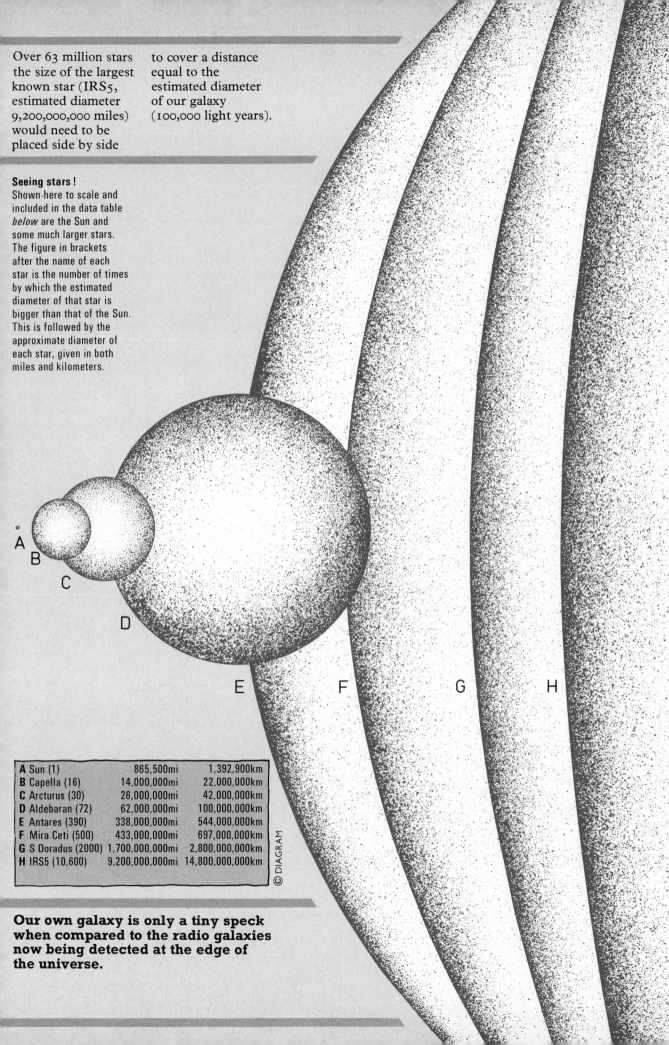

Over 63 million stars the size of the largest known star (IRS5, estimated diameter 9,200,000,000 miles) would need to be placed side by side to cover a distance equal to the estimated diameter of our galaxy (100,000 light years).

**Seeing stars!**
Shown here to scale and included in the data table *below* are the Sun and some much larger stars. The figure in brackets after the name of each star is the number of times by which the estimated diameter of that star is bigger than that of the Sun. This is followed by the approximate diameter of each star, given in both miles and kilometers.

| | | miles | kilometers |
|---|---|---|---|
| **A** | Sun (1) | 865,500mi | 1,392,900km |
| **B** | Capella (16) | 14,000,000mi | 22,000,000km |
| **C** | Arcturus (30) | 26,000,000mi | 42,000,000km |
| **D** | Aldebaran (72) | 62,000,000mi | 100,000,000km |
| **E** | Antares (390) | 338,000,000mi | 544,000,000km |
| **F** | Mira Ceti (500) | 433,000,000mi | 697,000,000km |
| **G** | S Doradus (2000) | 1,700,000,000mi | 2,800,000,000km |
| **H** | IRS5 (10,600) | 9,200,000,000mi | 14,800,000,000km |

© DIAGRAM

**Our own galaxy is only a tiny speck when compared to the radio galaxies now being detected at the edge of the universe.**

# CHAPTER 3

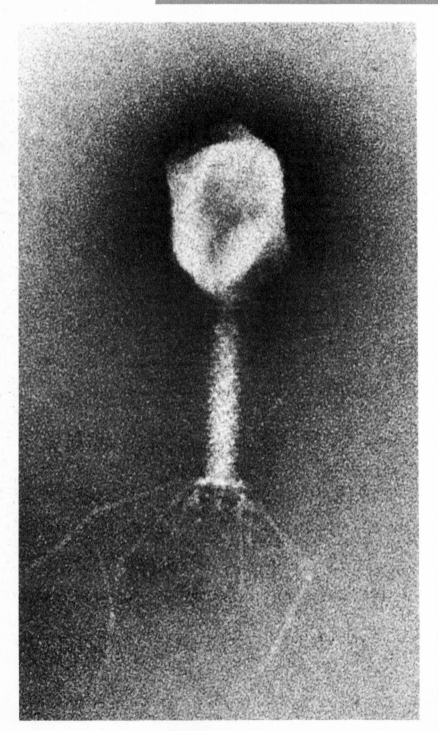

A T4 virus, which attacks the bacteria of the colon, is shown more than 400,000 times actual size in this enlarged negative-contrast electron micrograph (Basel University, Switzerland).

Post card showing a huge Californian water melon— evidence of an unofficial record-breaker, or a clever photomontage (Fred C. Moran; Smith International News, Los Angeles).

An 18th-century English engraving showing whale-men at work in Greenland. The whale's great size and strength are insufficient protection against the weapons and greed of man.

# SIZE: LIVING WORLD

A publicity photograph for
Giant Machnow, an
Irishman who appeared at
the London Hippodrome in
1905. He was billed as
being some 9ft 4in tall
(Mansell Collection).

# MICROSCOPIC LIFE

Microscopes and electron microscopes allow us to see in detail a host of living organisms that are invisible to the naked eye. On these two pages we use different degrees of magnification to compare some of these organisms, both plant and animal, unicellular and multicellular, simple and exceedingly complex.

**Small-scale creatures**
*below* Progressively greater magnifications are here used to show smaller and smaller life-forms.
**Magnification A** (x100)
**1** Euglena, which has plant and animal characteristics.
**2** Amoeba, a minute animal.
**3** Chlamydomonas, a plant.

**Magnification B** (x1000)
**3** Chlamydomonas, with its whiplike flagella, can now be seen quite clearly.
**4** A bacterium, however, is still only a tiny speck when magnified 1000 times.

**Not the bee's knees!**
*left* Here we compare the relative sizes of a queen honeybee and a parasite that lives upon it.
**a** A queen honeybee (1.5cm long) is shown here actual size. Drones are similar in size to the queen, but workers are smaller (1.2cm).
**b** One of the honeybee's legs is here magnified 10 times; the parasite (drawn in color) is also visible at this magnification.
**c** A magnification of 100 times actual size gives a detailed picture of the honeybee's unwelcome guest: *Braula caeca* (0.8mm long).

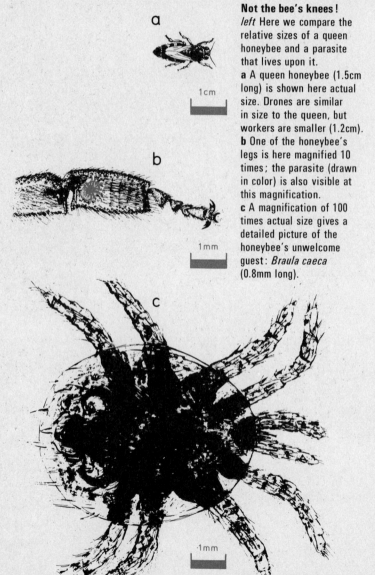

1cm

1mm

·1mm

1

2

3

·1mm

A

**Microscopic monsters**
*right* A magnification of 100 times actual size (similar to that used for the honeybee parasite *left*) shows huge variety among microscopic creatures. Here we show a small selection.
**d** *Phthirus pubis* (1–1.5mm long), crab louse, a blood-sucking parasite of humans.
**e** *Tetranychus urticae* (0.5mm), a reddish mite that sucks plant juices.
**f** *Folsomia fimetaria* (1mm), a springtail that lives in soil and attacks roots.
**g** *Knemidocoptes mutans* (0.25mm male; 0.45mm female), mange mite, gnaws the skin of many animals.

*Chondromyces* bacteria climb one on top of another to form towers several millimeters high. On a human scale, these towers would be over a mile high, or some four times the height of the World Trade Center in New York.

**Magnification C** (x10,000)
At this magnification we can clearly distinguish examples of the three basic types of bacterium.
**4** Cocci are spherical, and may be in groups or chains.
**5** Spirilla are spiral or comma-shaped.
**6** Bacilli are rod-shaped.

**Magnification D** (x100,000)
**6** Bacillus, with details of its structure now clearly visible.
**7** Virus, shown attacking the bacillus; viruses can reproduce only inside other living bodies.
**Magnification E** (x1,000,000)
**7** Part of the same virus.

**Quick scale-guide** *left*
Here we use well-known creatures to show the relative sizes of some of the life-forms *below*. If an amoeba (**2**) were as big as an elephant, chlamydomonas (**3**) would be the size of a cat, and a bacterium (**4**) the size of a flea.

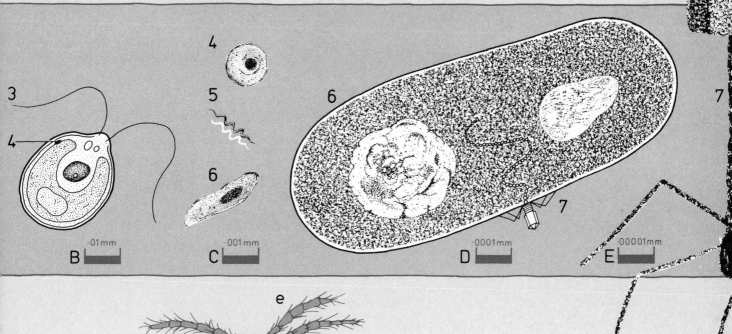

3
4
5
6
7

.01mm  B
.001mm  C
.0001mm  D
.00001mm  E

7

©DIAGRAM

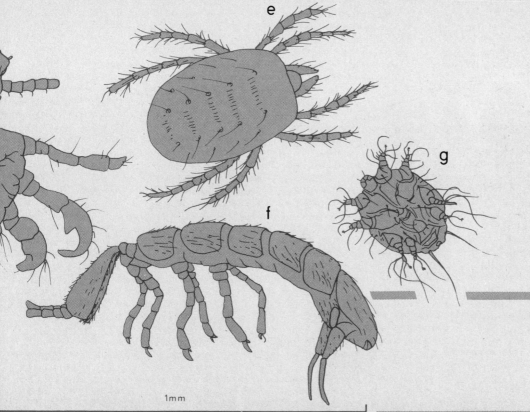

e
f
g

1mm

# PLANTS

On the previous two pages we compared some of the very smallest living things. Here we turn to some of the largest, all members of the plant kingdom. The Californian redwood is the tallest species of plant alive today. Also illustrated for comparison are some unusually large examples of generally much smaller plants.

**Tallest tree** *left*
Trees are the tallest of all living things, and the Californian redwood (**1**) is the tallest of all modern trees. Its record height of 366ft exceeds the length of a soccer pitch by 36ft, and is over 63 times the height of an average man.

**Tallest plants** *below*
Some record plants might not seem particularly tall when compared with the enormous Californian redwood, but each of the examples included here is a giant of its own kind.
**1** Californian redwood 366ft
**2** Bamboo 121ft
**3** Tree fern *Alsophila excelsa* 60ft
**4** Saguaro cactus 52ft
**5** Orchid *Grammatophyllum speciosum* 25ft
**6** Callie grass 18ft

**Floral phenomena** *right*
How about considering one or two of these splendid specimens for an impressive floral display? They are drawn here to scale along with a gardener, a man of average height (5ft 9in).
**A** The world's tallest orchid, *Grammatophyllum speciosum* from Malaysia, is sometimes 25ft tall.
**B** The tallest sunflower measured in the UK was 23ft 6½in high.
**C** The US record height for a hollyhock is an imposing 18ft 9½in.
**D** The tallest recorded dahlia measured 9ft 10¾in and was grown in Australia.
**E** The British record for a lupin is 6ft 0½in.

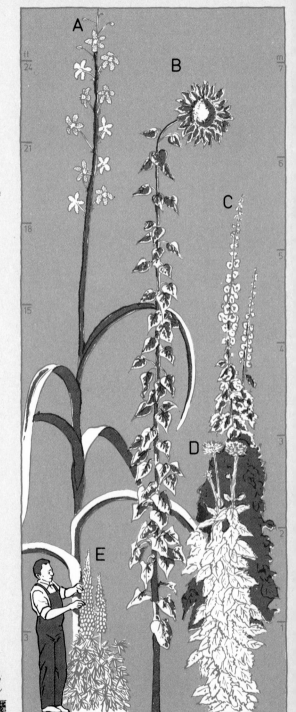

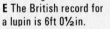

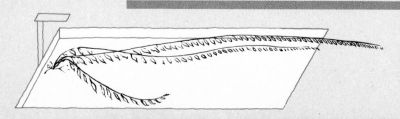

The longest recorded strand of seaweed measured 196ft, 31ft longer than the length of an Olympic swimming pool.

To quote a poem by David Everett (1769–1813), "tall oaks from little acorns grow," but to be more precise, 120ft oak trees grow from ¾in long acorns.

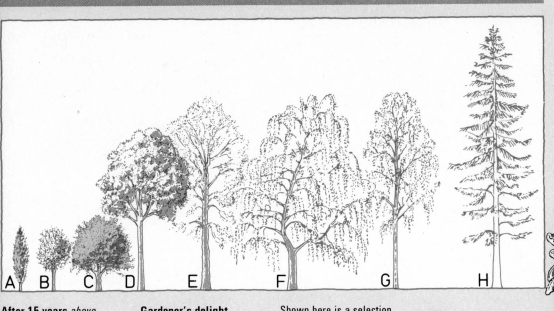

**After 15 years** *above*
Some typical heights:
**A** Juniper 10ft
**B** Holly 10ft
**C** Yew 12ft
**D** Oak 25ft
**E** Poplar 30ft
**F** Weeping willow 30ft
**G** Silver birch 30ft
**H** Douglas fir 40ft

**Gardener's delight**
*right* Man is always trying to grow bigger and better crops, but producing record-breakers is not without its problems. Imagine having to climb a ladder to pick a Brussels sprout from a plant that is over 10ft tall!

Shown here is a selection of record-breaking food plants, with their normal heights given in brackets for comparison.
**1** Rhubarb 5ft 1in (2–3ft)
**2** Brussels sprout 10ft 8in (3ft)
**3** Kale 12ft (1–3ft)
**4** Tomato 20ft (3–4ft)

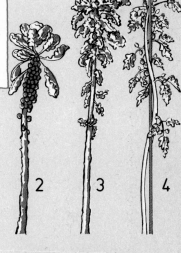

**Towering timber** *left*
All these record-breaking trees come from the USA.
**A** Californian redwood 366ft
**B** Douglas fir 302ft
**C** Fir noble 278ft
**D** Giant sequoia 272ft
**E** Ponderosa pine 223ft
**F** Cedar 219ft
**G** Sitka spruce 216ft
**H** Western larch 177ft
**I** Hemlock 163ft
**J** Beech 161ft
**K** Black cottonwood 147ft

**This letter o could contain over 20 blooms of the artillery plant *Pilea microphylla* from India. The smallest blooms known, their diameter is only 1/72 of an inch.**

The largest bloom is that of the stinking corpse lily *Rafflesia arnoldii*. Its diameter of up to 3ft is equal to the width of 4½ pages of this book.

59

©DIAGRAM

# MARINE CREATURES

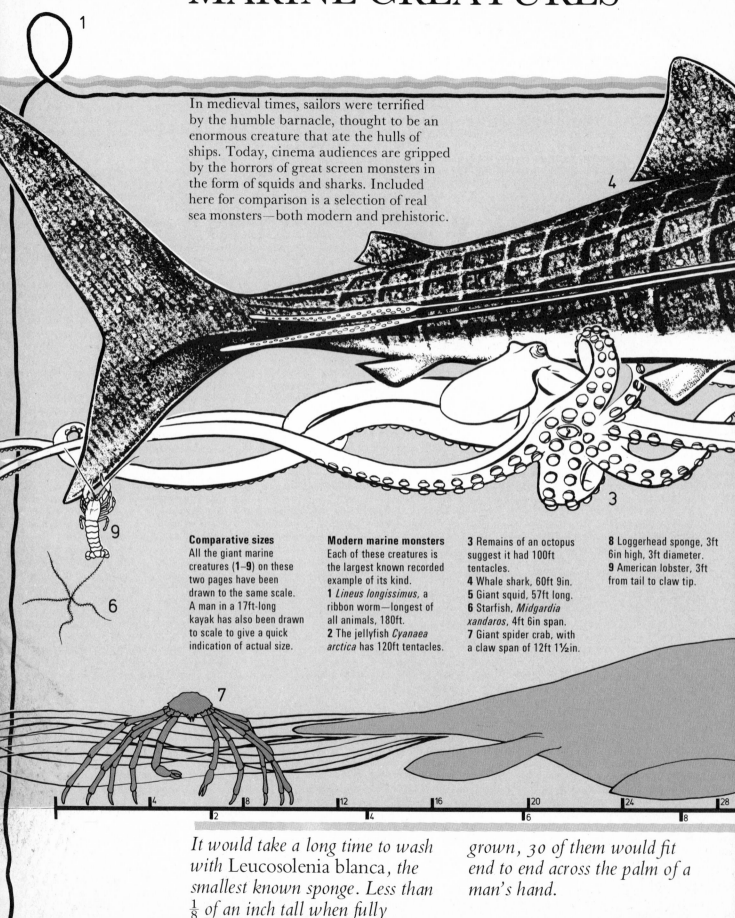

In medieval times, sailors were terrified by the humble barnacle, thought to be an enormous creature that ate the hulls of ships. Today, cinema audiences are gripped by the horrors of great screen monsters in the form of squids and sharks. Included here for comparison is a selection of real sea monsters—both modern and prehistoric.

**Comparative sizes**
All the giant marine creatures (1–9) on these two pages have been drawn to the same scale. A man in a 17ft-long kayak has also been drawn to scale to give a quick indication of actual size.

**Modern marine monsters**
Each of these creatures is the largest known recorded example of its kind.
1 *Lineus longissimus,* a ribbon worm—longest of all animals, 180ft.
2 The jellyfish *Cyanaea arctica* has 120ft tentacles.

3 Remains of an octopus suggest it had 100ft tentacles.
4 Whale shark, 60ft 9in.
5 Giant squid, 57ft long.
6 Starfish, *Midgardia xandaros,* 4ft 6in span.
7 Giant spider crab, with a claw span of 12ft 1½in.

8 Loggerhead sponge, 3ft 6in high, 3ft diameter.
9 American lobster, 3ft from tail to claw tip.

*It would take a long time to wash with* Leucosolenia blanca, *the smallest known sponge. Less than* $\frac{1}{8}$ *of an inch tall when fully grown, 30 of them would fit end to end across the palm of a man's hand.*

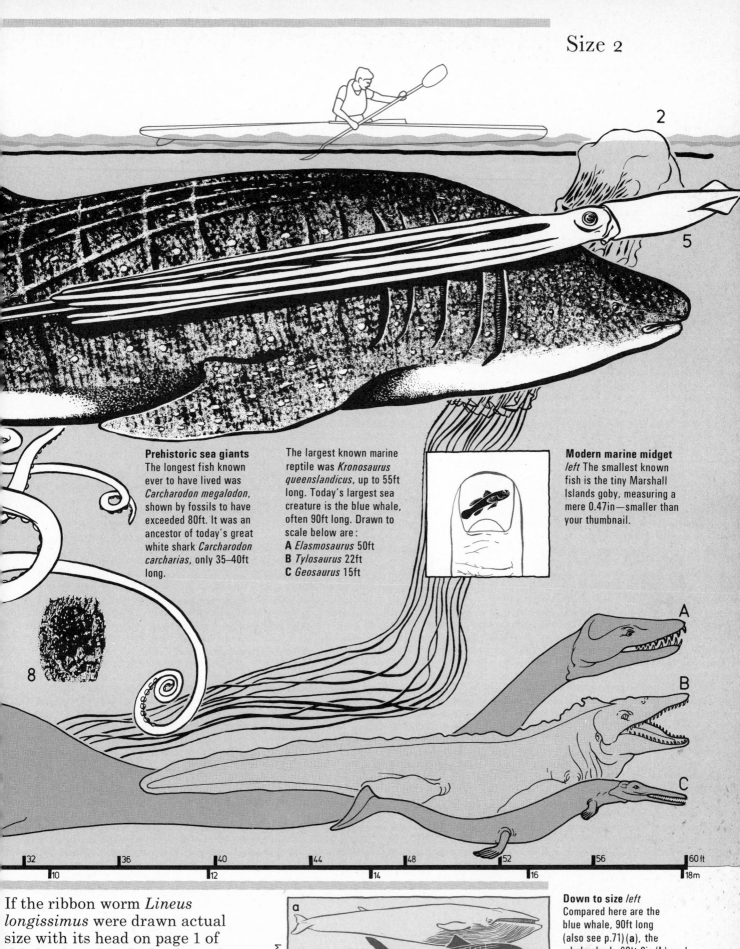

2

5

8

**Prehistoric sea giants**
The longest fish known ever to have lived was *Carcharodon megalodon*, shown by fossils to have exceeded 80ft. It was an ancestor of today's great white shark *Carcharodon carcharias*, only 35–40ft long.

The largest known marine reptile was *Kronosaurus queenslandicus*, up to 55ft long. Today's largest sea creature is the blue whale, often 90ft long. Drawn to scale below are:
**A** *Elasmosaurus* 50ft
**B** *Tylosaurus* 22ft
**C** *Geosaurus* 15ft

**Modern marine midget**
*left* The smallest known fish is the tiny Marshall Islands goby, measuring a mere 0.47in—smaller than your thumbnail.

A

B

C

| 32 | | 36 | | 40 | | 44 | | 48 | | 52 | | 56 | | 60 ft |
| 10 | | 12 | | | 14 | | 16 | | 18m |

If the ribbon worm *Lineus longissimus* were drawn actual size with its head on page 1 of this book and its body along the bottom of each page, its tail would dangle 15ft beyond the end!

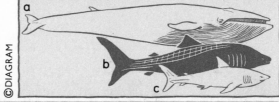

a

b

c

©DIAGRAM

**Down to size** *left*
Compared here are the blue whale, 90ft long (also see p.71) (**a**), the whale shark, 60ft 9in (**b**), and the aggressive great white shark, up to 40ft (**c**).

# REPTILES

The largest creatures ever to have roamed on Earth were probably reptiles—the huge dinosaurs of prehistoric times. *Diplodocus*, the longest dinosaur, makes today's largest lizard, the rare Komodo dragon, look like small fry. Today's largest crocodilian, the estuarine or saltwater crocodile, is certainly a force to be reckoned with, but at 20ft long it is much smaller than its 50ft-long prehistoric forebears. The biggest prehistoric turtle was probably about twice the length of the modern Pacific leatherback, but the largest prehistoric snakes are thought to have been little longer than modern anacondas and pythons.

**Snakes and ladders**
*left, below* A selection of present-day snakes—from the largest to the smallest—is illustrated here. Though often very large, constrictors, which kill by suffocation, are generally less dangerous than smaller venomous types.

**A** Anaconda, a constrictor from S America. Up to 30ft long, sometimes more.
**B** Reticulated python, a constrictor from SE Asia. May exceed 30ft.
**C** King cobra, from India. World's largest venomous snake, 18ft.
**D** Boa constrictor, from tropical America, 14ft.
**E** Eastern diamond-backed rattlesnake, venomous snake from N America. Largest rattler, 7–8ft.
**F** Mamba, venomous, from C and S Africa, 7ft.
**G** Grass snake, harmless European snake, 3ft.
**H** Thread snake, W Indies, world's shortest, 4½in.

**Smallest reptile** *above*
The smallest known reptile species, *Sphaerodactylus parthenopion*, is a type of gecko lizard. As shown here real size, adults measure less than ¾in from snout to vent, with a tail of approximately similar length.

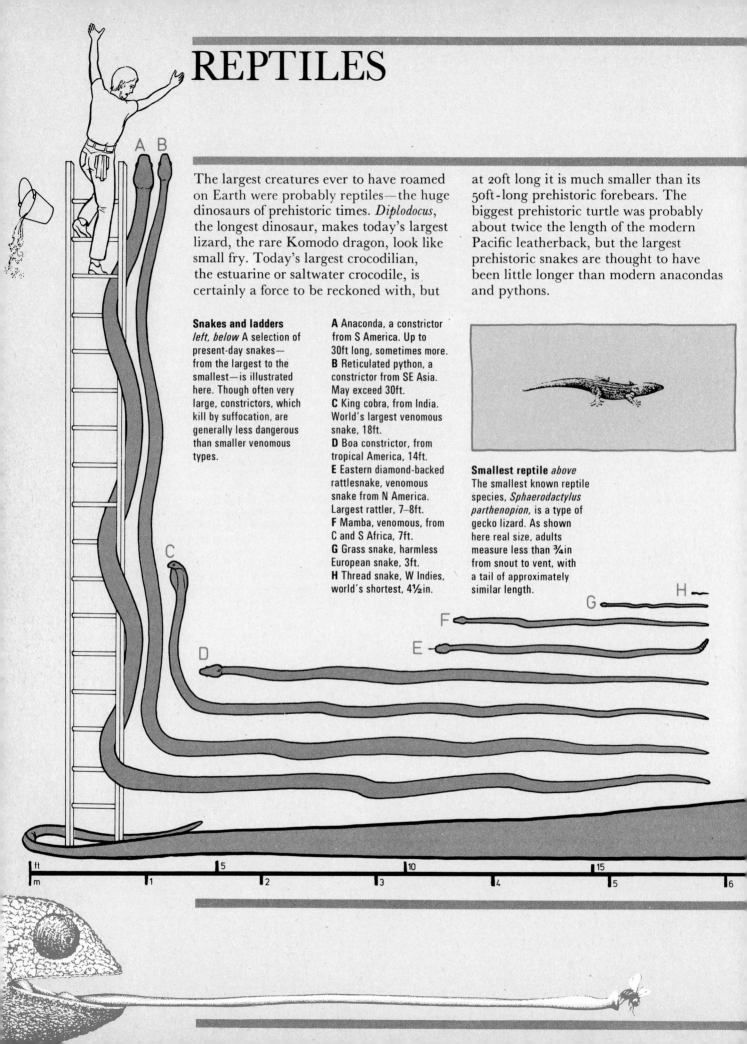

| ft | | 5 | | | 10 | | 15 | |
| m | 1 | 2 | 3 | 4 | 5 | 6 |

A crocodile's egg, about 3¼in long, is approximately the same size as a goose egg.

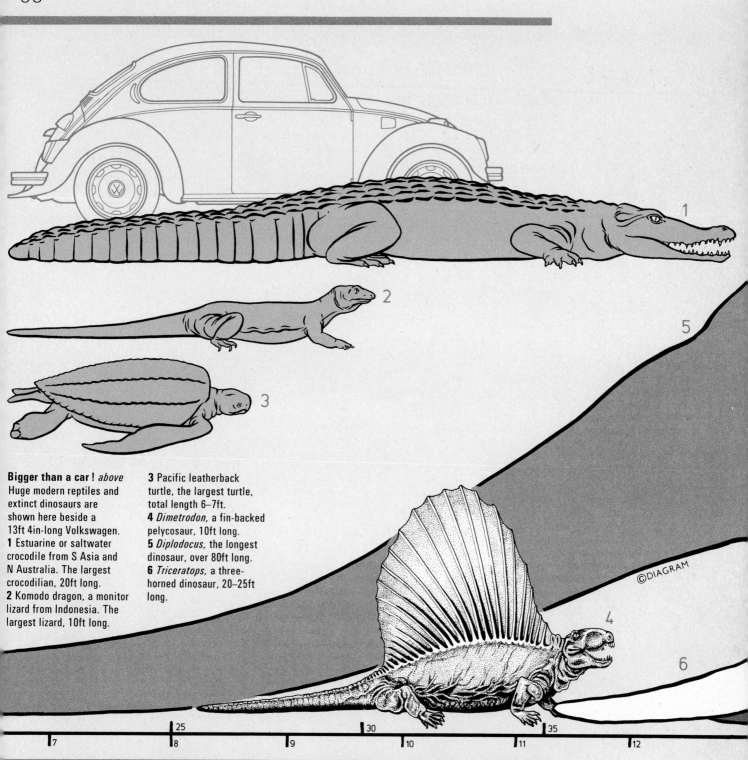

**Bigger than a car!** *above* Huge modern reptiles and extinct dinosaurs are shown here beside a 13ft 4in-long Volkswagen.
**1** Estuarine or saltwater crocodile from S Asia and N Australia. The largest crocodilian, 20ft long.
**2** Komodo dragon, a monitor lizard from Indonesia. The largest lizard, 10ft long.

**3** Pacific leatherback turtle, the largest turtle, total length 6–7ft.
**4** *Dimetrodon*, a fin-backed pelycosaur, 10ft long.
**5** *Diplodocus*, the longest dinosaur, over 80ft long.
**6** *Triceratops*, a three-horned dinosaur, 20–25ft long.

©DIAGRAM

**A chameleon can afford to "give you a piece of its tongue," for its tongue can be extended to a distance equal to its body length.**

Turn over the page to see the bodies and heads of the huge *Diplodocus* (5) and *Triceratops* (6).

# DINOSAURS

The huge dinosaurs or "terrible lizards" of Jurassic and Cretaceous times (190–65 million years ago) were the largest land creatures ever to have lived. Man did not appear for probably another 60 million years, but a man of average size (5ft 9in) is included here for comparison, drawn to the same scale as our six dinosaur examples.

**It's just possible that you could have jumped on the tail of a *Diplodocus* and got away with it—because of the time taken for a nerve** impulse to travel from the tail to the brain and back again.

*The Stegosaurus, a playful 25ft long, had a brain the size of a walnut.*

**1** *Parasaurolophus*, a duck-billed dinosaur with a large bony headcrest. A herbivore from late Cretaceous times, it was about 30ft long.
**2** *Tyrannosaurus*, the largest carnivorous dinosaur. Remains from the Cretaceous period suggest it was 18ft high and perhaps up to 47ft long.

**3** *Ornitholestes*, a small carnivorous dinosaur from Jurassic times. Its name means bird-catcher but it probably ate mainly reptiles. About 6ft long.
**4** *Stegosaurus*, a heavily armored herbivore with big triangular bony plates like sails along its spine. From the Jurassic period, 12–13ft tall, 18–25ft long.
**5** *Diplodocus*, a huge plant-eater from the Cretaceous period. The longest of the dinosaurs; a composite skeleton in Pittsburgh is 87½ft long.
**6** *Triceratops*, a late Cretaceous dinosaur with three horns and a bony neck frill. A strong and agile fighter, 8–10ft tall and 20–25ft long.

©DIAGRAM

Some horned dinosaurs had horns up to 3ft long, making them longer than the legs of an average man.

# INVERTEBRATES

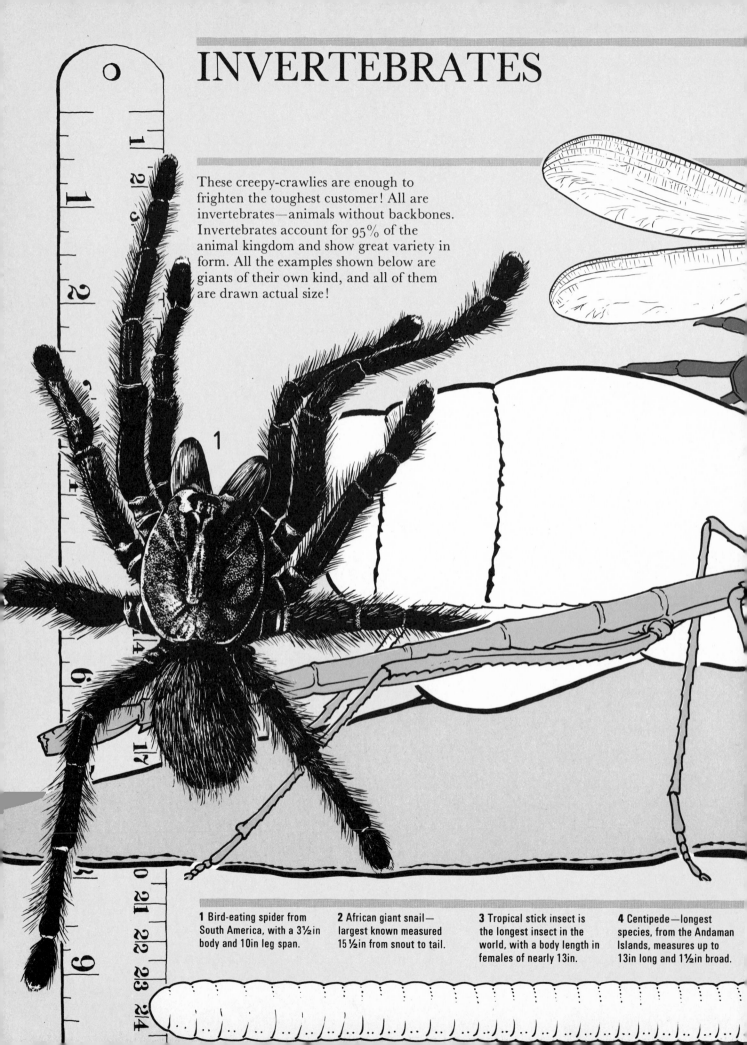

These creepy-crawlies are enough to frighten the toughest customer! All are invertebrates—animals without backbones. Invertebrates account for 95% of the animal kingdom and show great variety in form. All the examples shown below are giants of their own kind, and all of them are drawn actual size!

**1** Bird-eating spider from South America, with a 3½in body and 10in leg span.

**2** African giant snail— largest known measured 15½in from snout to tail.

**3** Tropical stick insect is the longest insect in the world, with a body length in females of nearly 13in.

**4** Centipede—longest species, from the Andaman Islands, measures up to 13in long and 1½in broad.

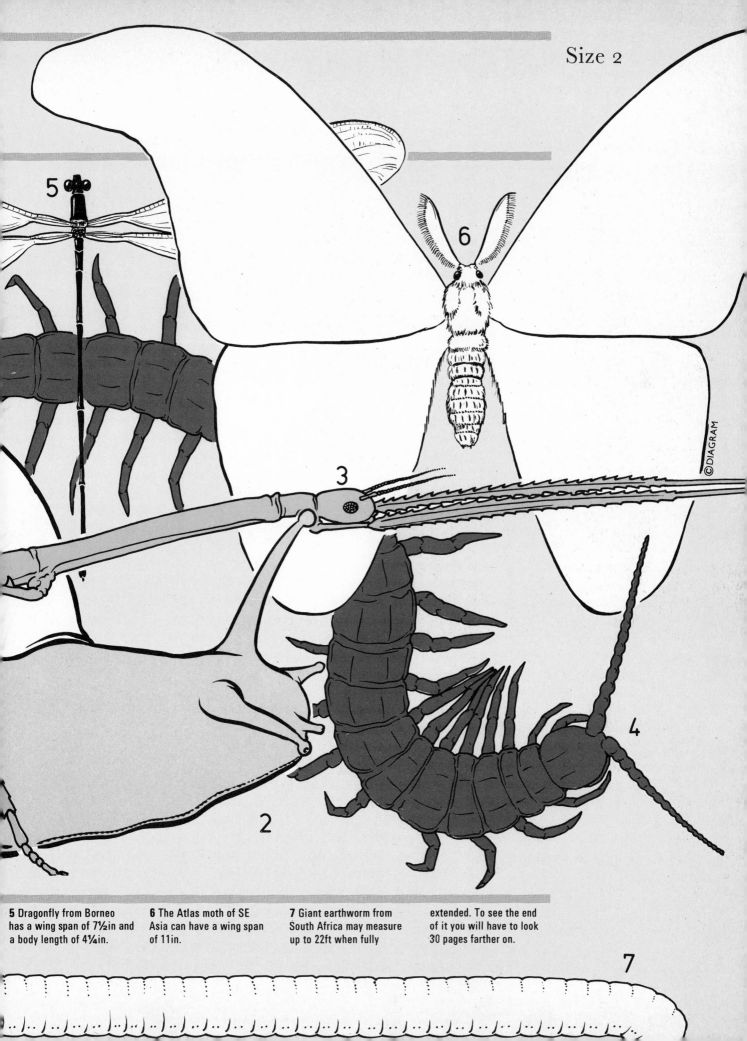

©DIAGRAM

**5** Dragonfly from Borneo has a wing span of 7½in and a body length of 4¼in.

**6** The Atlas moth of SE Asia can have a wing span of 11in.

**7** Giant earthworm from South Africa may measure up to 22ft when fully

extended. To see the end of it you will have to look 30 pages farther on.

# BIRDS

Fossils of birdlike creatures suggest that the early birds caught the records for size. In fact these huge creatures were not birds at all, but pterosaurs. The largest known prehistoric bird was the elephant bird. Today the largest bird is the ostrich, but the wandering albatross has the greatest wing span.

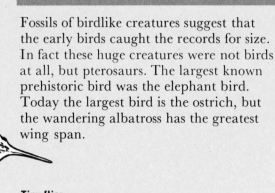

**Tiny flier**
*left* The smallest bird in the world, shown here real size, is Helena's hummingbird from Cuba. An average adult male measures only 2¼in from bill tip to tail.

**Domestic birds** *above*
The swan (**A**), goose (**B**), hen (**C**), duck (**D**) and pigeon (**E**) have such different body proportions that it is easier to make a visual assessment of their comparative sizes than it is to express this in statistics.

**Flightless giants**
*above* Flightless birds take the records for size. Our examples are shown to scale with a man of average height (5ft 9in).

**1** North African ostrich, the tallest bird alive today. Males are sometimes up to 9ft tall.
**2** Moa from New Zealand, probably the tallest extinct bird. May have been 13ft tall.
**3** Elephant bird from Madagascar, thought to have been the most massive but not the tallest prehistoric bird, 9–10ft tall.

**Exceptional eggs** *left*
The largest egg laid by any bird alive today is that of the ostrich, 6–8in long. The smallest is that of Helena's hummingbird, under ½in.

The kalong, a huge fruit bat from Indonesia, has a wing span of up to 5ft 7in—or roughly 1½ times the length of a baseball bat (3ft 6in).

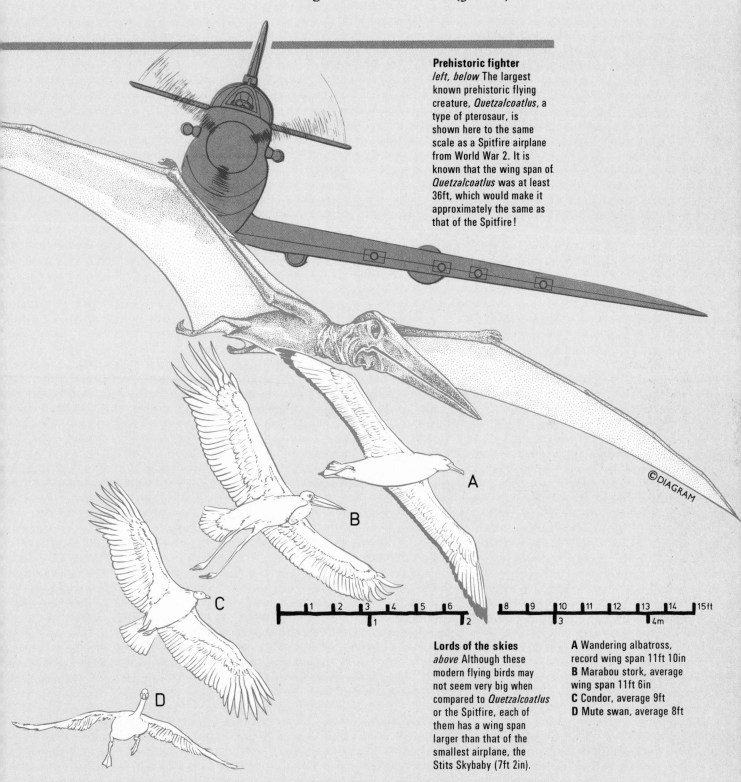

**Prehistoric fighter**
*left, below* The largest known prehistoric flying creature, *Quetzalcoatlus*, a type of pterosaur, is shown here to the same scale as a Spitfire airplane from World War 2. It is known that the wing span of *Quetzalcoatlus* was at least 36ft, which would make it approximately the same as that of the Spitfire!

©DIAGRAM

A

B

C

D

1 2 3 4 5 6 8 9 10 11 12 13 14 15ft
1 2 3 4m

**Lords of the skies**
*above* Although these modern flying birds may not seem very big when compared to *Quetzalcoatlus* or the Spitfire, each of them has a wing span larger than that of the smallest airplane, the Stits Skybaby (7ft 2in).

**A** Wandering albatross, record wing span 11ft 10in
**B** Marabou stork, average wing span 11ft 6in
**C** Condor, average 9ft
**D** Mute swan, average 8ft

The 11ft 10in wing span of a wandering albatross is approximately twice the arm span of a man of average height.

# MAMMALS

Today's largest mammal, the blue whale, is probably the largest mammal ever to have lived. The record for the largest land mammal, however, goes to a prehistoric creature, the *Paraceratherium*, a huge, hornless rhinolike creature that lived some 40 to 20 million years ago. The largest modern land animal is the African elephant. The tallest is the giraffe. Some of today's mammals, such as the tiger, rhino and armadillo, are smaller than their prehistoric forebears. Others, notably the horse, are very much bigger. All the extinct mammals below and the living mammals facing them are drawn to the same scale for easy visual comparison.

**Extinct land mammals**
**A** *Megatherium,* a type of sloth, about 20ft long.
**B** *Paraceratherium,* 35–37ft long, 18ft at shoulder.
**C** Mammoth, largest perhaps 14ft 9in at shoulder.
**D** Saber-toothed tiger, about 3ft 4in at shoulder.
**E** *Oxydactylus,* a Miocene camel, 4ft 6in at shoulder.
**F** *Synthetoceras,* 6ft long.
**G** *Glyptodon,* 9ft long.
**H** *Eohippus,* an early horse, 18in long, 9in at shoulder.

*Eohippus,* **a prehistoric horse, was approximately the same size as a modern cat.**

The mighty ape in the 1933 film "King Kong" appeared to be a terrifying 50ft tall—in reality, the model used was a mere 18in from head to toe.

**Monster whale**
*left* The blue whale is the largest of all mammals. Specimens 90ft long are not unusual; the longest ever recorded was over 110ft. To give an indication of comparative size, the illustration also includes an elephant and a giraffe.

**Modern land mammals**
**1** Giraffe may tower 19ft above ground.
**2** African elephant, male about 10ft 6in at shoulder.
**3** Horse, usually 5ft to 5ft 6in at shoulder. Record 6ft 6in (19.2 hands).
**4** Average man 5ft 9in tall; average woman 5ft 3¾in.

**5** White rhino, 6ft 6in at shoulder, 16ft long.
**6** Cow, 5ft at shoulder.
**7** Bactrian camel, 7ft to top of humps.
**8** Brown bear may be up to 8ft when standing erect.
**9** Armadillo, total length 2ft 6in.
**10** Cat, 9in at shoulder.

**The tiny shrew**
*above* Drawn actual size, the pygmy shrew has a head and body length of 1.7in. Its tail adds another 1.2in.

©DIAGRAM

A mammoth's shoulder height was a little greater than the height of a London double-decker bus (14ft 4½in); *Paraceratherium* could have looked over such a bus with ease.

# HUMANS

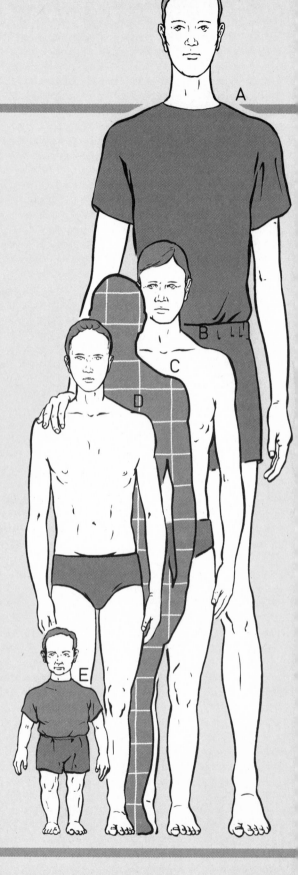

In reality there are no such persons as Mr and Mrs Average, but studies of the vital statistics of US adult males and females provide some interesting comparisons. For example, although the height range of the "normal" (95% of all males or females) is quite small (only 10in), the range of the possible is surprisingly great (about 6ft).

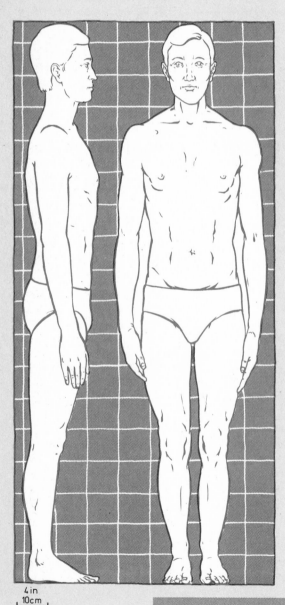

**Mr Average**
*left* The dimensions of the "average" US male are as follows:
Height 5ft 9in
Weight 162lb
Chest 38¾in
Waist 31¾in
Hips 37¾in

**Large and little**
*right* The "average" US male is shown here, plus figures representing the upper and lower limits of growth—both "normal" (95% of the adult male population) and extreme.
**A** The tallest reliably measured male was Robert Wadlow (1918–40) of the USA, 8ft 11in.
**B** Upper limit of normal range, 6ft 2in.
**C** Average US male, 5ft 9in.
**D** Lower limit of normal range, 5ft 4in.
**E** The shortest recorded adult male was Calvin Phillips (1791–1812) of the USA, who measured 2ft 2½in.

4 in
10cm

*While the head is one quarter of the total length at birth, it is only one sixth by the age of six and one eighth by adulthood.*

A baby grows fastest in the last three months before birth. If a child continued to grow at this rate he would be 18ft 4in tall at age 10 years!

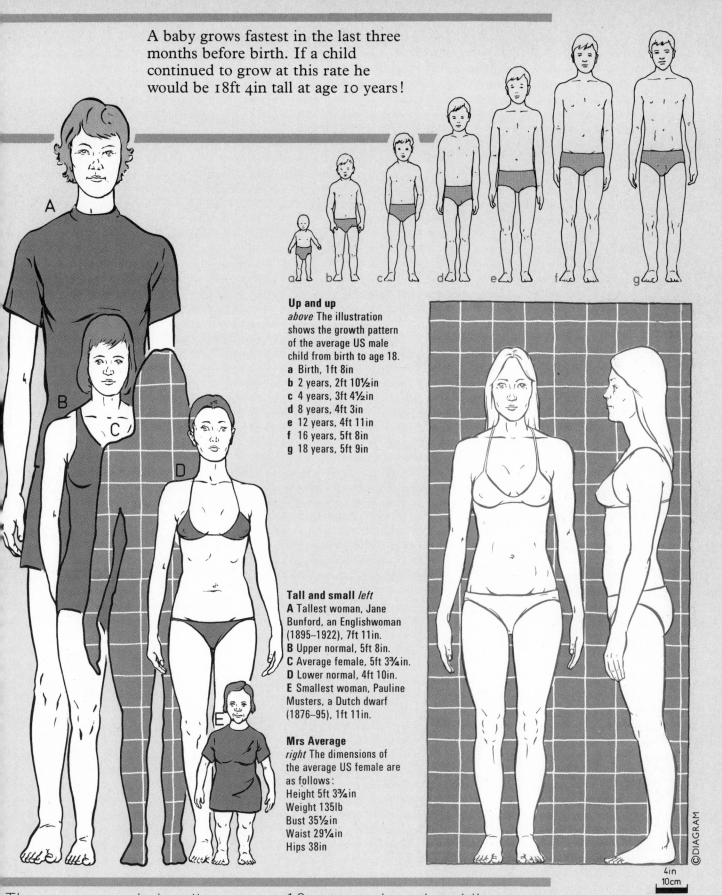

## Up and up
*above* The illustration shows the growth pattern of the average US male child from birth to age 18.
**a** Birth, 1ft 8in
**b** 2 years, 2ft 10½in
**c** 4 years, 3ft 4½in
**d** 8 years, 4ft 3in
**e** 12 years, 4ft 11in
**f** 16 years, 5ft 8in
**g** 18 years, 5ft 9in

## Tall and small *left*
**A** Tallest woman, Jane Bunford, an Englishwoman (1895–1922), 7ft 11in.
**B** Upper normal, 5ft 8in.
**C** Average female, 5ft 3¾in.
**D** Lower normal, 4ft 10in.
**E** Smallest woman, Pauline Musters, a Dutch dwarf (1876–95), 1ft 11in.

## Mrs Average
*right* The dimensions of the average US female are as follows:
Height 5ft 3¾in
Weight 135lb
Bust 35½in
Waist 29¼in
Hips 38in

4in
10cm

©DIAGRAM

The average male is taller than the average female at all ages except around age 12 years, when the girl's pre-puberty growth spurt puts her briefly ahead.

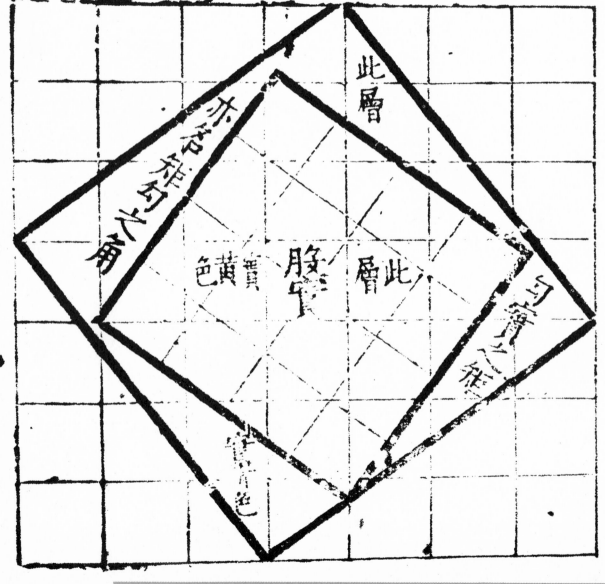

# CHAPTER 4

圖　　左

This illustration of what is now generally known as Pythagoras' theorem is from *Ch'ou-pei Suan-king,* an ancient Chinese treatise dating from c.1100BC (British Museum).

# AREA AND VOLUME

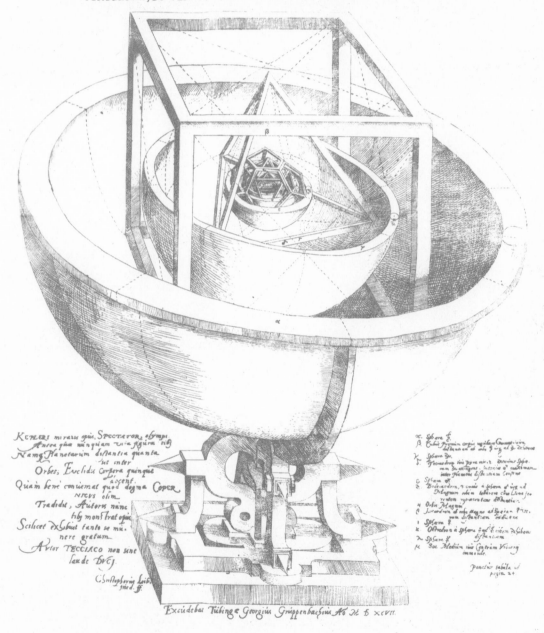

From Kepler's *Continens Misterium Cosmografica* of 1596, this diagram shows models of the five perfect solids fitted between spheres representing the orbits of the six planets known at that time (Science Museum, London).

# MEASURING AREA

Area measurements describe the size of surfaces, which may be either flat or curved, in terms of the number of square units that can be fitted within them. The sporadic development of the US/imperial units has resulted in a variety of multiplication factors, whereas the metric system is firmly based on multiples of 10.

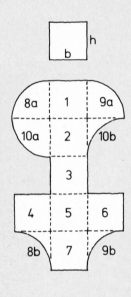

**Measuring area** *left*
The area of a square is its base (**b**) multiplied by its height (**h**). Shown is a square with sides of 1cm. Using this square centimeter (cm²) as a unit of measurement we see that the irregular shape shown has an area of 10cm².

**Geometric areas** *left*
Written inside these common geometric shapes are the formulae for calculating their areas.
Shapes shown are:
**1** Rectangle
**2** Parallelogram
**3** Triangle
**4** Trapezium
**5** Circle
Abbreviations used are:
**A** = area
**a** = top
**b** = base
**h** = height
$\pi$ = 3.1416
**r** = radius

**Metric area units** *right*
The table gives the basic units. Square millimeters, centimeters, meters and kilometers have been expressed by the standard abbreviations (mm², cm², m² and km²). Not used here are the abbreviations for are (a) and hectare (ha).

**Visualizing areas** *below*
All these areas are drawn to a common scale.
**A** A square chain (484yd²) is shown together with a basketball court (427yd²).
**B** An acre (4840yd²) is a little larger than two ice hockey rinks (2 x 2222yd²).
**C** An are (119.6yd²) is shown with a boxing ring (44yd²).

**D** A hectare (11,960yd²) is about $\frac{1}{3}$ as big again as a soccer pitch (8800yd²).

### Basic US customary/imperial units of area
144 square inches (in², sq.in) = 1 square foot (ft², sq.ft)
9 square feet = 1 square yard (yd², sq.yd)
4840 square yards = 1 acre (a, ac)
640 acres = 1 square mile (mi², sq.mi)
### Other US/imperial units of area
1 square rod, pole or perch = 30¼yd²
1 square chain = 16 square rods = 484yd²
1 rood = 2½ square chains = ¼ acre = 1210yd²

### Metric units of area
| | |
|---|---|
| 100mm² | = 1cm² |
| 10,000cm² | = 1m² |
| 100m² | = 1 are |
| 100 ares | = 1 hectare |
| 100 hectares | = 1km² |

**US/imperial units of area** *above* Included here are basic and also less common units of area from the US and imperial systems. Given in brackets are alternative abbreviations in common use; the abbreviations given first, for example in², are the ones used in this book.

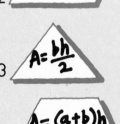

1  $A = bh$

2  $A = bh$

3  $A = \dfrac{bh}{2}$

4  $A = \dfrac{(a+b)h}{2}$

5  $A = \pi r^2$

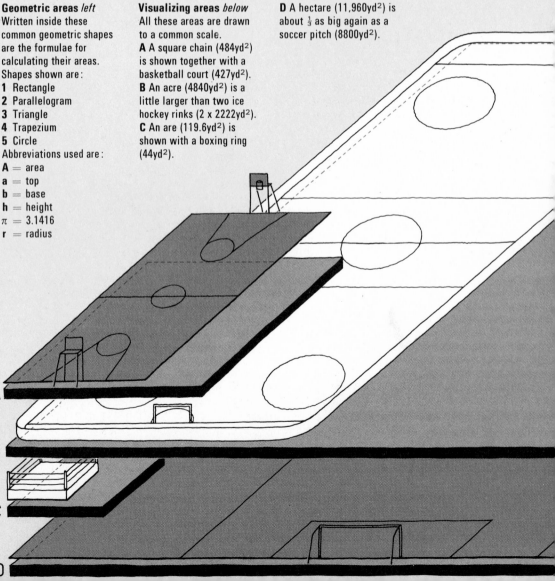

A
B
C
D

1 square foot = 1.6 pages of this book.
1 square yard = 14.3 pages of this book.
1 square meter = 17.1 pages of this book.

**Square measures** *right*
Shown here real size for easy visual comparison are a square inch (**1**) and a square centimeter (**2**).

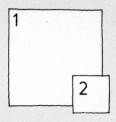

**Conversion tables** *left*
To convert US/imperial area measurements into metric, and vice versa, find the figure to be converted—US/imperial or metric—in the central column. Its equivalent will be in the appropriate column to the right or the left.

| in² | | cm² | yd² | | m² | acre | | ha | mi² | | km² |
|---|---|---|---|---|---|---|---|---|---|---|---|
| 0.1550 | 1 | 6.4516 | 1.1960 | 1 | 0.8361 | 2.4710 | 1 | 0.4047 | 0.3861 | 1 | 2.5900 |
| 0.3100 | 2 | 12.903 | 2.3920 | 2 | 1.6722 | 4.9421 | 2 | 0.8094 | 0.7722 | 2 | 5.1800 |
| 0.4650 | 3 | 19.355 | 3.5880 | 3 | 2.5084 | 7.4131 | 3 | 1.2141 | 1.1583 | 3 | 7.7699 |
| 0.6200 | 4 | 25.806 | 4.7840 | 4 | 3.3445 | 9.8842 | 4 | 1.6187 | 1.5444 | 4 | 10.360 |
| 0.7750 | 5 | 32.258 | 5.9800 | 5 | 4.1806 | 12.355 | 5 | 2.0234 | 1.9305 | 5 | 12.950 |
| 0.9300 | 6 | 38.710 | 7.1759 | 6 | 5.0168 | 14.826 | 6 | 2.4281 | 2.3166 | 6 | 15.540 |
| 1.0850 | 7 | 45.161 | 8.3719 | 7 | 5.8529 | 17.297 | 7 | 2.8328 | 2.7027 | 7 | 18.130 |
| 1.2400 | 8 | 51.613 | 9.5679 | 8 | 6.6890 | 19.768 | 8 | 3.2375 | 3.0888 | 8 | 20.720 |
| 1.3950 | 9 | 58.064 | 10.764 | 9 | 7.5251 | 22.239 | 9 | 3.6422 | 3.4749 | 9 | 23.310 |
| 2.3500 | 15 | 96.774 | 17.940 | 15 | 12.542 | 37.066 | 15 | 6.0703 | 5.7915 | 15 | 38.850 |
| 3.8750 | 25 | 161.29 | 29.900 | 25 | 20.903 | 61.776 | 25 | 10.117 | 9.6525 | 25 | 64.750 |
| 5.4250 | 35 | 225.81 | 41.860 | 35 | 29.264 | 86.487 | 35 | 14.164 | 13.514 | 35 | 90.650 |
| 6.9750 | 45 | 290.32 | 53.820 | 45 | 37.626 | 111.20 | 45 | 18.211 | 17.375 | 45 | 116.55 |
| 8.5250 | 55 | 354.84 | 65.779 | 55 | 45.987 | 135.91 | 55 | 22.258 | 21.236 | 55 | 142.45 |
| 10.075 | 65 | 419.35 | 77.739 | 65 | 54.348 | 160.62 | 65 | 26.305 | 25.097 | 65 | 168.35 |
| 11.625 | 75 | 483.87 | 89.699 | 75 | 62.710 | 172.97 | 75 | 30.351 | 28.958 | 75 | 194.25 |
| 13.175 | 85 | 548.39 | 101.66 | 85 | 71.071 | 210.04 | 85 | 34.398 | 32.819 | 85 | 220.15 |
| 14.725 | 95 | 612.90 | 113.62 | 95 | 79.432 | 234.75 | 95 | 38.445 | 36.680 | 95 | 246.05 |

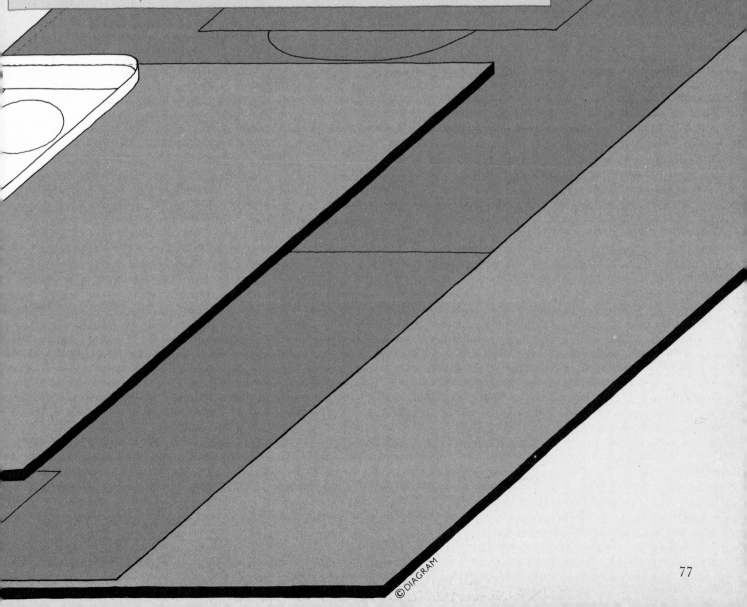

©DIAGRAM

# COMPARATIVE AREAS

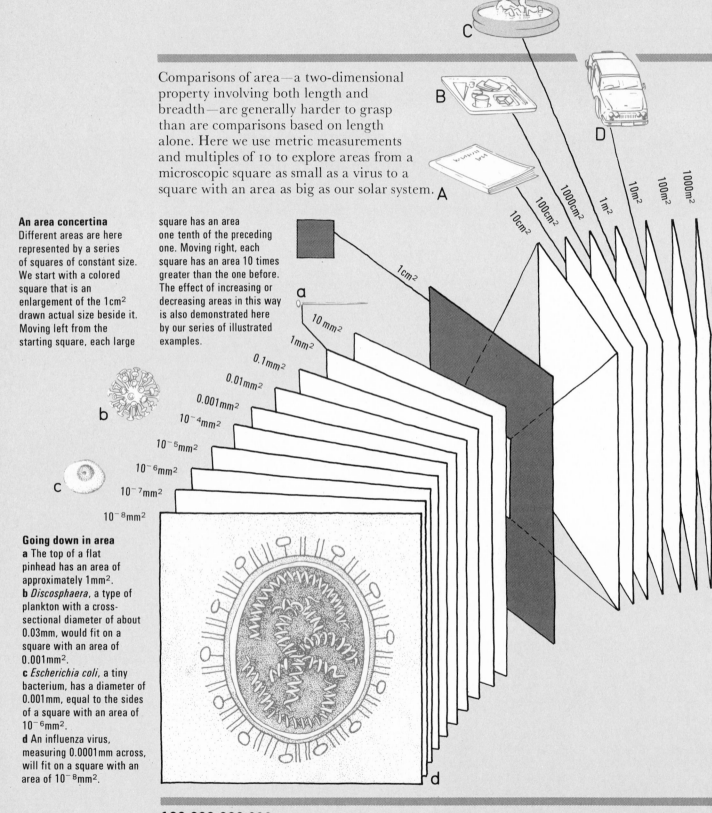

Comparisons of area—a two-dimensional property involving both length and breadth—are generally harder to grasp than are comparisons based on length alone. Here we use metric measurements and multiples of 10 to explore areas from a microscopic square as small as a virus to a square with an area as big as our solar system.

**An area concertina**
Different areas are here represented by a series of squares of constant size. We start with a colored square that is an enlargement of the 1cm² drawn actual size beside it. Moving left from the starting square, each large square has an area one tenth of the preceding one. Moving right, each square has an area 10 times greater than the one before. The effect of increasing or decreasing areas in this way is also demonstrated here by our series of illustrated examples.

1000cm²
100cm²
1m²
10m²
100m²
1000m²

1cm²
10cm²
100cm²

10 mm²
1mm²
0.1mm²
0.01mm²
0.001mm²
10⁻⁴mm²
10⁻⁵mm²
10⁻⁶mm²
10⁻⁷mm²
10⁻⁸mm²

**Going down in area**
**a** The top of a flat pinhead has an area of approximately 1mm².
**b** *Discosphaera*, a type of plankton with a cross-sectional diameter of about 0.03mm, would fit on a square with an area of 0.001mm².
**c** *Escherichia coli*, a tiny bacterium, has a diameter of 0.001mm, equal to the sides of a square with an area of 10⁻⁶mm².
**d** An influenza virus, measuring 0.0001mm across, will fit on a square with an area of 10⁻⁸mm².

**100,000,000,000 bacteria the size of *Escherichia coli* could fit on a food tray measuring 40x25cm.**

*The total skin area of an average man (20ft²) and an average woman (17ft²) can easily be covered by a sheet for a single bed (48ft²).*

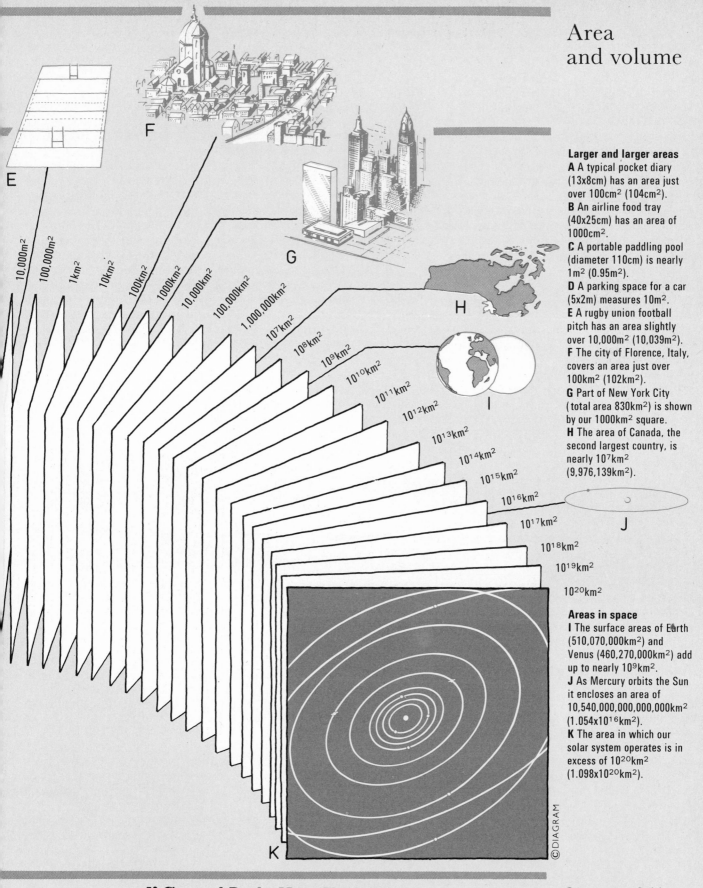

# Area and volume

## Larger and larger areas

**A** A typical pocket diary (13x8cm) has an area just over 100cm² (104cm²).

**B** An airline food tray (40x25cm) has an area of 1000cm².

**C** A portable paddling pool (diameter 110cm) is nearly 1m² (0.95m²).

**D** A parking space for a car (5x2m) measures 10m².

**E** A rugby union football pitch has an area slightly over 10,000m² (10,039m²).

**F** The city of Florence, Italy, covers an area just over 100km² (102km²).

**G** Part of New York City (total area 830km²) is shown by our 1000km² square.

**H** The area of Canada, the second largest country, is nearly 10⁷km² (9,976,139km²).

## Areas in space

**I** The surface areas of Earth (510,070,000km²) and Venus (460,270,000km²) add up to nearly 10⁹km².

**J** As Mercury orbits the Sun it encloses an area of 10,540,000,000,000,000km² (1.054x10¹⁶km²).

**K** The area in which our solar system operates is in excess of 10²⁰km² (1.098x10²⁰km²).

If Central Park, New York City were transformed into a vast parking lot, there would be space for over 300,000 cars.

One page of this book has a surface area of 585.48cm² or 90.75in².

# THE PLANETS

The diameter of Jupiter, the largest planet, is nearly 30 times as big as that of Mercury, the smallest planet, but its estimated surface area is over 850 times as big. On Earth's surface there is over twice as much sea as land, and one ocean, the Pacific, has an area over six million square miles bigger than the entire land surface.

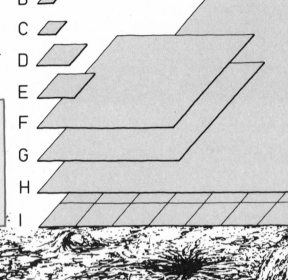

**Surface area of planets**
Listed in the table *right* and shown to a common scale as squares *far right* are estimated surface areas of the planets. The small squares on square **I** show how many times Earth's surface area will fit into that of Jupiter (125).

| | | | |
|---|---|---|---|
| A | Mercury | 28,880,000mi² | 74,800,000km² |
| B | Pluto | 43,000,000mi² | 111,000,000km² |
| C | Mars | 55,870,000mi² | 144,700,000km² |
| D | Venus | 177,710,000mi² | 460,270,000km² |
| E | Earth | 196,940,000mi² | 510,070,000km² |
| F | Neptune | 2,980,200,000mi² | 7,718,700,000km² |
| G | Uranus | 3,257,300,000mi² | 8,436,400,000km² |
| H | Saturn | 17,483,000,000mi² | 45,281,000,000km² |
| I | Jupiter | 24,717,000,000mi² | 64,017,000,000km² |

**Area of continents**
Listed in the table *right* and shown to scale in the diagram *far right* are the areas of the continents. Asia is 795,000mi² larger than N and S America combined. Asia and Africa together make up just over half the total land area.

| | | | |
|---|---|---|---|
| 1 | Asia | 17,085,000mi² | 44,250,000km² |
| 2 | Africa | 11,685,000mi² | 30,264,000km² |
| 3 | N America | 9,420,000mi² | 24,398,000km² |
| 4 | S America | 6,870,000mi² | 17,793,000km² |
| 5 | Antarctica | 5,100,000mi² | 13,209,000km² |
| 6 | Europe | 3,825,000mi² | 9,907,000km² |
| 7 | Oceania | 3,295,000mi² | 8,534,000km² |

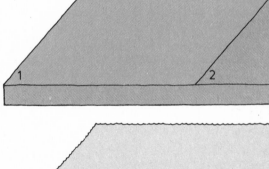

**Oceans and seas**
Listed *right* and shown to scale in the diagram *far right* are the world's oceans and five largest seas. The four oceans combined account for approximately 92% of the total sea area, with the Pacific alone accounting for about 46%.

| | | | |
|---|---|---|---|
| a | Pacific Ocean | 63,800,000mi² | 165,242,000km² |
| b | Atlantic Ocean | 31,800,000mi² | 82,362,000km² |
| c | Indian Ocean | 28,400,000mi² | 73,556,000km² |
| d | Arctic Ocean | 5,400,000mi² | 13,986,000km² |
| e | Malay Sea | 3,144,000mi² | 8,143,000km² |
| f | Caribbean Sea | 1,063,000mi² | 2,753,000km² |
| g | Mediterranean Sea | 967,000mi² | 2,505,000km² |
| h | Bering Sea | 876,000mi² | 2,269,000km² |
| i | Gulf of Mexico | 596,000mi² | 1,544,000km² |

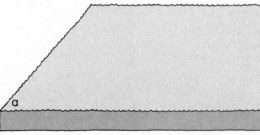

If the world's total land area were shared equally among the world's population, each person would have a plot of 8.5 acres. Climate and terrain, however, mean that perhaps 80% of these plots would be useless.

*The surface area of the smallest planet in our solar system, Mercury (28,880,000mi²), is approximately equal to the combined areas of Asia and Africa (28,770,000mi²).*

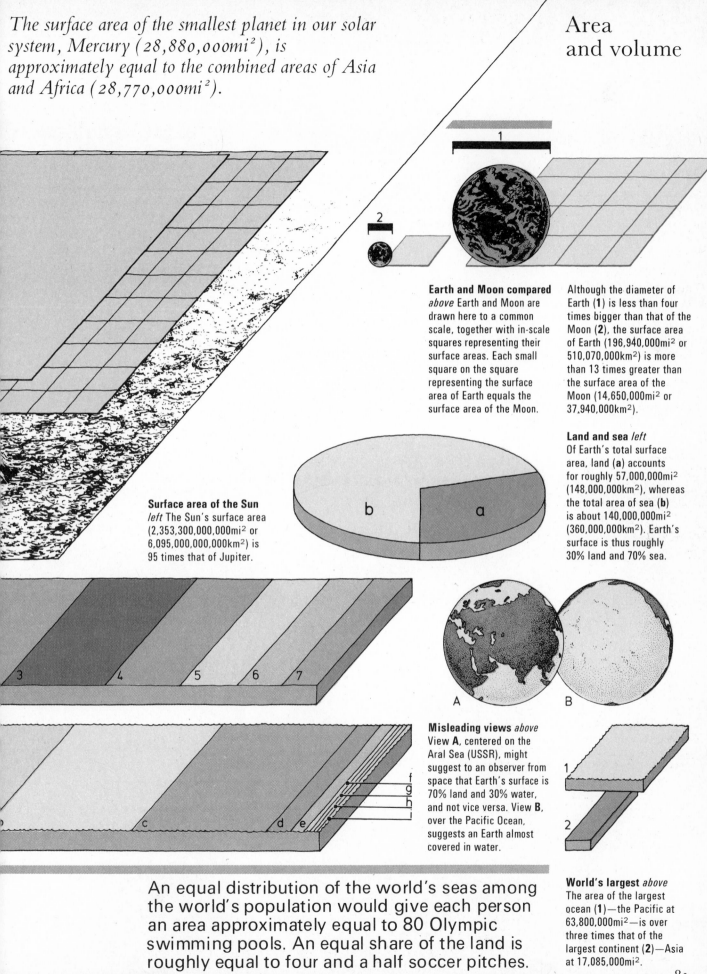

**Earth and Moon compared**
*above* Earth and Moon are drawn here to a common scale, together with in-scale squares representing their surface areas. Each small square on the square representing the surface area of Earth equals the surface area of the Moon.

Although the diameter of Earth (**1**) is less than four times bigger than that of the Moon (**2**), the surface area of Earth (196,940,000mi² or 510,070,000km²) is more than 13 times greater than the surface area of the Moon (14,650,000mi² or 37,940,000km²).

**Land and sea** *left*
Of Earth's total surface area, land (**a**) accounts for roughly 57,000,000mi² (148,000,000km²), whereas the total area of sea (**b**) is about 140,000,000mi² (360,000,000km²). Earth's surface is thus roughly 30% land and 70% sea.

**Surface area of the Sun**
*left* The Sun's surface area (2,353,300,000,000mi² or 6,095,000,000,000km²) is 95 times that of Jupiter.

**Misleading views** *above*
View **A**, centered on the Aral Sea (USSR), might suggest to an observer from space that Earth's surface is 70% land and 30% water, and not vice versa. View **B**, over the Pacific Ocean, suggests an Earth almost covered in water.

An equal distribution of the world's seas among the world's population would give each person an area approximately equal to 80 Olympic swimming pools. An equal share of the land is roughly equal to four and a half soccer pitches.

**World's largest** *above*
The area of the largest ocean (**1**)—the Pacific at 63,800,000mi²—is over three times that of the largest continent (**2**)—Asia at 17,085,000mi².

©DIAGRAM

# LAKES AND ISLANDS

Here we compare the areas of the world's largest lakes and islands. North America's Great Lakes include the world's largest freshwater lake (Superior) and three more from the top 10 (Huron, Michigan, Erie). Greenland, the largest island, is larger than the next three largest put together (New Guinea, Borneo, Madagascar).

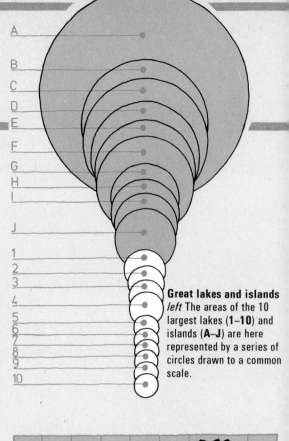

**Great lakes and islands**
*left* The areas of the 10 largest lakes (**1–10**) and islands (**A–J**) are here represented by a series of circles drawn to a common scale.

**World's largest lakes**
The world's 10 largest freshwater lakes are listed *right*, located on the map *below* and drawn to an equal area projection *below right*. The largest saltwater lake, the Caspian Sea (USSR), has an area of 143,550mi².

| | | | |
|---|---|---|---|
| **1** | Superior | 31,820mi² | 82,414km² |
| **2** | Victoria | 26,828mi² | 69,485km² |
| **3** | Huron | 23,010mi² | 59,596km² |
| **4** | Michigan | 22,400mi² | 58,016km² |
| **5** | Great Bear | 12,275mi² | 31,792km² |
| **6** | Baykal | 12,159mi² | 31,492km² |
| **7** | Great Slave | 10,980mi² | 28,438km² |
| **8** | Tanganyika | 10,965mi² | 28,399km² |
| **9** | Malawi | 10,900mi² | 28,231km² |
| **10** | Erie | 9,940mi² | 25,745km² |

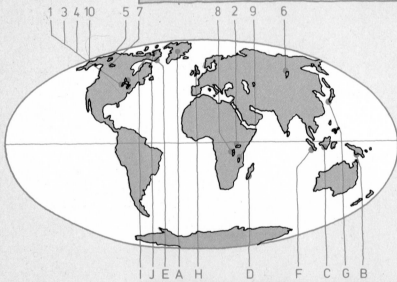

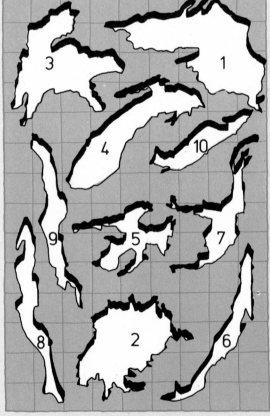

**World's largest islands**
The 10 largest are listed *right* and located *above*. Australia (2,941,526mi²) is not included, being classed as a continental land mass. Drawn with the islands to an equal area projection *far right* is the USA (Alaska/Hawaii excepted).

| | | | |
|---|---|---|---|
| **A** | Greenland | 840,000mi² | 2,175,600km² |
| **B** | New Guinea | 316,856mi² | 820,657km² |
| **C** | Borneo | 286,967mi² | 743,245km² |
| **D** | Madagascar | 227,000mi² | 587,930km² |
| **E** | Baffin (Canada) | 183,810mi² | 476,068km² |
| **F** | Sumatra | 182,866mi² | 473,623km² |
| **G** | Honshu (Japan) | 88,930mi² | 230,329km² |
| **H** | Great Britain | 88,756mi² | 229,878km² |
| **I** | Victoria (Canada) | 82,119mi² | 212,688km² |
| **J** | Ellesmere (Canada) | 81,930mi² | 212,199km² |

**The world's largest desert, the Sahara, with an area of 3,250,000mi², is over three times bigger than the Mediterranean Sea to its north.**

If Lake Superior (31,820mi²) were to be drained, the area of regained land would be just over twice the area of the Netherlands (15,770mi²).

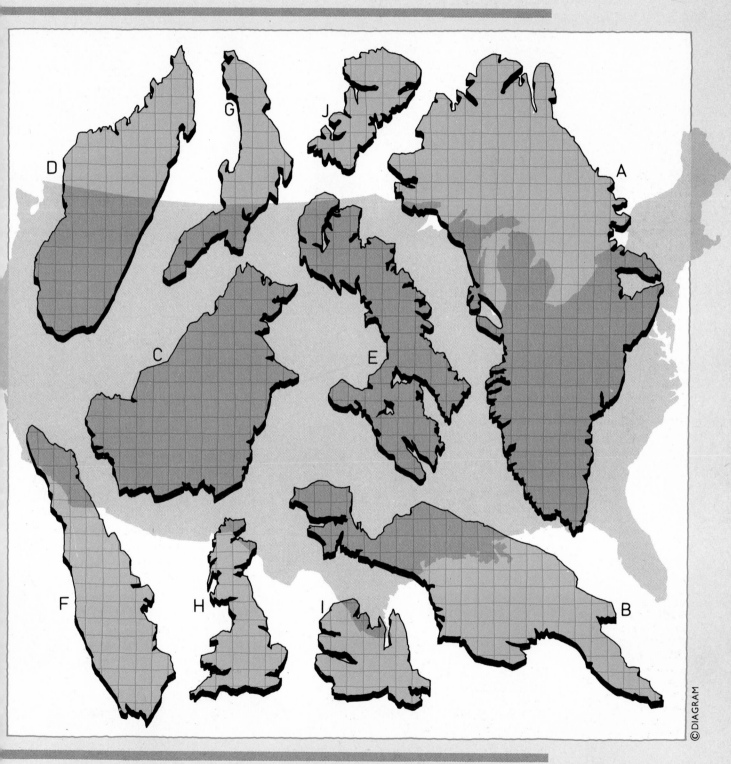

*Lake Malawi (10,900mi²) is
almost a quarter as big as the
country of the same name
(45,747mi²).*

©DIAGRAM

# COUNTRIES AND STATES 1

Different political and geographical factors have produced nation states of widely differing size. The smallest country in the world, the Vatican City State, is less than a quarter of a square mile in area, whereas the largest country in the world, the USSR has an area exceeding eight and a half million square miles.

**Largest countries**
The areas of the world's 10 largest countries are included in the list *below* and represented by the scaled squares beneath it. In the illustration *right* these same countries are drawn to an equal area projection, with the Moon drawn to the same scale in the center. Square **A** represents the land area of Earth (57,000,000mi²), and square **B** the surface of the Moon (14,650,000mi²). The USSR, with an area of 8,649,489mi², would cover well over half of the Moon's surface.

**Smallest countries**
*right* Listed here in ascending order of size are the 10 smallest countries in the world. Their combined areas (770mi²) would fit almost 1½ times into the state of Rhode Island, USA (area 1,049mi²).

| | | | |
|---|---|---|---|
| **A** | Vatican City | 0.17mi² | 0.44km² |
| **B** | Monaco | 0.73mi² | 1.89km² |
| **C** | Nauru | 8.1mi² | 21km² |
| **D** | San Marino | 23.4mi² | 60.5km² |
| **E** | Liechtenstein | 61.8mi² | 160km² |
| **F** | Maldive Islands | 115mi² | 298km² |
| **G** | Malta | 122mi² | 316km² |
| **H** | Grenada | 133mi² | 344km² |
| **I** | St Vincent | 150mi² | 389km² |
| **J** | Seychelles | 156mi² | 404km² |

| | | | |
|---|---|---|---|
| **1** | USSR | 8,649,489mi² | 22,402,200km² |
| **2** | Canada | 3,851,787mi² | 9,976,139km² |
| **3** | China (CPR) | 3,691,502mi² | 9,561,000km² |
| **4** | USA | 3,675,547mi² | 9,519,666km² |
| **5** | Brazil | 3,286,470mi² | 8,511,965km² |
| **6** | Australia | 2,966,136mi² | 7,682,300km² |
| **7** | India | 1,269,338mi² | 3,287,590km² |
| **8** | Argentina | 1,072,157mi² | 2,776,889km² |
| **9** | Sudan | 967,494mi² | 2,505,813km² |
| **10** | Zaire | 905,360mi² | 2,344,885km² |

**Country parks?**
The areas of the world's 10 smallest countries are represented *right* by 10 scaled squares. As shown *below*, New York City's Central Park (**a**) area 1.3mi², is nearly twice as big as the second-smallest country, Monaco (**b**) 0.73mi².

**Bigger than Europe**
*right* The USA (excluding Alaska and Hawaii) is here drawn to the same scale as Europe. The area of the entire USA (3,675,547mi²) exceeds by over one million square miles the area of all of Europe west of the USSR (2,572,600mi²).

**Only six states?**
*far right* The state of Alaska (586,412mi²) is here superimposed over the main area of the USA. If all the states were the size of Alaska there would be room for only six complete states in the entire area of the USA (3,675,547mi²).

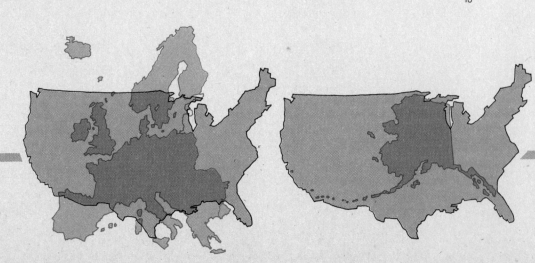

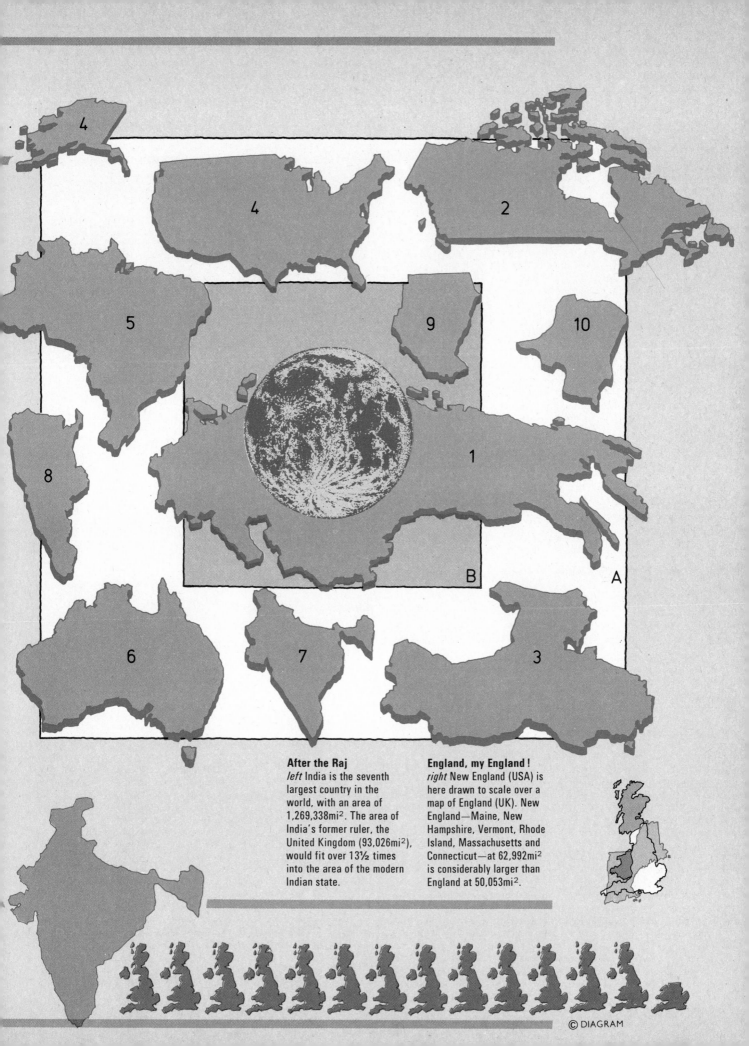

**After the Raj**
*left* India is the seventh largest country in the world, with an area of 1,269,338mi². The area of India's former ruler, the United Kingdom (93,026mi²), would fit over 13½ times into the area of the modern Indian state.

**England, my England!**
*right* New England (USA) is here drawn to scale over a map of England (UK). New England—Maine, New Hampshire, Vermont, Rhode Island, Massachusetts and Connecticut—at 62,992mi² is considerably larger than England at 50,053mi².

© DIAGRAM

# COUNTRIES AND STATES 2

For its area, Europe has more countries than any other continent. Even France, Europe's largest country (211,207mi²), ranks only forty-fourth in the world in terms of size. Canada's Northwest Territories (1,304,900mi²) is six times bigger than France, and, if a country, would be 19th largest in the world.

| | | | |
|---|---|---|---|
| **1** | France | 211,207mi² | 547,026km² |
| **2** | Spain | 194,896mi² | 504,782km² |
| **3** | Sweden | 173,731mi² | 449,964km² |
| **4** | Finland | 130,119mi² | 337,009km² |
| **5** | Norway | 125,181mi² | 324,219km² |
| **6** | Poland | 120,725mi² | 312,677km² |
| **7** | Italy | 116,316mi² | 301,260km² |
| **8** | Yugoslavia | 98,766mi² | 255,804km² |
| **9** | West Germany | 95,992mi² | 248,620km² |
| **10** | United Kingdom | 93,026mi² | 240,937km² |
| **11** | Romania | 91,699mi² | 237,500km² |
| **12** | Greece | 50,944mi² | 131,944km² |
| **13** | Czechoslovakia | 49,373mi² | 127,876km² |
| **14** | Bulgaria | 42,823mi² | 110,912km² |
| **15** | East Germany | 41,768mi² | 108,178km² |
| **16** | Iceland | 39,768mi² | 103,000km² |
| **17** | Hungary | 35,920mi² | 93,032km² |
| **18** | Portugal | 35,553mi² | 92,082km² |
| **19** | Austria | 32,374mi² | 83,850km² |
| **20** | Irish Republic | 27,136mi² | 70,282km² |

**Largest in Europe**
The areas of the 20 largest countries in Europe are listed in the table *left*, drawn to an equal area projection *right* and represented as rectangles drawn to scale *below*. The remaining 12 countries that are completely in Europe have a combined area of just under 75,000mi².

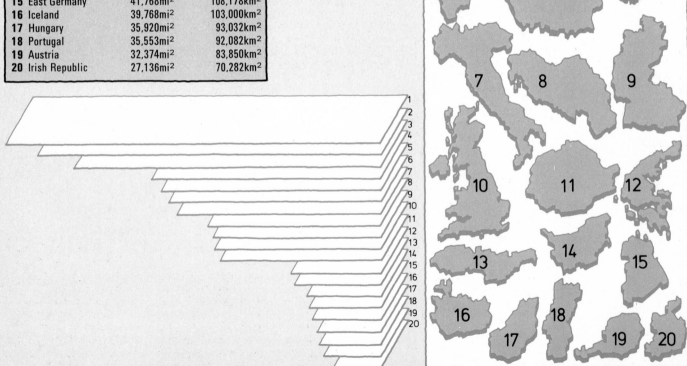

**If Mexico (761,604mi²) were to annex New Mexico, Texas and California, its new total area (1,309,048mi²) would move it up from the thirteenth to the seventh largest country in the world.**

In Iceland, the least densely populated country
in Europe, there is enough land for each person
to have 123.5 acres in an equal share-out; in Malta,
the most densely populated European country,
68 people would have to share each acre.

**Common denominator**
*right* France is the largest
country in the Common
Market (EEC), with an area
of 211,207mi². The diagram
shows the number of times
that each of the other eight
countries would fit into the
area of France.

Italy
(116,316mi², 301,260km²) x 1.8

West Germany
(95,992mi², 248,620km²) x 2.2

United Kingdom
(93,026mi², 240,937km²) x 2.3

Ireland
(27,136mi², 70,282km²) x 7.8

Denmark
(16,629mi², 43,069km²) x 12.7

Netherlands
(15,770mi², 40,844km²) x 13.4

Belgium
(11,781mi², 30,513km²) x 17.9

Luxembourg
(998mi², 2586km²) x 211.6

**USSR: largest republics**

| | | |
|---|---|---|
| 1 Kazakhstan | 1,049,100mi² | 2,717,300km² |
| 2 Ukraine | 233,100mi² | 603,700km² |
| 3 Turkmenistan | 188,500mi² | 488,100km² |
| 4 Uzbekistan | 172,700mi² | 447,400km² |
| 5 Belorussia | 80,200mi² | 207,600km² |

**Canada: largest provinces/territories**

| | | |
|---|---|---|
| 1 Northwest Territories | 1,304,900mi² | 3,379,700km² |
| 2 Quebec | 594,900mi² | 1,540,700km² |
| 3 Ontario | 412,600mi² | 1,068,600km² |
| 4 British Columbia | 366,300mi² | 948,600km² |
| 5 Alberta | 255,300mi² | 661,200km² |

**China: largest administrative regions**

| | | |
|---|---|---|
| 1 Sian | 1,260,100mi² | 3,263,600km² |
| 2 Chungking | 926,900mi² | 2,400,800km² |
| 3 Shenyang | 474,900mi² | 1,230,000km² |
| 4 Wuhan | 392,600mi² | 1,016,800km² |
| 5 Peking | 321,100mi² | 831,600km² |

**USA: largest states**

| | | |
|---|---|---|
| 1 Alaska | 586,400mi² | 1,518,800km² |
| 2 Texas | 267,300mi² | 692,300km² |
| 3 California | 158,700mi² | 411,000km² |
| 4 Montana | 147,100mi² | 381,000km² |
| 5 New Mexico | 121,400mi² | 314,400km² |

**Political parts** *left*
The table lists the areas of
the largest five political
subdivisions in each of the
four largest countries in the
world—the USSR, Canada,
China and the USA. Largest
of all is Canada's Northwest
Territories (1,304,900mi²).

**Some of the parts** *above*
The diagram shows the
comparative areas of the
largest land division in
each of the four largest
countries (in color), and
compares them with the
areas of countries that
are similar in size (in
white). See list *right*.

**A** Northwest Territories,
Canada (1,304,900mi²) and
India (1,269,338mi²).
**B** Sian, China (1,260,100mi²)
and India (1,269,338mi²).
**C** Kazakhstan, USSR
(1,049,100mi²) and
Argentina (1,072,157mi²).
**D** Alaska, USA (586,400mi²)
and Iran (636,293mi²).

*Europe's northernmost countries—
Sweden, Finland and Norway—
rank third, fourth and fifth in
Europe in terms of size. Their*
*combined area (429,031mi²),
however, is less than one third of
that of Canada's Northwest
Territories (1,304,900mi²).*

©DIAGRAM

1

2

# BUILDINGS

Scale drawings of the plans of some
famous buildings are used here to show
their comparative ground areas. Our
selection ranges from the Great Pyramid of
Cheops, one of the world's largest ancient
structures, to the Pentagon in Washington
DC, which has a larger ground area than
any other office building in the world.

3

6

5

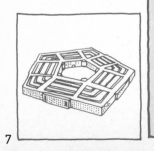

7

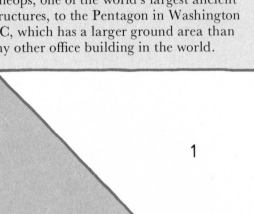

2

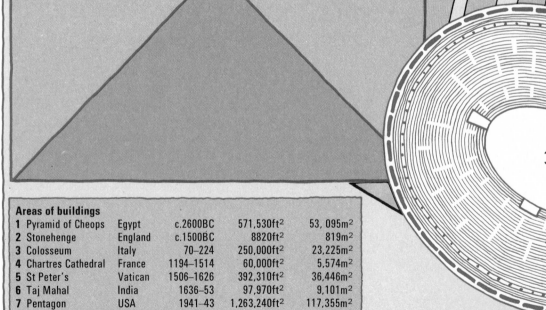

1

3

### Areas of buildings

| | | | | |
|---|---|---|---|---|
| 1 Pyramid of Cheops | Egypt | c.2600BC | 571,530ft² | 53, 095m² |
| 2 Stonehenge | England | c.1500BC | 8820ft² | 819m² |
| 3 Colosseum | Italy | 70–224 | 250,000ft² | 23,225m² |
| 4 Chartres Cathedral | France | 1194–1514 | 60,000ft² | 5,574m² |
| 5 St Peter's | Vatican | 1506–1626 | 392,310ft² | 36,446m² |
| 6 Taj Mahal | India | 1636–53 | 97,970ft² | 9,101m² |
| 7 Pentagon | USA | 1941–43 | 1,263,240ft² | 117,355m² |

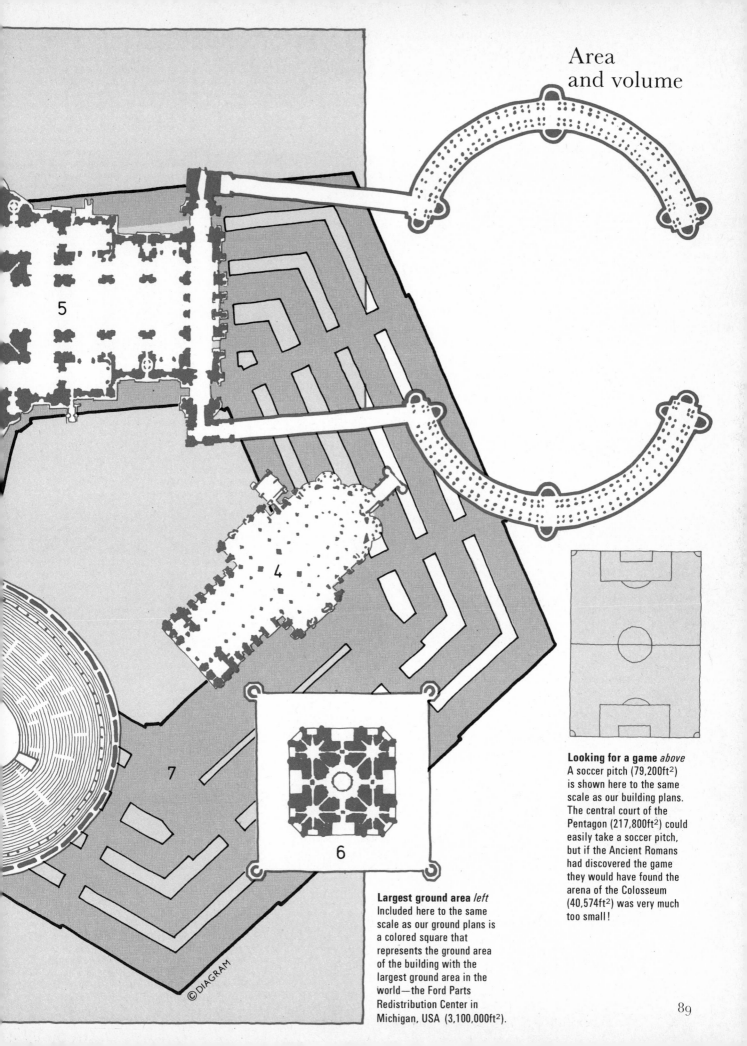

5

4

7

6

**Looking for a game** *above*
A soccer pitch (79,200ft²)
is shown here to the same
scale as our building plans.
The central court of the
Pentagon (217,800ft²) could
easily take a soccer pitch,
but if the Ancient Romans
had discovered the game
they would have found the
arena of the Colosseum
(40,574ft²) was very much
too small!

**Largest ground area** *left*
Included here to the same
scale as our ground plans is
a colored square that
represents the ground area
of the building with the
largest ground area in the
world—the Ford Parts
Redistribution Center in
Michigan, USA (3,100,000ft²).

©DIAGRAM

89

# SPORTS AREAS

The area in which a sport is played is an important element in determining the character of play. Playing area dimensions are therefore closely defined in official sports rules. In general, size is a compromise between an area in which the sport can be easily played, and an area calling for the use of extra energy or skill.

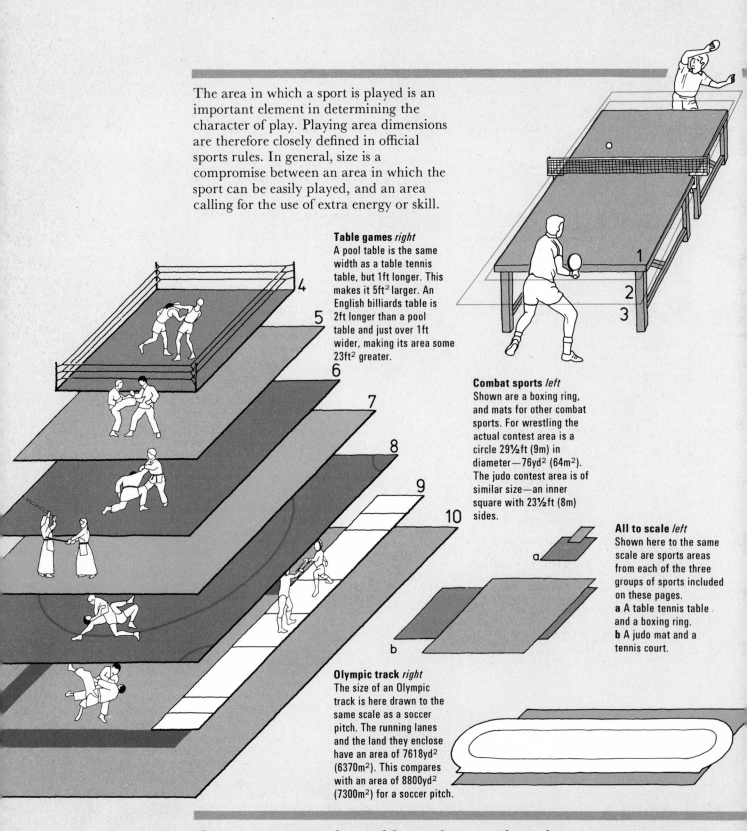

**Table games** *right*
A pool table is the same width as a table tennis table, but 1ft longer. This makes it 5ft² larger. An English billiards table is 2ft longer than a pool table and just over 1ft wider, making its area some 23ft² greater.

**Combat sports** *left*
Shown are a boxing ring, and mats for other combat sports. For wrestling the actual contest area is a circle 29½ft (9m) in diameter—76yd² (64m²). The judo contest area is of similar size—an inner square with 23½ft (8m) sides.

**All to scale** *left*
Shown here to the same scale are sports areas from each of the three groups of sports included on these pages.
**a** A table tennis table and a boxing ring.
**b** A judo mat and a tennis court.

**Olympic track** *right*
The size of an Olympic track is here drawn to the same scale as a soccer pitch. The running lanes and the land they enclose have an area of 7618yd² (6370m²). This compares with an area of 8800yd² (7300m²) for a soccer pitch.

Over 37,000 people could stand on an American football field. More than 51,000 would fit on a soccer pitch.

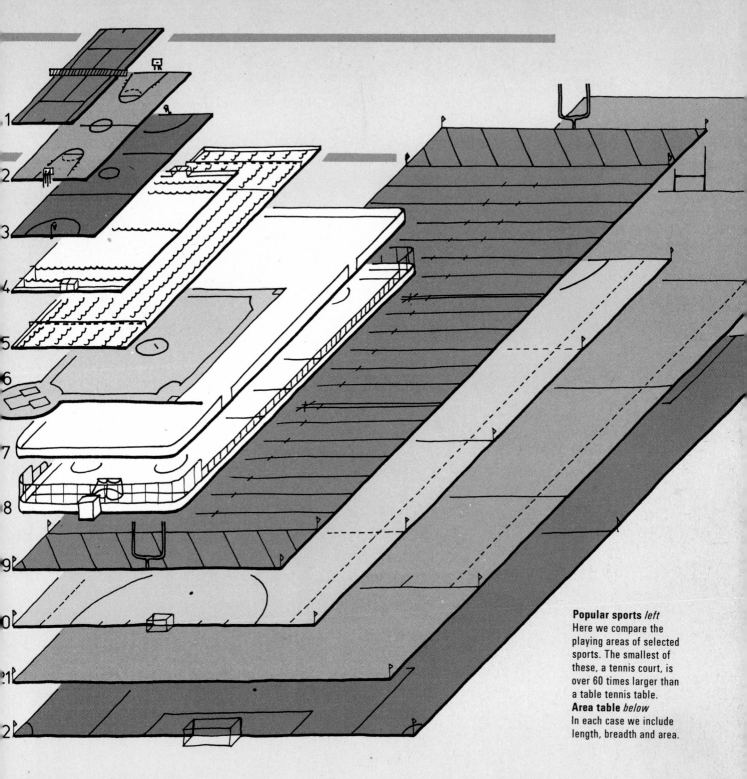

**Popular sports** *left*
Here we compare the playing areas of selected sports. The smallest of these, a tennis court, is over 60 times larger than a table tennis table.
**Area table** *below*
In each case we include length, breadth and area.

| | Sport | Dimensions | Area |
|---|---|---|---|
| **1** | Table tennis | 9x5ft (2.74x1.52m) | 5yd² (4.16m²) |
| **2** | Pool | 10x5ft (3.05x1.52m) | 5.6yd² (4.63m²) |
| **3** | Billiards, English | 12x6ft 1½ in (3.66x1.86m) | 8.1yd² (6.80m²) |
| **4** | Boxing | 20x20ft (6.10x6.10m) | 44yd² (37m²) |
| **5** | Karate | 26x26ft (8x8m) | 75yd² (64m²) |
| **6** | Aikido | 29ft 6inx29ft 6in (9x9m) | 96.7yd² (81m²) |
| **7** | Kendo | 36x33ft (11x10m) | 132yd² (110m²) |
| **8** | Wrestling | 39ft 3inx39ft 3in (12x12m) | 171yd² (144m²) |
| **9** | Fencing | 46x6ft 6in (14x2m) | 33yd² (28m²) |
| **10** | Judo | 52ft 6inx52ft 6in (16x16m) | 306yd² (256m²) |

| | Sport | Dimensions | Area |
|---|---|---|---|
| **11** | Tennis | 26x12yd (23.77x10.97m) | 312yd² (260.75m²) |
| **12** | Basketball | 28x15yd 9in (26x14m) | 427yd² (364m²) |
| **13** | Netball | 33yd 1ftx16yd 2ft (30.5x15.25m) | 555yd² (465.1m²) |
| **14** | Water polo | 33x22yd (30x20m) | 726yd² (600m²) |
| **15** | Swimming | 55x23yd (50x21m) | 1265yd² (1050m²) |
| **16** | Baseball | 30x30yd (27.45x27.45m) | 900yd² (753.5m²) |
| **17** | Ice skating | 66x33yd (60x30m) | 2178yd² (1800m²) |
| **18** | Ice hockey | 66yd 2ftx33yd 1ft (61x30.5m) | 2222yd² (1860.5m²) |
| **19** | US football | 120x53yd 1ft (109.8x48.8m) | 6399yd² (5358.2m²) |
| **20** | Field hockey | 100x60yd (91.5x54.9m) | 6000yd² (5063.35m²) |
| **21** | Rugby union | 160x75yd (146.3x68.62m) | 1200yd² (10,039m²) |
| **22** | Soccer | 110x80yd (100x73m) | 8800yd² (7300m²) |

©DIAGRAM

# MEASURING VOLUME 1

Volume is a measure of the space occupied or contained by a three-dimensional object possessing length, breadth and height. On these two pages we compare cubic units from the US/imperial and metric systems, and use a series of cubes to show progressive increases in volume that take us from the size of a sugar cube to the volume of Earth.

**US customary/imperial units of volume**
1728 cubic inches (in$^3$, cu.in) = 1 cubic foot (ft$^3$, cu.ft)
27 cubic feet = 1 cubic yard (yd$^3$, cu.yd)
5,451,776,000yd$^3$ = 1 cubic mile (mi$^3$)
**Metric units of volume**
1000 cubic millimeters (mm$^3$, cu.mm) = 1 cubic centimeter (cm$^3$, cu.cm, cc)
1,000,000 cubic centimeters = 1 cubic meter (m$^3$, cu.m)
1,000,000,000 cubic meters = 1 cubic kilometer (km$^3$, cu.km)

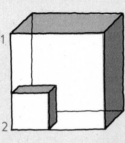

**Cubic measures** *left*
A cubic inch (**1**) and a cubic centimeter (**2**) are drawn here to give an indication of their real size. The volume of a cube equals the area of its base (length x breadth) multiplied by its height.

**Units of volume** *above*
Included here, with alternative abbreviations in brackets, are units of volume obtained by "cubing" units of linear measurement from the US/imperial and metric systems. (Other units of volume are given on p. 94.)

**Conversion tables** *right*
To convert US/imperial volume measurements into metric, and vice versa, find the figure to be converted—US/imperial or metric—in the central column. Its equivalent will be in the appropriate column to the right or the left.

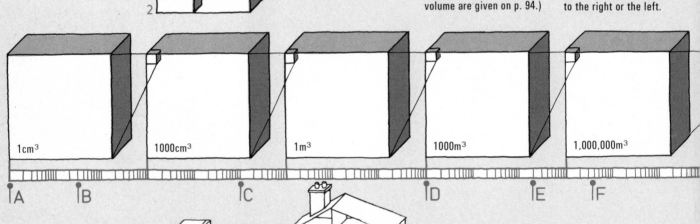

1cm$^3$    1000cm$^3$    1m$^3$    1000m$^3$    1,000,000m$^3$

A    B    C    D    E    F

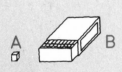

A    B    C    D    F    E

**Increasing volumes** *above*
A series of cubes drawn to a constant size is here used to represent progressively larger cubes. Note that a tenfold increase in the length of a cube's sides produces a cube whose volume is 1000 times that of its predecessor. The volumes of our cubes are also used to provide fixed points on the logarithmic scale below them, and illustrated examples are used to give a clearer impression of the actual volumes involved.

**Illustrated examples**
**A** A sugar cube with 1cm sides is 1cm$^3$ in volume.
**B** A matchbox measuring 5x3.5x1.7cm has a volume of 29.75cm$^3$.
**C** A large traveling bag (80x50x25cm) is 100,000cm$^3$.
**D** A typical two-storied, four bed-roomed house with a 150m$^2$ ground area has a volume of roughly 1000m$^3$.
**E** The volume of St Paul's Cathedral in London is approximately 190,000m$^3$.
**F** The John F. Kennedy Space Center, Florida, boasts a Vehicle Assembly Building with a capacity of 3,666,500m$^3$.

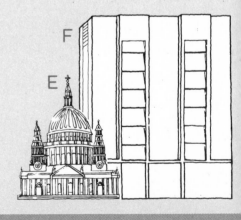

*The volume of a typical two-storied, four-bedroomed house (1000m$^3$) would fit 3666 times into the massive Vehicle Assembly Building at Florida's John F. Kennedy Space Center.*

**The estimated volume of Earth's oceans (1,285,600,000km$^3$) is over 36 times as great as the estimated volume of freshwater on Earth (35,000,000km$^3$).**

**The world's largest pyramid, the Quetzalcóatl at Cholula de Rivadabia in Mexico, had an estimated volume of 3,300,000m³ — compared with the Pyramid of Cheops, which has an estimated volume of 2,500,000m³.**

| in³ | | cm³ | ft³ | | m³ |
|---|---|---|---|---|---|
| 0.0610 | 1 | 16.387 | 35.315 | 1 | 0.0283 |
| 0.1220 | 2 | 32.774 | 70.629 | 2 | 0.0566 |
| 0.1831 | 3 | 49.161 | 105.94 | 3 | 0.0849 |
| 0.2441 | 4 | 65.548 | 141.26 | 4 | 0.1133 |
| 0.3051 | 5 | 81.935 | 176.57 | 5 | 0.1416 |
| 0.3661 | 6 | 98.322 | 211.89 | 6 | 0.1699 |
| 0.4272 | 7 | 114.71 | 247.20 | 7 | 0.1982 |
| 0.4882 | 8 | 131.10 | 282.52 | 8 | 0.2265 |
| 0.5492 | 9 | 147.48 | 317.83 | 9 | 0.2549 |
| 0.9154 | 15 | 245.81 | 529.72 | 15 | 0.4248 |
| 1.5256 | 25 | 409.68 | 882.87 | 25 | 0.7079 |
| 2.1358 | 35 | 573.55 | 1236.0 | 35 | 0.9911 |
| 2.7461 | 45 | 737.42 | 1589.2 | 45 | 1.2743 |
| 3.3563 | 55 | 901.29 | 1942.3 | 55 | 1.5574 |
| 3.9665 | 65 | 1065.2 | 2295.5 | 65 | 1.8406 |
| 4.5768 | 75 | 1229.0 | 2648.6 | 75 | 2.1238 |
| 5.1870 | 85 | 1392.9 | 3001.7 | 85 | 2.4069 |
| 5.7973 | 95 | 1556.8 | 3354.9 | 95 | 2.6901 |

$$V = bhl$$

$$V = \frac{bhl}{2}$$

$$V = \frac{blh}{3}$$

$$V = \pi r^2 l$$

$$V = \frac{\pi r^2 h}{3}$$

$$V = \frac{4\pi r^3}{3}$$

**Calculating volumes** *left*
Given here are formulae for calculating the volume of some common solid forms:
**1** Cube or cuboid
**2** Prism
**3** Pyramid
**4** Cylinder
**5** Cone
**6** Sphere
Abbreviations used are:
**A** = area
**b** = breadth
**h** = height
**l** = length
**π** = 3.1416
**r** = radius
**V** = volume

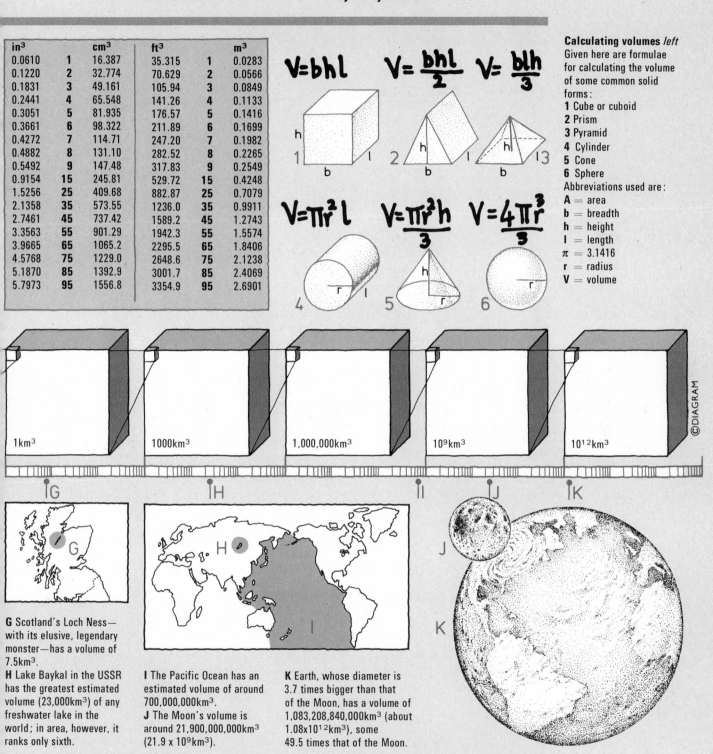

1km³   1000km³   1,000,000km³   10⁹km³   10¹²km³

G   H   I   J   K

**G** Scotland's Loch Ness — with its elusive, legendary monster — has a volume of 7.5km³.
**H** Lake Baykal in the USSR has the greatest estimated volume (23,000km³) of any freshwater lake in the world; in area, however, it ranks only sixth.

**I** The Pacific Ocean has an estimated volume of around 700,000,000km³.
**J** The Moon's volume is around 21,900,000,000km³ (21.9 x 10⁹km³).

**K** Earth, whose diameter is 3.7 times bigger than that of the Moon, has a volume of 1,083,208,840,000km³ (about 1.08x10¹²km³), some 49.5 times that of the Moon.

©DIAGRAM

Earth's volume is equivalent to 1,083,208,840,000,000,000,000,000,000 (approximately 10²⁷) sugar lumps.

# MEASURING VOLUME 2

Here we look at a further aspect of measuring volume: the use of special units for measuring the capacity of containers and thus also the quantity of substances that can be held within them. US and UK systems differ markedly in this area: the names of the units are the same, but the volumes are different in every case.

**Units of capacity** *right*
Listed in the table are capacity units from the US customary, UK/imperial, and metric systems of measurement. Recognized abbreviations are given in brackets. The final column gives equivalent volumes in cubic units, and serves to demonstrate the extent to which units with common names vary between the systems. Note that in the US system there are 4 fluid ounces in a gill, whereas in the UK/imperial system there are 5; otherwise multiples of units are generally similar.

### US units of liquid capacity
| | | |
|---|---|---|
| 60 minims (min) | = 1 fluid dram (fl.dr) | = $0.2256\text{in}^3$ |
| 8 fluid drams | = 1 fluid ounce (fl.oz) | = $1.8047\text{in}^3$ |
| 4 fluid ounces | = 1 gill (gi) | = $7.2187\text{in}^3$ |
| 4 gills | = 1 pint (pt) | = $28.875\text{in}^3$ |
| 2 pints | = 1 quart (qt) | = $57.750\text{in}^3$ |
| 4 quarts | = 1 gallon (gal) | = $231.00\text{in}^3$ |

### US units of dry capacity
| | | |
|---|---|---|
| 1 dry pint (dry pt) | = ½ dry quart (dry qt) | = $33.600\text{in}^3$ |
| 2 dry pints | = 1 dry quart | = $67.201\text{in}^3$ |
| 8 dry quarts | = 1 peck (pk) | = $537.60\text{in}^3$ |
| 4 pecks | = 1 bushel (bu) | = $2150.4\text{in}^3$ |

### UK/imperial units of liquid and dry capacity
| | | |
|---|---|---|
| 60 minims (min) | = 1 fluid drachm (fl.dr) | = $0.2167\text{in}^3$ |
| 8 fluid drachms | = 1 fluid ounce (fl.oz) | = $1.7339\text{in}^3$ |
| 5 fluid ounces | = 1 gill (gi) | = $8.6690\text{in}^3$ |
| 4 gills | = 1 pint (pt) | = $34.677\text{in}^3$ |
| 2 pints | = 1 quart (qt) | = $69.355\text{in}^3$ |
| 4 quarts | = 1 gallon (gal) | = $277.42\text{in}^3$ |
| 2 gallons | = 1 peck (pk) | = $554.84\text{in}^3$ |
| 4 pecks | = 1 bushel (bu) | = $2219.4\text{in}^3$ |
| 36 bushels | = 1 chaldron | = $7979,898\text{in}^3$ |

### Metric units of capacity
| | | |
|---|---|---|
| 1000 microliters or lambdas ($\lambda$) | = 1 mil (ml) | = $0.000001\text{m}^3$ |
| 10 milliliters or mils | = 1 centiliter (cl) | = $0.00001\text{m}^3$ |
| 10 centiliters | = 1 deciliter (dl) | = $0.0001\text{m}^3$ |
| 10 deciliters | = 1 liter (l) | = $0.001\text{m}^3$ |
| 1000 liters | = 1 stère (st) | = $1\text{m}^3$ |

**Comparative capacities** *right* The diagram allows a quick comparison of capacity units: US pints (**A**), UK pints (**B**), and liters (**C**). Alongside the scales is a selection of common objects, chosen to illustrate the range of capacities involved.

a Wine glass
b Beer bottle
c Wine bottle
d Thermos (4-cup size)
e Mixing bowl
f Medium saucepan
g Earthenware casserole
h Large saucepan
i Pressure cooker
j Plastic bucket

**Roll out which barrel? Among the diverse quantities for which the unit of a "barrel" has been used are: 32 gallons of herrings; 200lb of meat; 2cwt of butter; 5826 cubic inches of cranberries; and 36 gallons of beer!**

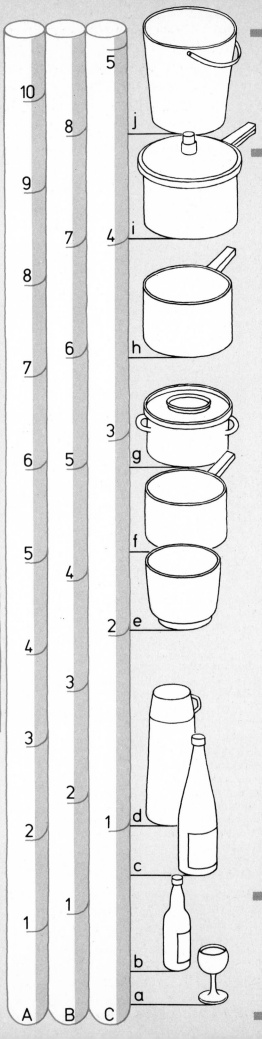

Different English versions of the Bible use three different units to express the size of the jars of water turned into wine by Jesus at the wedding at Cana (John 2:6)—two or three metretes (Wycliffe's English Bible of 1388); two or three firkins (King James Bible); twenty to thirty gallons (New English Bible). Although the units differ, the quantities are roughly similar.

# Area and volume

| US pt | | UK pt | | US pt | | l | | UK pt | | l |
|---|---|---|---|---|---|---|---|---|---|---|
| 1.2010 | 1 | 0.8327 | | 2.1134 | 1 | 0.4732 | | 1.7598 | 1 | 0.5683 |
| 2.4020 | 2 | 1.6653 | | 4.2269 | 2 | 0.9463 | | 3.5095 | 2 | 1.1365 |
| 3.6030 | 3 | 2.4980 | | 6.3403 | 3 | 1.4195 | | 5.2793 | 3 | 1.7048 |
| 4.8039 | 4 | 3.3306 | | 8.4537 | 4 | 1.8926 | | 7.0390 | 4 | 2.2730 |
| 6.0049 | 5 | 4.1633 | | 10.567 | 5 | 2.3658 | | 8.7988 | 5 | 2.8413 |
| 7.2059 | 6 | 4.9959 | | 12.681 | 6 | 2.8390 | | 10.559 | 6 | 3.4096 |
| 8.4069 | 7 | 5.8286 | | 14.794 | 7 | 3.3121 | | 12.318 | 7 | 3.9778 |
| 9.6079 | 8 | 6.6612 | | 16.907 | 8 | 3.7853 | | 14.078 | 8 | 4.5461 |

| US gal | | UK gal | | US gal | | l | | UK gal | | l |
|---|---|---|---|---|---|---|---|---|---|---|
| 1.2009 | 1 | 0.8327 | | 0.2642 | 1 | 3.7853 | | 0.2200 | 1 | 4.5460 |
| 2.4019 | 2 | 1.6653 | | 0.5284 | 2 | 7.5706 | | 0.4400 | 2 | 9.0919 |
| 3.6029 | 3 | 2.4980 | | 0.7925 | 3 | 11.356 | | 0.6599 | 3 | 13.638 |
| 4.8038 | 4 | 3.3307 | | 1.0567 | 4 | 15.141 | | 0.8799 | 4 | 18.184 |
| 6.0047 | 5 | 4.1634 | | 1.3209 | 5 | 18.926 | | 1.0999 | 5 | 22.730 |
| 7.2057 | 6 | 4.9960 | | 1.5851 | 6 | 22.712 | | 1.3199 | 6 | 27.276 |
| 8.4066 | 7 | 5.8287 | | 1.8492 | 7 | 26.497 | | 1.5398 | 7 | 31.822 |
| 9.6076 | 8 | 6.6614 | | 2.1134 | 8 | 30.282 | | 1.7598 | 8 | 36.368 |
| 10.809 | 9 | 7.4941 | | 2.3776 | 9 | 34.067 | | 1.9798 | 9 | 40.914 |
| 18.014 | 15 | 12.490 | | 3.9627 | 15 | 56.780 | | 3.2996 | 15 | 68.189 |
| 30.024 | 25 | 20.817 | | 6.6045 | 25 | 94.633 | | 5.4994 | 25 | 113.65 |
| 42.033 | 35 | 29.144 | | 9.2463 | 35 | 132.49 | | 7.6992 | 35 | 159.11 |
| 54.043 | 45 | 37.470 | | 11.888 | 45 | 170.34 | | 9.8989 | 45 | 181.84 |
| 66.052 | 55 | 45.797 | | 14.530 | 55 | 208.25 | | 12.099 | 55 | 204.57 |
| 78.062 | 65 | 54.124 | | 17.172 | 65 | 246.04 | | 14.298 | 65 | 295.49 |
| 90.071 | 75 | 62.451 | | 19.813 | 75 | 283.90 | | 16.498 | 75 | 340.95 |
| 102.08 | 85 | 70.777 | | 22.455 | 85 | 319.46 | | 18.698 | 85 | 386.41 |
| 114.09 | 95 | 79.104 | | 25.097 | 95 | 359.60 | | 20.898 | 95 | 431.87 |

| US fl.oz | | UK fl.oz | | US fl.oz | | cl | | UK fl.oz | | cl |
|---|---|---|---|---|---|---|---|---|---|---|
| 0.9608 | 1 | 1.0408 | | 0.3381 | 1 | 2.9573 | | 0.3520 | 1 | 2.8413 |
| 1.9216 | 2 | 2.0816 | | 0.6763 | 2 | 5.9145 | | 0.7039 | 2 | 5.6826 |
| 2.8824 | 3 | 3.1224 | | 1.0144 | 3 | 8.8718 | | 1.0559 | 3 | 8.5239 |
| 3.8431 | 4 | 4.1633 | | 1.3526 | 4 | 11.829 | | 1.4078 | 4 | 11.365 |
| 4.8039 | 5 | 5.2041 | | 1.6907 | 5 | 14.786 | | 1.7598 | 5 | 14.207 |
| 5.7647 | 6 | 6.2449 | | 2.0289 | 6 | 17.744 | | 2.1117 | 6 | 17.048 |
| 6.7255 | 7 | 7.2857 | | 2.3670 | 7 | 20.701 | | 2.4637 | 7 | 19.889 |
| 7.6863 | 8 | 8.3265 | | 2.7052 | 8 | 23.658 | | 2.8156 | 8 | 22.730 |
| 8.6471 | 9 | 9.3673 | | 3.0433 | 9 | 26.615 | | 3.1676 | 9 | 25.572 |

**Conversion tables** *left*
Included here are tables for converting US and UK/imperial liquid capacity measurements from one to the other, as well as tables for converting into metric units and vice versa. To use the tables, first find the figure to be converted—US, UK or metric—in the central column of the relevant table. Its equivalent can then be found in the appropriate column, either to the right or to the left as indicated by the headings above.

| US cookery measures | Metric equivalents |
|---|---|
| 1 teaspoon | 0.5cl |
| 1 tablespoon (= 3 teaspoons) | 1.5cl |
| 1 cup (= 16 tablespoons = ½ US pint) | 23.7cl |
| **UK cookery measures** | |
| 1 teaspoon | 0.6cl |
| 1 dessertspoon (= 2 teaspoons) | 1.2cl |
| 1 tablespoon (= 3 teaspoons) | 1.8cl |
| 1 cup (= 16 tablespoons = ½ UK pint) | 28.4cl |

©DIAGRAM

**Recipe for success**
The table *above* gives the centiliter equivalents of the standard measuring spoons and cups commonly used by cooks in the USA and UK. Note that the standard measuring cup is a ''breakfast'' cup rather than a teacup, which is half its size. As the diagram *right* further illustrates, US cooks' measures are roughly four-fifths as big as UK measures.
a UK tablespoon
b US tablespoon
c UK dessertspoon
d UK teaspoon
e US teaspoon

1.5 cl
1.0 cl
0.5 cl

a
b
c
d
e

**For a bubbly bath** *right*
The standard champagne bottle holds 80cl (5–10cl more than standard bottles for other wines). Champagne is also sold in larger bottles, of which the names and capacities (given as multiples of the standard 80cl bottle) are given here.

a Magnum (2)
b Jeroboam (4)
c Rehoboam (6)
d Methuselah (8)
e Salmanazar (12)
f Balthazar (16)
g Nebuchadnezzar (20)

If Scotland's Loch Ness were to be emptied in search of the monster, it would take 1650 billion UK one-gallon buckets, or 1981 billion US one-gallon buckets.

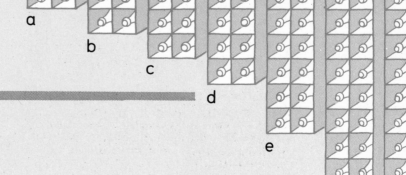

# OIL AND WATER

Man's largest oil tankers and storage tanks are tiny compared with the volumes of water contained in nature. Even the man-made lake with the greatest volume, at Owen Falls, would fit 113 times into the world's most voluminous natural freshwater lake (Baykal 5520mi³), and could be filled in $19\frac{1}{2}$ weeks by the flow over Boyoma Falls.

| A | Pierre Guillaumat | 678,000m³ | 3,307,317 |
|---|---|---|---|
| B | Bellamya | 677,362m³ | 3,304,205 |
| C | Batillus | 677,362m³ | 3,304,205 |
| D | Globtik London | 578,235m³ | 2,820,658 |
| E | Globtik Tokyo | 573,361m³ | 2,796,883 |
| F | Nissei Maru | 573,345m³ | 2,796,805 |
| G | Esso Mediterranean | 553,054m³ | 2,697,824 |
| H | Berge Emperor | 513,680m³ | 2,505,756 |
| I | Berge Empress | 513,680m³ | 2,505,756 |
| J | Al Rekkah | 512,920m³ | 2,502,049 |

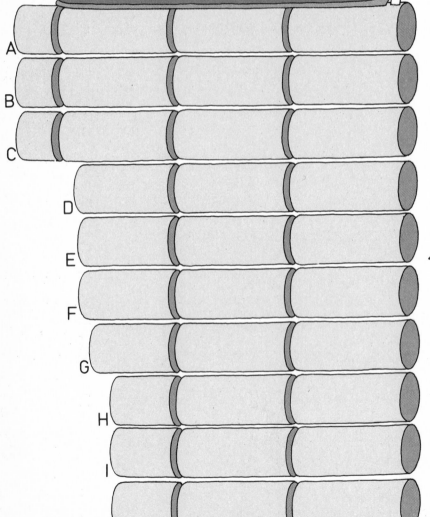

### Oil in the tanks
The table *above* and the diagram *left* show the oil-carrying capacity of the world's 10 largest supertankers. In the table, the ships' capacities are expressed first in cubic meters (in accordance with international practice in this area), and also in terms of standard international oil barrels (each with a capacity of 205 liters).

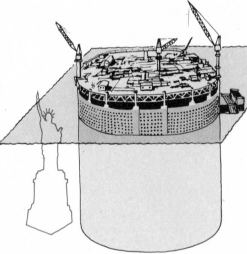

### Giant oil tank *above*
The world's largest oil storage tank—in the North Sea's Ekofisk field—is shown here to the same scale as the Statue of Liberty. Note, however, that the overall volume of the Ekofisk tank is roughly five times as great as the tank's oil capacity. When full, the tank holds some 160,000m³ of oil, equal to 780,466 standard international 205l oil barrels, or almost one-quarter of the capacity of the world's largest oil tanker, France's *Pierre Guillaumat* (678,000m³).

**The capacity of the world's largest oil tanker, the *Pierre Guillaumat*, is equivalent to the tanks of nearly 10 million average-sized US automobiles.**

**If the 48.5 cubic miles of water in the man-made lake at Owen Falls, Uganda, were to be put in a regularly shaped tank, the tank would be a cube with edges of 3.65 miles.**

©DIAGRAM

| | | | | |
|---|---|---|---|---|
| **a** | Boyoma (Stanley) | Zaïre | 600,000ft³/s | 0.47s |
| **b** | Guaíra | Brazil/Paraguay | 470,000ft³/s | 0.60s |
| **c** | Khône | Laos | 410,000ft³/s | 0.69s |
| **d** | Niagara | Canada/USA | 212,000ft³/s | 1.33s |
| **e** | Paulo Afonso | Brazil | 100,000ft³/s | 2.82s |
| **f** | Urubupungá | Brazil | 97,000ft³/s | 2.91s |
| **g** | Cataratas del Iguazú | Brazil/Argentina | 61,660ft³/s | 4.57s |
| **h** | Patos-Maribondo | Brazil | 53,000ft³/s | 5.32s |
| **i** | Victoria | Zimbabwe-Rhodesia | 38,430ft³/s | 7.34s |
| **j** | Churchill (Grand) | Canada | 35,000ft³/s | 8.06s |

a  b  c  d  e  f  g  h  i  j

**Over the falls** *above*
The table shows the world's top 10 waterfalls in terms of volume. The first column of figures gives their mean annual water flow, expressed in cubic feet per second, or cusecs (ft³/s). The other column of figures, and the accompanying diagram, show the amount of time, in seconds, that would be needed for each of these waterfalls to fill the dome of London's St Paul's Cathedral (282,000ft³).

| | | | |
|---|---|---|---|
| **1** | Owen Falls | Victoria Nile, Uganda | 48.5mi³ |
| **2** | Bratsk | Angara, USSR | 40.6mi³ |
| **3** | Aswan High | Nile, Egypt | 39.4mi³ |
| **4** | Kariba | Zambesi, Zambia/Rhodesia | 38.4mi³ |
| **5** | Akosombo | Volta, Ghana | 35.5mi³ |
| **6** | Daniel Johnson | Manicouagan, Canada | 34.1mi³ |
| **7** | Krasnoyarsk | Yenisey, USSR | 17.6mi³ |
| **8** | WAC Bennett | Peace, Canada | 16.8mi³ |
| **9** | Zeya | Zeya, USSR | 16.4mi³ |
| **10** | Wadi Tharthar | Tigris, Iraq | 16.0mi³ |

**Behind the dams**
The table *above* gives the names of the world's greatest dams, the rivers that they dam, the countries in which they are situated and the volume of water in the lakes behind them. The diagram *left* provides a visual comparison of these volumes. Greatest among them is the volume of water in the lake behind Uganda's Owen Falls— some 48.5mi³, a volume sufficient to fill more than 1,762,000,000,000 average bathtubs!

1  2  3  4  5  6  7  8  9  10

Here we see at last the head of the 22ft-long giant earthworm whose tail is on page 66.

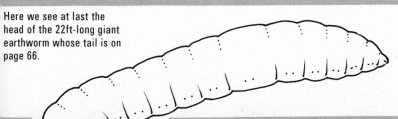

**A fast-running domestic tap would take 308 days to fill the dome of London's St Paul's Cathedral.**

# THE UNIVERSE

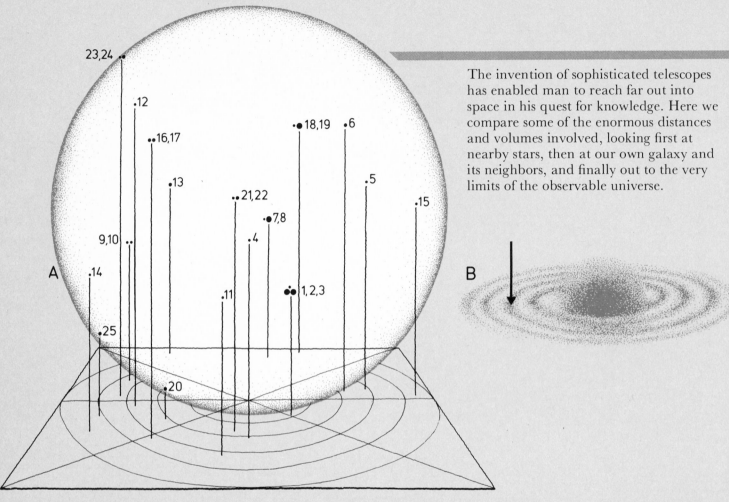

The invention of sophisticated telescopes has enabled man to reach far out into space in his quest for knowledge. Here we compare some of the enormous distances and volumes involved, looking first at nearby stars, then at our own galaxy and its neighbors, and finally out to the very limits of the observable universe.

**Light years away** *below right* Here we use spheres of constant size to represent progressively larger spheres. Each new sphere has a radius (**r**) 10 times bigger than that of its predecessor, giving it a volume (**V**) that is 1000 times as great. Dimensions are expressed in light years (ly) and cubic light years (ly³). Drawn within four of the spheres are colored spheres (**A,B,C,D**) indicating the comparative volumes of the various space features shown in more detail *above*.
**A** Sphere with radius of 12 ly, containing our Sun's stellar neighbors.
**B** Sphere representing the volume of our galaxy.
**C** Sphere with radius of 2,500,000 ly, containing our neighboring galaxies.
**D** Sphere representing the theoretical edge of the universe.

**A) Stellar neighbors**
*above* This sphere, with its center at our Sun, has a radius of 12 ly and a volume of 7238 ly³. Stellar neighbors situated within these limits are listed *right* and located both within the sphere and on the plan view below it.

| | | | | | |
|---|---|---|---|---|---|
| **1** | Proxima Centauri | **11** | Ross 154 | **21** | Sigma 2398 A |
| **2** | Alpha Centauri | **12** | Ross 248 | **22** | Sigma 2398 B |
| **3** | Beta Centauri | **13** | Epsilon Eridani | **23** | Groombridge 34A |
| **4** | Barnard's star | **14** | Lutyens 789-6 | **24** | Groombridge 34B |
| **5** | Wolf 359 | **15** | Ross 128 | **25** | Lacertae 9352 |
| **6** | LAL 21185 | **16** | 61 Cygni A | | |
| **7** | Sirius A | **17** | 61 Cygni B | | |
| **8** | Sirius B | **18** | Procyon A | | |
| **9** | UV Ceti A | **19** | Procyon B | | |
| **10** | UV Ceti B | **20** | Epsilon Indi | | |

**B) Volume of our galaxy**
*above* Here we show our galaxy, with its well-defined nucleus and spiral arms. The Sun's approximate position is indicated by an arrow. Our galaxy's volume (mass divided by density) is about $3.7 \times 10^{13}$ ly³, represented *bottom* by sphere **B**.

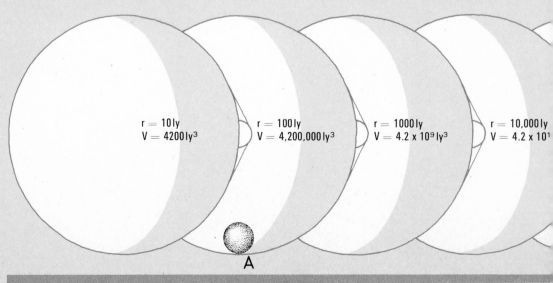

r = 10 ly
V = 4200 ly³

r = 100 ly
V = 4,200,000 ly³

r = 1000 ly
V = 4.2 x 10⁹ ly³

r = 10,000 ly
V = 4.2 x 10¹

A

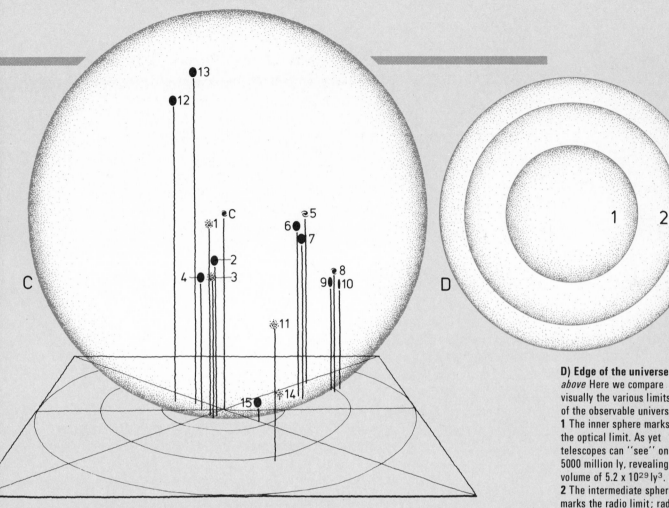

**C) Neighboring galaxies**
*above* This sphere, centered on our galaxy (**c**), has a radius of 2,500,000 ly and a volume of $65.5 \times 10^{18}$ ly$^3$. It contains our nearest galactic neighbors, which are identified on the illustration by numbers and named in the list *right*.

| | | | |
|---|---|---|---|
| **1** | Nubecula Major | **11** | NGC 6822 |
| **2** | Sculptor | **12** | Leo I |
| **3** | Nubecula Minor | **13** | Leo II |
| **4** | Fornax | **14** | IC 1613 |
| **5** | M33 | **15** | Wolf-Lundmark |
| **6** | NGC 185 | | |
| **7** | NGC 147 | | |
| **8** | M31 | | |
| **9** | M32 | | |
| **10** | NGC 205 | | |

**D) Edge of the universe**
*above* Here we compare visually the various limits of the observable universe.
**1** The inner sphere marks the optical limit. As yet telescopes can "see" only 5000 million ly, revealing a volume of $5.2 \times 10^{29}$ ly$^3$.
**2** The intermediate sphere marks the radio limit; radio telescopes can reach about 8000 million ly, giving us a volume of $21.4 \times 10^{29}$ ly$^3$.
**3** The outer sphere (r = $10^{10}$ ly; V = $4.2 \times 10^{30}$ ly$^3$) marks the "ultimate horizon" since at this distance objects are receding at the speed of light—and so cannot be detected.

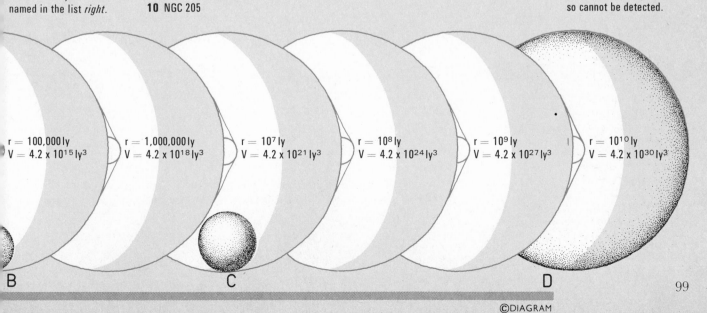

r = 100,000 ly
V = $4.2 \times 10^{15}$ ly$^3$

r = 1,000,000 ly
V = $4.2 \times 10^{18}$ ly$^3$

r = $10^7$ ly
V = $4.2 \times 10^{21}$ ly$^3$

r = $10^8$ ly
V = $4.2 \times 10^{24}$ ly$^3$

r = $10^9$ ly
V = $4.2 \times 10^{27}$ ly$^3$

r = $10^{10}$ ly
V = $4.2 \times 10^{30}$ ly$^3$

B                    C                    D

©DIAGRAM

# CHAPTER 5

Drawings of Japanese Sumo wrestlers from the book *Sumo Nyakunenshi* (published by Kodansha of Tokyo). The minimum weight for a Sumo wrestler is 350 lb—more than twice the weight of an average man. Perhaps the heaviest *sumatori* of all was the 430 lb Dewayatake.

# MASS, WEIGHT AND DENSITY

This photograph taken during the 1969 Apollo 11 mission shows Astronaut Edwin Aldrin walking on the surface of the Moon, where gravity—and hence a person's weight—is only about one sixth of that on Earth (NASA, Washington DC).

# MEASURING MASS, WEIGHT AND DENSITY

Mass measures the amount of matter, or substance, in an object. Density is the mass per unit volume, which varies with temperature and pressure. Weight measures the pull of gravity on an object and is directly related to the object's mass. For most purposes mass and weight are the same, as the gravitational force on which weight depends is for most of us always that of Earth (although even this varies slightly with latitude and altitude, see p.112). Systems of weights use multiples and divisions of the weight of commonly agreed objects. Base weights range from a sack of grain, popular among agricultural societies, to the metric system's standard kilogram—a cylinder of platinum-iridium alloy.

**Weight and gravity** *left*
Weight measures the force of attraction between an object and (for us) Earth. The stronger this force, the heavier the object. It is measured most simply by a spring scale marked in commonly agreed units of weight.

**Systems of weights** *right*
Listed are units for measuring mass and weight. Standard abbreviations are given in brackets. "Short" or "net" hundredweights and tons are fuller names for these US units, "long" or "gross" hundredweights and tons for the UK units.

**US units of mass and weight (avoirdupois)**

| | | |
|---|---|---|
| 16 drams (dr) | = 1 ounce (oz) | |
| 16 ounces | = 1 pound (lb) | |
| 100 pounds | = 1 hundredweight (cwt) | |
| 5 hundredweights | = 1 quarter (qr) | = 500 lb |
| 4 quarters | = 1 ton (tn) | = 2000 lb |

**UK/imperial units of mass and weight (avoirdupois)**

| | | |
|---|---|---|
| 16 drachms (dr) | = 1 ounce (oz) | |
| 16 ounces | = 1 pound (lb) | |
| 14 pounds | = 1 stone (st) | |
| 2 stones | = 1 quarter (qr) | = 28 lb |
| 4 quarters | = 1 hundredweight (cwt) | = 112 lb |
| 20 hundredweights | = 1 ton (tn) | = 2240 lb |

**Metric units of mass and weight**

| | |
|---|---|
| 1000 milligrams (mg) | = 1 gram (g) |
| 1000 grams | = 1 kilogram (kg) |
| 1000 kilograms | = 1 tonne (t) |

**Troy (jewelers') units of weight**

| | | |
|---|---|---|
| 24 grains (gr) | = 1 pennyweight (dwt) | |
| 20 pennyweights | = 1 ounce (oz.t) | = 1.097oz |
| 12 ounces | = 1 pound (lb.t) | = 0.823 lb |

**Apothecaries' units of weight**

| | | |
|---|---|---|
| 20 grains (gr) | = 1 scruple (s.ap) | |
| 3 scruples | = 1 dram (dr.ap) | |
| 8 drams | = 1 ounce (oz.ap) | = 1.097oz |
| 12 ounces | = 1 pound (lb.ap) | = 0.823 lb |

**Conversion tables** *right*
To convert US/imperial weight measurements into metric, and vice versa, find the figure to be converted—US/imperial or metric—in the central column. Its equivalent will be in the appropriate column to the right or to the left.

**Tons and tons and tonnes** *far right* These conversion tables enable us to convert short tons to tonnes, and long tons to tonnes. Short tons can be converted to long tons (and vice versa) by first converting into tonnes and then to short or to long tons.

| oz | | g | lb | | kg |
|---|---|---|---|---|---|
| 0.0353 | 1 | 28.350 | 2.2046 | 1 | 0.4536 |
| 0.0705 | 2 | 56.699 | 4.4092 | 2 | 0.9072 |
| 0.1058 | 3 | 85.049 | 6.6139 | 3 | 1.3608 |
| 0.1411 | 4 | 113.40 | 8.8185 | 4 | 1.8144 |
| 0.1764 | 5 | 141.75 | 11.023 | 5 | 2.2680 |
| 0.2116 | 6 | 170.10 | 13.228 | 6 | 2.7216 |
| 0.2469 | 7 | 198.45 | 15.432 | 7 | 3.1752 |
| 0.2822 | 8 | 226.80 | 17.637 | 8 | 3.6287 |
| 0.3175 | 9 | 255.15 | 19.842 | 9 | 4.0823 |
| 0.5291 | 15 | 425.24 | 33.069 | 15 | 6.8039 |
| 0.8819 | 25 | 708.74 | 55.116 | 25 | 11.340 |
| 1.2346 | 35 | 992.23 | 77.162 | 35 | 15.876 |
| 1.5873 | 45 | 1275.7 | 99.208 | 45 | 20.412 |
| 1.9401 | 55 | 1559.2 | 121.25 | 55 | 24.948 |
| 2.2928 | 65 | 1842.7 | 143.30 | 65 | 29.484 |
| 2.6456 | 75 | 2126.2 | 165.35 | 75 | 34.019 |
| 2.9983 | 85 | 2409.7 | 187.39 | 85 | 38.555 |
| 3.3510 | 95 | 2693.2 | 209.44 | 95 | 43.091 |

| short tons | | tonnes | long tons | | tonnes |
|---|---|---|---|---|---|
| 1.1023 | 1 | 0.9072 | 0.9842 | 1 | 1.0161 |
| 2.2046 | 2 | 1.8144 | 1.9684 | 2 | 2.0321 |
| 3.3069 | 3 | 2.7216 | 2.9526 | 3 | 3.0482 |
| 4.4092 | 4 | 3.6287 | 3.9368 | 4 | 4.0642 |
| 5.5116 | 5 | 4.5359 | 4.9210 | 5 | 5.0803 |
| 6.6139 | 6 | 5.4431 | 5.9052 | 6 | 6.0963 |
| 7.7162 | 7 | 6.3503 | 6.8895 | 7 | 7.1124 |
| 8.8185 | 8 | 7.2575 | 7.8737 | 8 | 8.1284 |
| 9.9208 | 9 | 8.1647 | 8.8579 | 9 | 9.1445 |
| 16.535 | 15 | 13.607 | 14.763 | 15 | 15.241 |
| 27.558 | 25 | 22.680 | 24.605 | 25 | 25.401 |
| 38.581 | 35 | 31.751 | 34.447 | 35 | 35.562 |
| 49.604 | 45 | 40.823 | 44.289 | 45 | 45.722 |
| 60.627 | 55 | 49.895 | 54.131 | 55 | 55.883 |
| 71.650 | 65 | 58.967 | 63.973 | 65 | 66.043 |
| 82.673 | 75 | 68.039 | 73.816 | 75 | 76.204 |
| 93.696 | 85 | 77.111 | 83.658 | 85 | 86.364 |
| 104.72 | 95 | 86.182 | 93.500 | 95 | 96.525 |

Use of the term carat can lead to confusion when describing an engagement ring. When applied to precious stones, such as a diamond, a carat is a unit of weight equal to 200 milligrams. When applied to gold, however, a carat (more properly spelled karat in this case) is a measure of purity not of weight, being equal to 1/24th part of pure gold in an alloy.

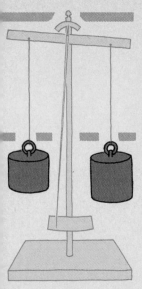

**Mass and matter** *above*
Mass measures the amount of matter in an object, and is measured by comparing an object with others of known mass on a balance. Mass is expressed in the same units as weight (lb, kg, etc), but unlike weight it does not depend on gravity.

**Determining density**
The density of an object is its mass divided by its volume. The greater the density of a substance, then the more concentrated is its matter, the more mass it will have per unit volume, and, volume for volume, the heavier it will seem.

|  | lb/ft³ | g/cm³ |
|---|---|---|
| Platinum | 1338.48 | 21.45 |
| Gold | 1203.70 | 19.29 |
| Lead | 709.49 | 11.37 |
| Silver | 651.46 | 10.44 |
| Granite | 164.74 | 2.64 |
| Concrete | 134.78* | 2.16* |
| Sugar | 100.00* | 1.61* |
| Coal | 84.50* | 1.35* |
| Boxwood | 64.90* | 1.04* |
| 0 Milk | 64.27 | 1.03 |
| 1 Water | 62.40 | 1 |
| 2 Rubber | 58.03 | 0.93 |
| 3 Petroleum | 54.80 | 0.88 |
| 4 Alcohol | 49.30 | 0.79 |
| 5 Beechwood | 44.93* | 0.72* |
| 6 Charcoal | 21.53* | 0.345* |
| 7 Air (62°F) | 0.08 | 0.00128 |

Mean density

**Density, mass and volume**
The table *left* lists the densities of selected substances. The diagram *above* shows, real size, the volumes that 4g (about the weight of an airmail envelope and one sheet of paper) of these substances would occupy.

**The densest elements**
*below* This table shows the 10 densest elements at 20°C. The order depends on temperature because different substances expand and contract at different rates in response to the addition or subtraction of heat.

| 1 | Osmium | 1409.62 lb/ft³ | 22.59g/cm³ |
|---|---|---|---|
| 2 | Iridium | 1407.74 lb/ft³ | 22.56g/cm³ |
| 3 | Platinum | 1338.48 lb/ft³ | 21.45g/cm³ |
| 4 | Rhenium | 1311.02 lb/ft³ | 21.01g/cm³ |
| 5 | Gold | 1203.70 lb/ft³ | 19.29g/cm³ |
| 6 | Tungsten | 1201.82 lb/ft³ | 19.26g/cm³ |
| 7 | Uranium | 1188.72 lb/ft³ | 19.05g/cm³ |
| 8 | Tantalum | 1040.21 lb/ft³ | 16.67g/cm³ |
| 9 | Protactinium | 961.58 lb/ft³ | 15.41g/cm³ |
| 10 | Mercury | 845.52 lb/ft³ | 13.55g/cm³ |

**Relative density** *right*
Comparisons of density can be made with reference to the "specific gravity" of different substances. The specific gravity (sg) of water is 1; the sg of other substances is the ratio, at a certain temperature (usually 60°F), of the weight of the substance to the weight of the same volume of water. The weight of the same volume of water is the difference between the weight of the substance when weighed in air (**a**) or in water (**b**). More often, sg is measured with a special instrument—a hydrometer.

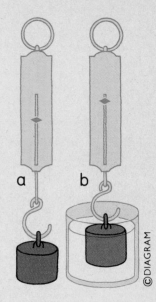

©DIAGRAM

*A table top measuring 6ft by 2ft by 1in thick would weigh 32lb if made of yellow pine. If made of marble it would weigh over five times as much (165lb).*

# COMPARATIVE MASSES

On these two pages we look at the whole range of masses, from the mass of a neutrino, the smallest known mass at $5 \times 10^{-34}$ kg, to the largest, which is the estimated mass of the universe, at $10^{51}$ kg. Masses within the living world range from that of a virus at $10^{-21}$ kg, to that of a blue whale at $1.38 \times 10^5$ kg.

## Mass in the living world

*below* Plotted on this enlarged section of the scale are examples showing the wide range of masses in the living world.
**8** Virus $10^{-21}$ kg.
**9** Bacteria $10^{-13}$ to $10^{-14}$ kg.
**10** Parasitic wasp, the smallest insect, $5 \times 10^{-9}$ kg.
**11** House spider $10^{-4}$ kg.
**12** Helena's hummingbird $2 \times 10^{-3}$ kg.
**13** Chicken 3.15 kg.
**14** Average man $7.29 \times 10$ kg.
**15** Polar bear $3.22 \times 10^2$ kg.
**16** African elephant $6.3 \times 10^3$ kg.
**17** Blue whale, the most massive animal, $1.38 \times 10^5$ kg.

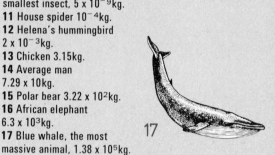

## Universal scale of mass

*below* The logarithmic scale across these pages shows the whole range of known or estimated masses, allowing us to compare the masses of things as diverse as a subatomic particle, a hummingbird, a Chieftain tank, and the Moon.

Enlarged sections of the main scale have made it possible to plot a greater number of examples, and so allow more detailed comparisons of very tiny masses, of the masses of living and man-made things, and of the huge masses to be found in space.

| 8 | 9 | 10 | 11 | 12 | 13 | 14 | 15 |

$10^{-20}$   $10^{-15}$   $10^{-10}$   $10^{-5}$   1

$10^{-30}$   $10^{-25}$   1

| 1 | 2 | 3 4 | 5 6 | 7 | 18 | 19 | 20 | 21 | 22 | 23 |

## Minute masses *above*

Plotted on this enlarged section are the masses of subatomic particles, atoms and molecules.
**1** Neutrino, a stable, electrically neutral particle, $5 \times 10^{-34}$ kg.
**2** Electron $9.1096 \times 10^{-31}$ kg.
**3** Proton $1.6726 \times 10^{-27}$ kg.
**4** Neutron, a long-lived, neutral particle, $1.6748 \times 10^{-27}$ kg.
**5** Carbon 12 atom $1.9924 \times 10^{-26}$ kg.
**6** Molecule of water ($H_2O$) $2.99 \times 10^{-26}$ kg.
**7** Molecule of a complex biochemical compound $10^{-22}$ kg.

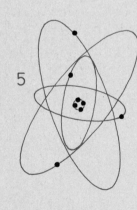

The mass of a virus is to the mass of an average man as the mass of an average man is to the mass of Earth.

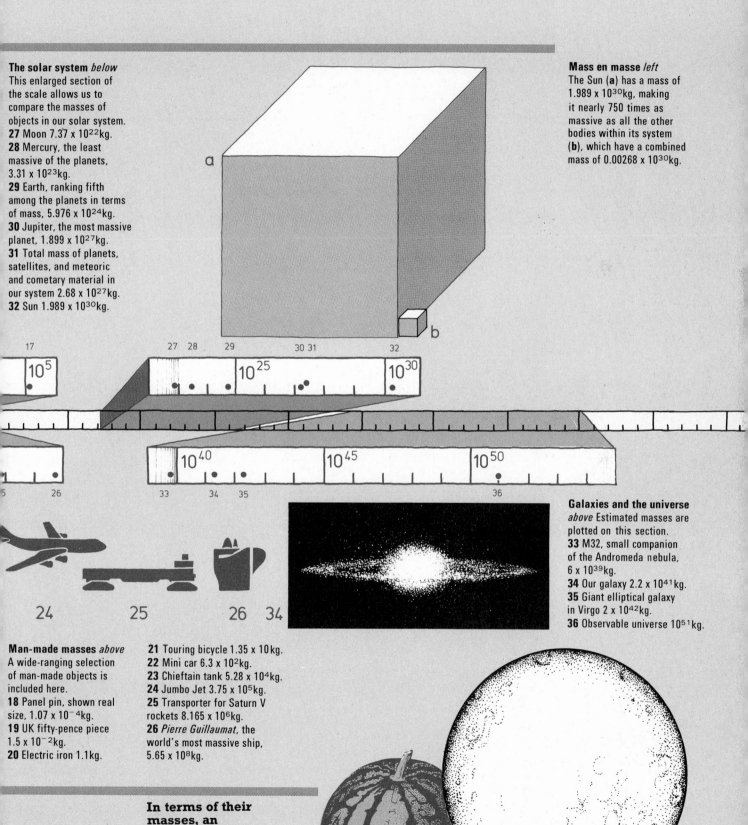

*Among subatomic particles, the mass of a neutron, at $1.6748 \times 10^{-27}$ kg, is over three million times greater than the mass of a neutrino, at $5 \times 10^{-34}$ kg.*

**The solar system** *below*
This enlarged section of the scale allows us to compare the masses of objects in our solar system.
**27** Moon $7.37 \times 10^{22}$ kg.
**28** Mercury, the least massive of the planets, $3.31 \times 10^{23}$ kg.
**29** Earth, ranking fifth among the planets in terms of mass, $5.976 \times 10^{24}$ kg.
**30** Jupiter, the most massive planet, $1.899 \times 10^{27}$ kg.
**31** Total mass of planets, satellites, and meteoric and cometary material in our system $2.68 \times 10^{27}$ kg.
**32** Sun $1.989 \times 10^{30}$ kg.

**Mass en masse** *left*
The Sun (**a**) has a mass of $1.989 \times 10^{30}$ kg, making it nearly 750 times as massive as all the other bodies within its system (**b**), which have a combined mass of $0.00268 \times 10^{30}$ kg.

**Galaxies and the universe**
*above* Estimated masses are plotted on this section.
**33** M32, small companion of the Andromeda nebula, $6 \times 10^{39}$ kg.
**34** Our galaxy $2.2 \times 10^{41}$ kg.
**35** Giant elliptical galaxy in Virgo $2 \times 10^{42}$ kg.
**36** Observable universe $10^{51}$ kg.

**Man-made masses** *above*
A wide-ranging selection of man-made objects is included here.
**18** Panel pin, shown real size, $1.07 \times 10^{-4}$ kg.
**19** UK fifty-pence piece $1.5 \times 10^{-2}$ kg.
**20** Electric iron 1.1 kg.

**21** Touring bicycle $1.35 \times 10$ kg.
**22** Mini car $6.3 \times 10^{2}$ kg.
**23** Chieftain tank $5.28 \times 10^{4}$ kg.
**24** Jumbo Jet $3.75 \times 10^{5}$ kg.
**25** Transporter for Saturn V rockets $8.165 \times 10^{6}$ kg.
**26** *Pierre Guillaumat*, the world's most massive ship, $5.65 \times 10^{8}$ kg.

**In terms of their masses, an electron is to a water melon as a water melon is to the Sun.**

©DIAGRAM

# MATTER

All matter consists of atoms, which combine to form "elements" and "compounds." Here we use the "periodic table" as a means of comparing elements. Substances as different as hydrogen, calcium and gold are all elements; each has distinctive chemical and physical properties and cannot be split chemically into simpler form.

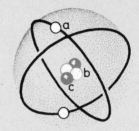

**Atomic structure** *left*
Electrons (**a**) orbit a nucleus of protons (**b**) and neutrons (**c**). Electrons have a negative charge and protons a positive charge; neutrons are neutral. There are always the same number of electrons as protons; the number of neutrons varies.

**How many elements?**
*below* When the Russian scientist Mendeleev drew up the first periodic table in 1869, only 65 elements were known. In the modern periodic table there are 104 known elements. 88 of these, from hydrogen to uranium, occur naturally, 16, including elements 43, 61, 85 and 87, are man-made or occur instantaneously during radioactive decay. Further elements have been predicted, and names already prepared for them.

**The pattern of the table**
*below* The table groups the elements into seven lines, or periods. In each horizontal line there is a repetition of chemical properties: as we read from left to right the elements of each line become less metallic.
The elements of each vertical group in the main table also have similar chemical properties.

The "lanthanides" or rare earths (numbers 57–71) and the "actinides" (numbers 89–103) form separate groups because, despite their atomic numbers, their properties are so similar that they fit the space of only one element in the main table.

| 1 H Hydrogen 1.0079 | | | | | | | | | |
|---|---|---|---|---|---|---|---|---|---|
| 3 Li Lithium 6.941 | 4 Be Beryllium 9.01218 | | | | | | | | |
| 11 Na Sodium 22.98977 | 12 Mg Magnesium 24.305 | | | | | | | | |
| 19 K Potassium 39.0983 | 20 Ca Calcium 40.08 | 21 Sc Scandium 44.9559 | 22 Ti Titanium 47.9 | 23 V Vanadium 50.9414 | 24 Cr Chromium 51.996 | 25 Mn Manganese 54.938 | 26 Fe Iron 55.847 | 27 Co Cobalt 58.9332 | C |
| 37 Rb Rubidium 85.4678 | 38 Sr Strontium 87.62 | 39 Y Yttrium 88.9059 | 40 Zr Zirconium 91.22 | 41 Nb Niobium 92.9064 | 42 Mo Molybdenum 95.94 | 43 Tc Technetium 96.9064* | 44 Ru Ruthenium 101.07 | 45 Rh Rhodium 102.9055 | R |
| 55 Cs Cesium 132.9054 | 56 Ba Barium 137.33 | 57–71 The lanthanides (rare earths) | 72 Hf Hafnium 178.49 | 73 Ta Tantalum 180.9479 | 74 W Tungsten 183.85 | 75 Re Rhenium 186.207 | 76 Os Osmium 190.2 | 77 Ir Iridium 192.22 | |
| 87 Fr Francium 223.0197* | 88 Ra Radium 226.0254* | 89–103 Actinide series | 104 Unq Unnilquadium | | | | | | |

| 57 La Lanthanum 138.9055 | 58 Ce Cerium 140.12 | 59 Pr Praseodymium 140.9077 | 60 Nd Neodymium 144.24 | 61 Pm Promethium 144.9128* | 62 Sm Samarium 150.35 | 63 Eu Europium 151.96 | E |
|---|---|---|---|---|---|---|---|
| 89 Ac Actinium 227.0278* | 90 Th Thorium 232.0381 | 91 Pa Protoactinium 231.0359 | 92 U Uranium 238.029* | 93 Np Neptunium 237.0482* | 94 Pu Plutonium 244.0642* | 95 Am Americium 243.0614* | Ar |

**Explanation of symbols and figures** *left*
**a** Atomic number
**b** Letter symbol for each element
**c** Element's name

**d** Atomic mass number (or atomic weight) in international amu's
**\*** Atomic weight of the isotope with the longest known half-life

a — 99
b — Es
c — Einsteinium
d — 254.0880*

**Es**

| Atomic mass units (amu) | | Derivation | | Equivalent in kg |
|---|---|---|---|---|
| 1 amu (international) | = | One-twelfth the mass of carbon 12, the principle isotope of carbon. | = | $1.66033 \times 10^{-27}$kg |
| 1 amu (physical) | = | One-sixteenth the mass of oxygen 16 (99.8% of all oxygen found on Earth). | = | $1.65981 \times 10^{-27}$kg |
| 1 amu (chemical) | = | One-sixteenth of the average mass of a mixture of three oxygen isotopes. | = | $1.66026 \times 10^{-27}$kg |

**Atomic mass units** *left*
An atom's mass (or weight) is measured in multiples of an atomic mass unit (amu). This table shows the three types of amu. Note that the amu differs from the ''atomic unit of mass,'' which is the electron's rest mass: $9.1084 \times 10^{-31}$kg.

**Elemental order** *below*
Elements are arranged in the periodic table according to their atomic numbers (the number of protons they have in their nucleus). Hydrogen (atomic number 1) has the lightest, smallest and simplest atom; Unnilquadium is the known element with the highest atomic number (104) and the most complex structure.

2 He Helium 4.0026

5 B Boron 10.81 | 6 C Carbon 12.011 | 7 N Nitrogen 14.0067 | 8 O Oxygen 15.9994 | 9 F Fluorine 18.9984 | 10 Ne Neon 20.179

13 Al Aluminum 26.98154 | 14 Si Silicon 28.0855 | 15 P Phosphorus 30.97376 | 16 S Sulfur 32.064 | 17 Cl Chlorine 35.453 | 18 Ar Argon 39.948

Ni | 29 Cu Copper 63.546 | 30 Zn Zinc 65.381 | 31 Ga Gallium 69.72 | 32 Ge Germanium 72.59 | 33 As Arsenic 74.9216 | 34 Se Selenium 78.96 | 35 Br Bromine 79.904 | 36 Kr Krypton 83.8

Pd | 47 Ag Silver 107.868 | 48 Cd Cadmium 112.41 | 49 In Indium 114.82 | 50 Sn Tin 118.69 | 51 Sb Antimony 121.75 | 52 Te Tellurium 127.6 | 53 I Iodine 126.9045 | 54 Xe Xenon 131.3

Pt | 79 Au Gold 196.9665 | 80 Hg Mercury 200.59 | 81 Tl Thallium 204.37 | 82 Pb Lead 207.19 | 83 Bi Bismuth 208.9804 | 84 Po Polonium 208.9824* | 85 At Astatine 209.9870* | 86 Rn Radon 222.0176*

Gd | 65 Tb Terbium 158.9254 | 66 Dy Dysprosium 162.5 | 67 Ho Holmium 164.9304 | 68 Er Erbium 167.26 | 69 Tm Thulium 168.9342 | 70 Yb Ytterbium 173.04 | 71 Lu Lutetium 174.97

Cm | 97 Bk Berkelium 247.0703* | 98 Cf Californium 251.0796* | 99 Es Einsteinium 254.0880* | 100 Fm Fermium 257.0951* | 101 Md Mendelevium 258.099* | 102 No Nobelium 259.101* | 103 Lr Lawrencium 260.105*

©DIAGRAM

# HARDNESS

Solids vary in their degree of hardness or softness. Their degree of hardness depends on their microscopic internal structure—the arrangement of the atoms from which they are made. Many solids are in the form of crystals, whose macroscopic, flat-sided, geometric shapes indicate the microscopic arrangement of their atoms.

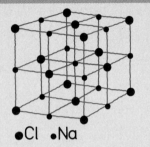

**Building with atoms** *left*
The regular shape of a crystal is an indication of its atomic structure. Salt crystals are cube-shaped because they are made up of cubic arrangements of alternating sodium (Na) and chlorine (Cl) atoms.

●Cl ●Na

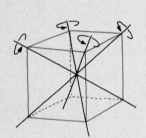

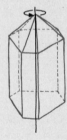

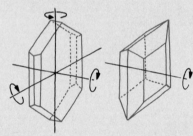
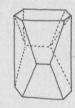

1    2    3    4    5    6    7

**Crystal symmetry**
Illustrated *above* and included in the table *right* are examples of seven basic types, or "systems," of crystal. A crystal's system depends on the symmetry of its structure, which can be determined, as here, from its "axes of symmetry." On the schematic diagram beneath each crystal we show the minimum number of axes of symmetry needed to classify a crystal within a system. These axes may be 2-, 3-, 4- or 6-fold depending on how many times the crystal presents an identical aspect when rotated through 360°.

| System | Minimum symmetry | Example | Composition | Uses |
|---|---|---|---|---|
| **1** Cubic or isometric | Four 3-fold axes | Diamond | Carbon | Drills, abrasives, cutting tools, gems |
| **2** Hexagonal | One 6-fold axis | Beryl (emerald) | Beryllium aluminum silicate | Gems |
| **3** Trigonal | One 3-fold axis | Tourmaline | Aluminum borosilicate | Electronics, gems, pressure gauges |
| **4** Tetragonal | One 4-fold axis | Cassiterite | Tin dioxide or tinstone | Source of tin |
| **5** Orthorhombic | Three 2-fold axes | Barite | Barium sulfate | Source of barium compounds |
| **6** Monoclinic | One 2-fold axis | Gypsum | Hydrated calcium sulfate | Plaster of Paris, cement, paint |
| **7** Triclinic | None | Albite | Sodium aluminum silicate | Glass, ceramics |

In the words of the song, "Diamonds are a girl's best friend." Certainly they are long lasting, being the hardest known naturally occurring substance. Among other precious stones, sapphires and rubies both rank second in terms of hardness, and emeralds third.

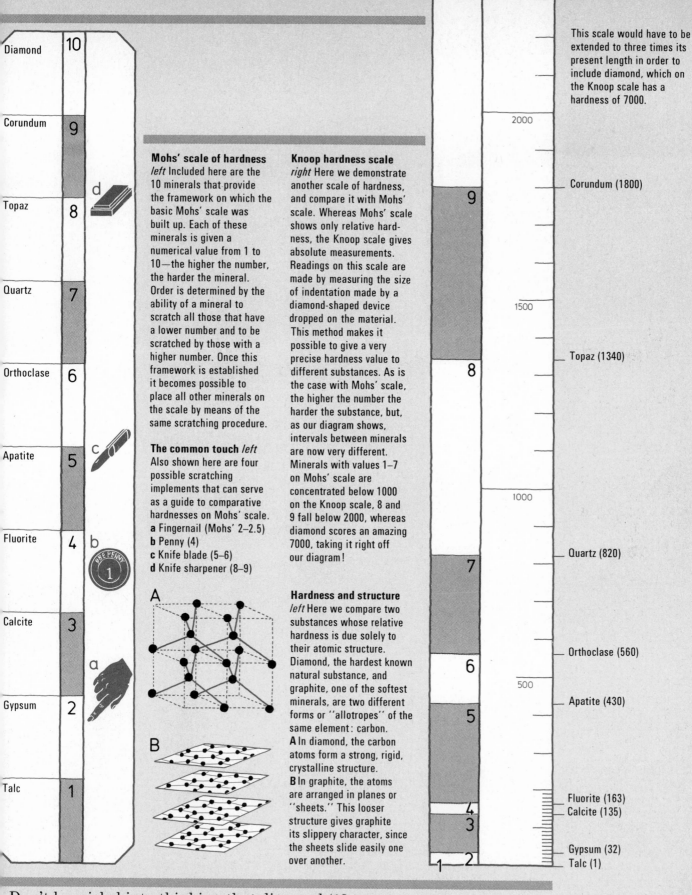

| | | |
|---|---|---|
| Diamond | 10 | |
| Corundum | 9 | |
| Topaz | 8 | |
| Quartz | 7 | |
| Orthoclase | 6 | |
| Apatite | 5 | |
| Fluorite | 4 | |
| Calcite | 3 | |
| Gypsum | 2 | |
| Talc | 1 | |

**Mohs' scale of hardness**
*left* Included here are the 10 minerals that provide the framework on which the basic Mohs' scale was built up. Each of these minerals is given a numerical value from 1 to 10—the higher the number, the harder the mineral. Order is determined by the ability of a mineral to scratch all those that have a lower number and to be scratched by those with a higher number. Once this framework is established it becomes possible to place all other minerals on the scale by means of the same scratching procedure.

**The common touch** *left*
Also shown here are four possible scratching implements that can serve as a guide to comparative hardnesses on Mohs' scale.
**a** Fingernail (Mohs' 2–2.5)
**b** Penny (4)
**c** Knife blade (5–6)
**d** Knife sharpener (8–9)

**Knoop hardness scale**
*right* Here we demonstrate another scale of hardness, and compare it with Mohs' scale. Whereas Mohs' scale shows only relative hardness, the Knoop scale gives absolute measurements. Readings on this scale are made by measuring the size of indentation made by a diamond-shaped device dropped on the material. This method makes it possible to give a very precise hardness value to different substances. As is the case with Mohs' scale, the higher the number the harder the substance, but, as our diagram shows, intervals between minerals are now very different. Minerals with values 1–7 on Mohs' scale are concentrated below 1000 on the Knoop scale, 8 and 9 fall below 2000, whereas diamond scores an amazing 7000, taking it right off our diagram!

**Hardness and structure**
*left* Here we compare two substances whose relative hardness is due solely to their atomic structure. Diamond, the hardest known natural substance, and graphite, one of the softest minerals, are two different forms or "allotropes" of the same element: carbon.
**A** In diamond, the carbon atoms form a strong, rigid, crystalline structure.
**B** In graphite, the atoms are arranged in planes or "sheets." This looser structure gives graphite its slippery character, since the sheets slide easily one over another.

This scale would have to be extended to three times its present length in order to include diamond, which on the Knoop scale has a hardness of 7000.

2000

Corundum (1800)

1500

Topaz (1340)

1000

Quartz (820)

Orthoclase (560)

500

Apatite (430)

Fluorite (163)
Calcite (135)

Gypsum (32)
Talc (1)

Don't be misled into thinking that diamond (10 on Mohs' scale) is twice as hard as apatite (5 on the same scale). If the same two minerals are measured on the Knoop scale, diamond has a hardness of 7000, compared with only 430 for apatite.

©DIAGRAM

# THE PLANETS

On these pages we compare the composition, mass and density of the planets, using information based on theories of planetary formation and on the investigation of other factors such as magnetic and gravitational fields. As space exploration proceeds, our theories about other planets will be tested scientifically.

| Planet | Mass | Density |
|---|---|---|
| Mercury | $0.331 \times 10^{27}$g | 5.4g/cm$^3$ |
| Venus | $4.870 \times 10^{27}$g | 5.2g/cm$^3$ |
| Earth | $5.976 \times 10^{27}$g | 5.518g/cm$^3$ |
| Mars | $0.642 \times 10^{27}$g | 3.95g/cm$^3$ |
| Jupiter | $1899.350 \times 10^{27}$g | 1.34g/cm$^3$ |
| Saturn | $568.598 \times 10^{27}$g | 0.7g/cm$^3$ |
| Uranus | $86.891 \times 10^{27}$g | 1.2g/cm$^3$ |
| Neptune | $102.966 \times 10^{27}$g | 1.7g/cm$^3$ |
| Pluto | (?) $1.016 \times 10^{27}$g | (?) |

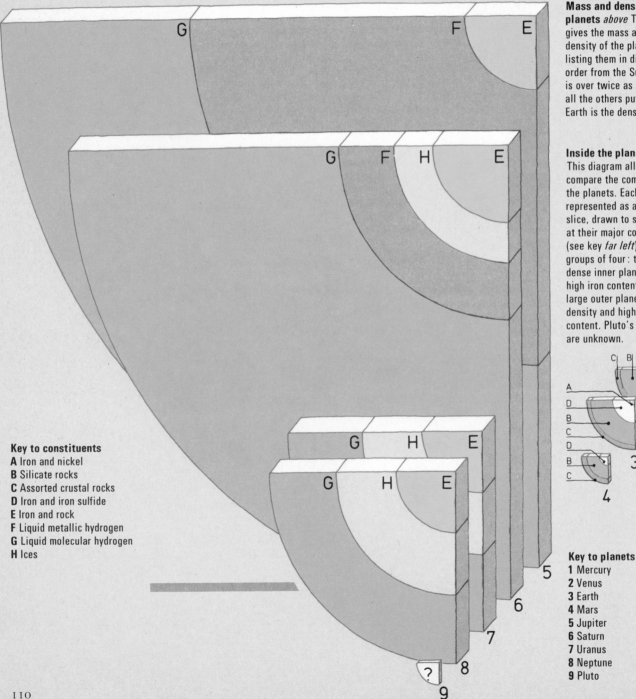

**Mass and density of the planets** *above* This table gives the mass and the density of the planets, listing them in distance order from the Sun. Jupiter is over twice as massive as all the others put together. Earth is the densest planet.

**Inside the planets** *left* This diagram allows us to compare the composition of the planets. Each planet is represented as a quarter slice, drawn to scale. A look at their major constituents (see key *far left*) shows two groups of four: the small, dense inner planets with a high iron content; and the large outer planets of low density and high hydrogen content. Pluto's constituents are unknown.

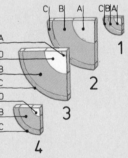

**Key to constituents**
A Iron and nickel
B Silicate rocks
C Assorted crustal rocks
D Iron and iron sulfide
E Iron and rock
F Liquid metallic hydrogen
G Liquid molecular hydrogen
H Ices

**Key to planets**
1 Mercury
2 Venus
3 Earth
4 Mars
5 Jupiter
6 Saturn
7 Uranus
8 Neptune
9 Pluto

# Among the planets of the solar system, Earth ranks only fifth in terms of mass and of volume, but first in terms of density.

## Density

| | | |
|---|---|---|
| **A** | Earth | 1.00 |
| **B** | Mercury | 0.98 |
| **C** | Venus | 0.94 |
| **D** | Mars | 0.72 |
| **E** | Neptune | 0.31 |
| **F** | Jupiter | 0.24 |
| **G** | Uranus | 0.22 |
| **H** | Saturn | 0.13 |
| **I** | Pluto | (?) |

## Mass

| | | |
|---|---|---|
| **F** | Jupiter | 317.83 |
| **H** | Saturn | 95.15 |
| **E** | Neptune | 17.23 |
| **G** | Uranus | 14.54 |
| **A** | Earth | 1 |
| **C** | Venus | 0.81 |
| **I** | Pluto | 0.17(?) |
| **D** | Mars | 0.11 |
| **B** | Mercury | 0.06 |

| Region | Mass | Density |
|---|---|---|
| **a** Crust | 2.014 x 10²⁵g | 2.8g/cm³ |
| **b** Mantle | 415.347 x 10²⁵g | 4.75g/cm³ |
| **c** Outer core | 166.749 x 10²⁵g | 11.1g/cm³ |
| **d** Inner core | 13.245 x 10²⁵g | 12.75g/cm³ |

**Comparative densities**
The table *left* and the shaded disks *right* rank the planets in order of density. For easy comparison, the density of Earth—the densest of all the planets—is here taken as "1."

**Comparative masses**
The table *left* ranks the planets in order of mass, with the mass of Earth taken as "1." The rows of blocks *right* allow us to compare the planets' masses alongside their densities, and serve to illustrate the difference in their ranking.

**Inside the Earth**
The diagram *right* shows the four regions of Earth's interior; the table *left* lists their masses and densities. Knowledge of the crust is based on direct observation; information about the interior is from studies of seismic waves.

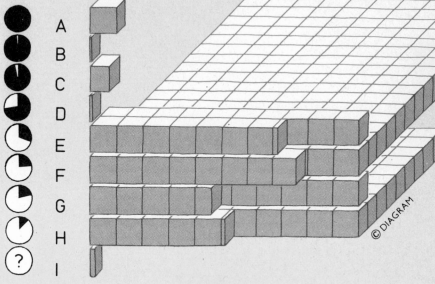

© DIAGRAM

**Earth's crust** *left, below*
About 90 elements make up Earth's crust, but over 98% of it is accounted for by just eight of these. The slices in our diagram show the proportions of these first eight elements. The ninth slice, which represents all the other crustal elements, has been extended to show the proportions of a further eight elements. For the proportions of gold and platinum (five parts per billion) to appear on our diagram as 10mm slivers it would be necessary to increase the circle's radius to 1.978mi (3.183km).

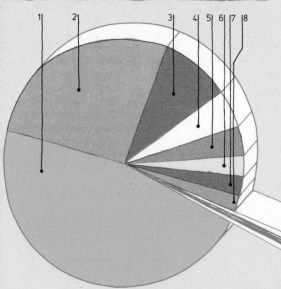

| | | |
|---|---|---|
| **1** | Oxygen (O) | 46.60% |
| **2** | Silicon (Si) | 27.72% |
| **3** | Aluminum (Al) | 8.13% |
| **4** | Iron (Fe) | 5.00% |
| **5** | Calcium (Ca) | 3.63% |
| **6** | Sodium (Na) | 2.83% |
| **7** | Potassium (K) | 2.59% |
| **8** | Magnesium (Mg) | 2.09% |
| **9** | Titanium (Ti) | 0.44% |
| **10** | Hydrogen (H) | 0.14% |
| **11** | Phosphorus (P) | 0.12% |
| **12** | Manganese (Mn) | 0.10% |
| **13** | Fluorine (F) | 0.08% |
| **14** | Sulfur (S) | 0.05% |
| **15** | Chlorine (Cl) | 0.04% |
| **16** | Carbon (C) | 0.03% |
| **17** | Others | 0.41% |

# GRAVITY AND WEIGHT

All objects are attracted to each other by a force known as "gravity." The degree of gravitational attraction increases with the mass of an object, and thus it follows that objects within Earth's gravitational pull are attracted to Earth more than to each other. Here we investigate gravity on Earth, in the solar system and in the universe.

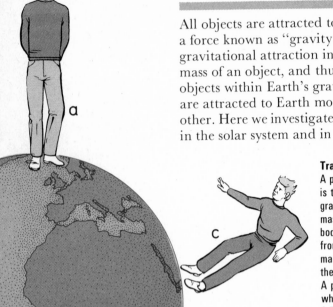

**Travel to reduce** *left*
A person's weight on Earth is the measure of the gravitational pull of Earth's mass on the mass of his body. The farther he is from the center of Earth's mass, the less its pull and the less he weighs.
A person on the Equator, where Earth bulges, weighs 0.5% less than at the Poles, where the globe is flattened. Thus a person who weighs 162lb at the North Pole (**a**) loses 13oz by traveling to the Equator (**b**). There is also a 0.5% weight loss for every 6.6mi (10.7km) ascended above sea level (**c**).

**How high can you jump?**
The table *below* and the diagram *right* show the effect of gravity on the height you can jump. The greater the gravitational force, the more difficult it is to make a high jump. Here we take a jump on Earth of 3ft and show how high a similar jump would be if made elsewhere in the solar system. In the table, gravity is given as the acceleration of a falling object (expressed in feet per second per second), and then, in brackets, relative to that of Earth, which is taken as "1."

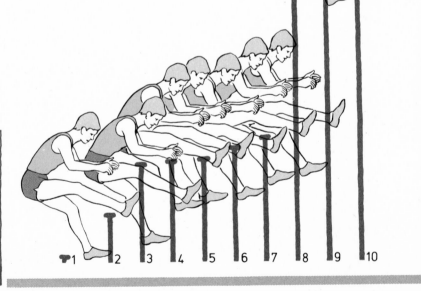

| Venue | Gravity | | Height jumped |
|---|---|---|---|
| **1** Sun | 898.88ft/s$^2$ | (27.90) | 1¼in |
| **2** Jupiter | 75.39ft/s$^2$ | (2.34) | 1ft 3½in |
| **3** Neptune | 38.02ft/s$^2$ | (1.18) | 2ft 6½in |
| **4** Uranus | 37.69ft/s$^2$ | (1.17) | 2ft 6¾in |
| **5** Saturn | 37.04ft/s$^2$ | (1.15) | 2ft 7¼in |
| **6** Earth | 32.22ft/s$^2$ | (1.00) | 3ft 0in |
| **7** Venus | 28.35ft/s$^2$ | (0.88) | 3ft 4¾in |
| **8** Mars | 12.24ft/s$^2$ | (0.38) | 7ft 10¾in |
| **9** Mercury | 11.91ft/s$^2$ | (0.37) | 8ft 1¼in |
| **10** Moon | 5.31ft/s$^2$ | (0.16) | 18ft 9in |

The world record for an overhead lift is 564¼lb. A similar effort on the Moon, where gravity is less, would have resulted in a lift of 3526½lb—equal to lifting 2½ Mini cars.

10,000km

1000km

100km

10km

1km

100m

10m

1m

**Black hole weight gain**
*left, below* Here we
demonstrate the rate at
which the weight of an
object is believed to
increase in response to the
gravitational pull of a black
hole with the same mass as
Earth. Starting with an
object with the same weight
as a bag of sugar (1kg), we
have used a logarithmic
kilometer scale to show its
accelerating weight gain,
indicating its weight at
different distances from the
black hole by means of
objects which, on Earth,
would weigh an equivalent
amount.

A
B
C

**Bending the rules** *above*
**A** Here we represent space
as a flat surface with light
and time running in straight
lines across it.
**B** The great mass of a star
exerts such a strong
gravitational force that it
pulls these lines toward
itself, bending the lines and
producing the effect of a
dent in the curved surface.
Since the lines representing
light and time are now
longer, it follows that the
passage of light and time
will be slowed down.

**C** In this representation of a
"black hole" our original
flat surface is distorted to
the extreme and is pulled
down to a point in the
center. A black hole is
thought to result from the
collapse of a heavy star under
the force of its own gravity.
The same amount of matter
occupies a smaller and
smaller volume, and the
force of gravity that it exerts
becomes so intense that it
is impossible even for light
to escape from it, so making
it appear black.

| Distance | Weight | Equivalent |
|----------|--------|------------|
| 6378km | 1kg | **a** Bag of sugar |
| 744km | 73.5kg | **b** Average US man |
| 74km | $7.4 \times 10^3$kg | **c** Tractor |
| 10.7km | $3.5 \times 10^5$kg | **d** Jumbo Jet |
| 268m | $5.6 \times 10^8$kg | **e** Largest oil tanker |
| 6.3m | $2 \times 10^{12}$kg | **f** World population |

©DIAGRAM

**This black dot shows the
calculated size of a black hole
with the same mass as Earth.**

# COMPARATIVE WEIGHTS

Even when objects are small enough to hold in the hands it is by no means easy to estimate comparative weights with any degree of accuracy. With very heavy objects the problem is even greater. One useful guide is, as here, to measure unfamiliar weights in terms of other, generally more familiar ones.

**Tons of bricks** *below*
Walls built from a ton of standard bricks show considerable variations in size depending on the type of ton—US (short), UK/imperial (long), or metric. Here we compare the lengths of three walls built from a "ton" of bricks. In each case the wall is 4ft high and built from bricks measuring, with mortar, 3 x 4½ x 9in.
**a** Wall from a UK/imperial ton of bricks 39ft.
**b** Wall from a metric tonne of bricks 38ft 3in.
**c** Wall from a US ton of bricks 34ft 6in.

a b     c

**Vehicular heavyweights** *right* These heavy land vehicles have all been drawn to a common scale. Weights are given here in short tons (each 2000 lb).
**1** Tractor 8.2 tons.
**2** American Greyhound bus (model MC8) 13.4 tons.
**3** London double-decker bus (model RML) 13.8 tons.
**4** Excavator 16.5 tons.
**5** Articulated truck (with load) 31.3 tons.
**6** Transcontinental truck (with load) 48.5 tons.
**7** Chieftain tank, the heaviest tank in current use, 58.2 tons.

**Weight in elephants** *right* These same vehicle weights are now given in elephants.
**1** Tractor 1.2
**2** Greyhound bus 1.9
**3** London bus 2
**4** Excavator 2.4
**5** Articulated truck 4.5
**6** Transcontinental truck 6.9
**7** Chieftain tank 8.3

**Fair weights for balls**
Shown to scale *right* and listed in the table *far right* in order of weight, from the lightest to the heaviest, are officially approved balls for selected sporting activities.

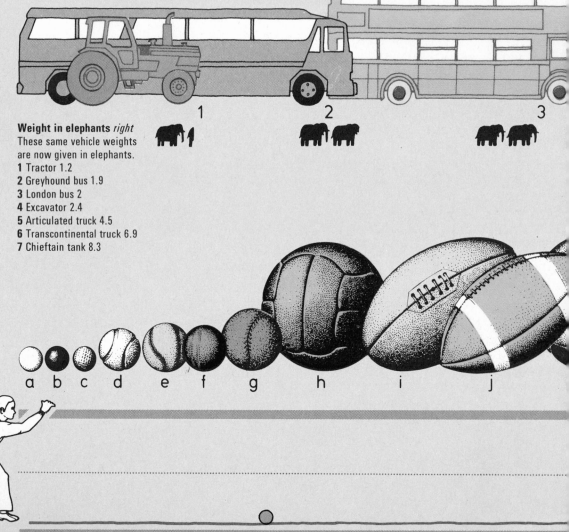

a b c d e f g h i j

*One stone at Stonehenge is equal in weight to 37,200 standard bricks. These bricks (each $3 \times 4\frac{1}{2} \times 9in$) would be sufficient to build a one brick thick chimney with a diameter of 12ft and a height of 186ft.*

**Weighty stones** *right*
Limestone blocks used for the Great Pyramid of Cheops (**1**) weigh an average 2.8 short tons, equal to four Minis (each 1406 lb). Sarsen blocks at England's Stonehenge (**2**) weigh over 50 short tons each, equal to over 71 Minis.

| | | | |
|---|---|---|---|
| **a** Table tennis | 0.085–0.09oz | 2.40–2.53g |
| **b** Squash | 0.821–0.912oz | 23.3–24.6g |
| **c** Golf | 1.62oz (max) | 45.9g (max) |
| **d** Tennis | 2–2.06oz | 56.7–58.5g |
| **e** Baseball | 5–5.5oz | 141.7–155.9g |
| **f** Cricket | 5.5–5.75oz | 155.9–163.0g |
| **g** Softball | 6.25–7oz | 177.2–198.4g |
| **h** Volleyball | 9.17–9.88oz | 260–280g |
| **i** Rugby | 13.5–15.5oz | 383–439g |
| **j** US football | 14–15oz | 397–425g |
| **k** Soccer | 14–16oz | 397–454g |
| **l** Croquet | 15.75–16.25oz | 447–461g |
| **m** Basketball | 21.16–22.93oz | 600–650g |
| **n** Boccie/boules | 24.69–45.86oz | 700–1300g |
| **o** Flat green bowls | 48–56oz | 1361–1588g |
| **p** 10-pin bowling | 256oz (max) | 7258g (max) |

©DIAGRAM

$2868\frac{1}{2}$ maximum-weight table tennis balls are needed to equal the weight of one maximum-weight bowl for 10-pin bowling. To show them all at this scale it would be necessary to continue our row for a further $6\frac{2}{3}$ pages.

# AIRCRAFT

With its pilot, the Wright Brothers' aircraft *Flyer 1* weighed only 750lb, less than five times the weight of an average US man (162lb). The wide-bodied Boeing 747 "Jumbo Jet" has a maximum take-off weight of 775,000lb, equal to the weight of 4784 average men or 55 times the weight of an average African elephant (14,000lb).

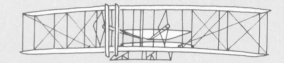

**Much heavier than air**
Listed from the lightest to the heaviest in the table *right*, and illustrated and plotted by weight on the logarithmic scale *below* is a selection of aircraft, both civil and military, old and new. The weight given for *Flyer I* includes the weight of the pilot. All other weights are maximum take-off weights.

| | | | Civil aircraft |
|---|---|---|---|
| 750 lb | 340kg | A | Wright brothers' *Flyer I*, first flown in 1903 |
| 1600 lb | 726kg | B | Beagle B121 Pup-150, 2/3 seat cabin monoplane |
| 25,000 lb | 11,340kg | C | HS 125 Series 600, light executive transport |
| 333,600 lb | 151,321kg | D | Boeing 707-320B, long-range airliner |
| 408,000 lb | 185,069kg | E | BAC/Aérospatiale Concorde, supersonic transport |
| 775,000 lb | 351,540kg | F | Boeing 747 ''Jumbo Jet,'' wide-bodied long-range airliner |
| | | | **Military aircraft** |
| 1453 lb | 659kg | G | Sopwith F1 Camel, WW1 Allied fighter |
| 7700 lb | 3493kg | H | Messerschmitt Bf 109G-X, WW2 German fighter |
| 8745 lb | 3967kg | I | Gotha GVb, WW1 German bomber |
| 56,000 lb | 25,402kg | J | McDonnell Douglas F-15 Eagle, modern fighter |
| 68,000 lb | 30,845kg | K | Avro Lancaster B1, WW2 British bomber |
| 488,000 lb | 221,357kg | L | Boeing B-52H, heaviest modern bomber |
| 672,000 lb | 304,819kg | M | British Hovercraft Corporation SRA4 Mark 3 |
| 6,526,000 lb | 2,960,194kg | N | Saturn V rocket |

**Bicycles to airplanes**
*above* Before turning to making airplanes, Orville and Wilbur Wright were bicycle makers. *Flyer I*, in which Orville made the first controlled and sustained flight ever, weighed 605 lb when empty—20 times the weight of a modern touring bicycle.

**Civil aircraft** *right*
Selected civil aircraft, listed in the table *above*, are here plotted against a logarithmic weight scale. Except for the pioneering *Flyer I*, all of the civil planes shown are in current use.

**Military aircraft** *right*
Included here are representative fighters and bombers from the two world wars and from the present day. The modern fighter is similar in weight to a WW2 bomber; a WW2 fighter is similar in weight to a WW1 bomber.

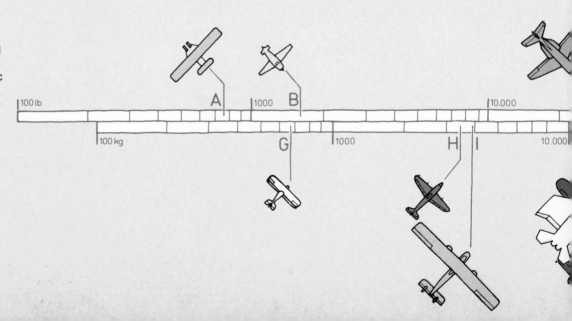

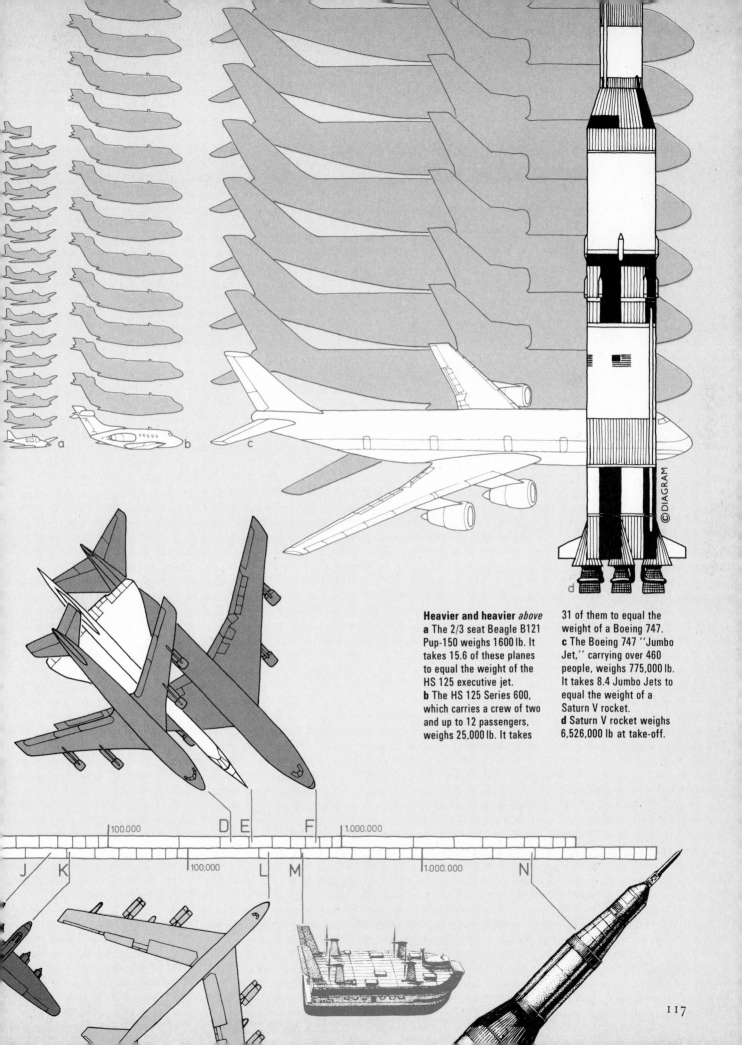

**Heavier and heavier** *above*
**a** The 2/3 seat Beagle B121 Pup-150 weighs 1600 lb. It takes 15.6 of these planes to equal the weight of the HS 125 executive jet.
**b** The HS 125 Series 600, which carries a crew of two and up to 12 passengers, weighs 25,000 lb. It takes

31 of them to equal the weight of a Boeing 747.
**c** The Boeing 747 "Jumbo Jet," carrying over 460 people, weighs 775,000 lb. It takes 8.4 Jumbo Jets to equal the weight of a Saturn V rocket.
**d** Saturn V rocket weighs 6,526,000 lb at take-off.

100.000

D E F 1.000.000

100,000

J K L M 1.000.000 N

©DIAGRAM

# ANIMALS

The weights of living creatures range from the infinitesimal weights of microscopic organisms to the tons of an elephant or whale. The blue whale weighs over 70 million times more than the smallest bird, Helena's hummingbird, and 24,560 billion times more than the smallest insect, the parasitic wasp (0.0000002oz).

**Farmyard equivalents** *left, below* Here we show a farmer's wife—a US woman of average weight (135 lb)—and show how many chickens, cats and rats make up the same weight.
**a** Chickens 19.3
**b** Cats 9.6
**c** Rats 134.6

**Creatures great and small**
Plotted on the logarithmic scales *right* and listed in the table *far right* are likely average weights for animal species, from the smallest bird to the heaviest living creature, the blue whale. Also included for comparison is a *Brachiosaurus*, the heaviest known dinosaur. Average weights for animal species are always subject to some uncertainty, especially for wild animals. Man may not have weighed, or even seen, the heaviest or lightest of a species, and big seasonal variations in weight are a further complicating factor.

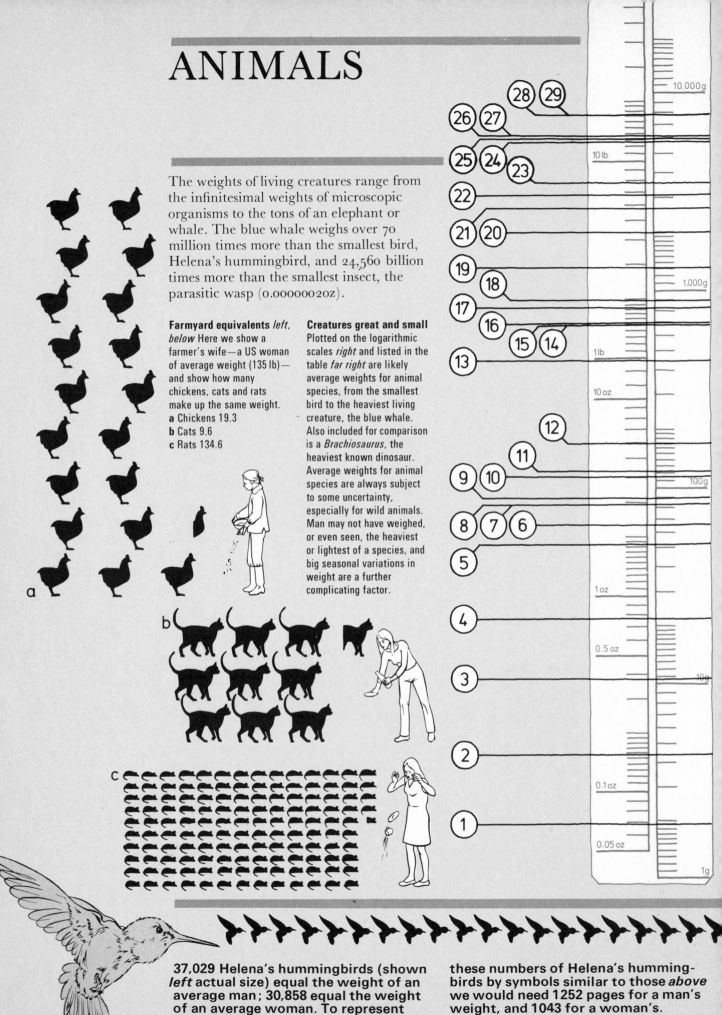

37,029 Helena's hummingbirds (shown *left* actual size) equal the weight of an average man; 30,858 equal the weight of an average woman. To represent these numbers of Helena's hummingbirds by symbols similar to those *above* we would need 1252 pages for a man's weight, and 1043 for a woman's.

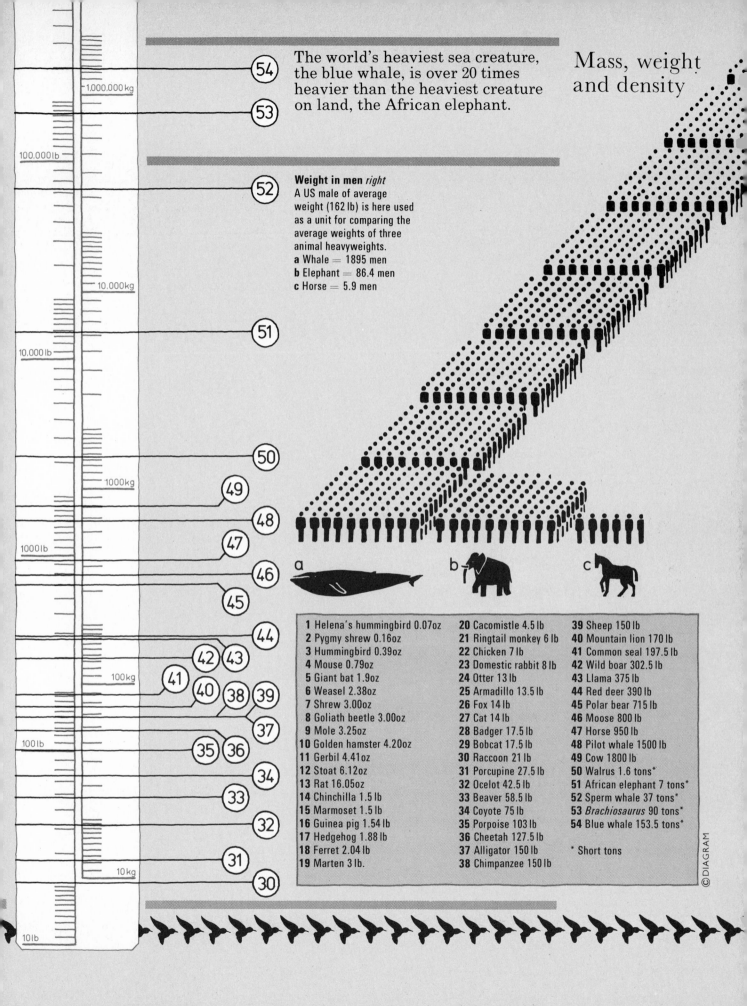

The world's heaviest sea creature, the blue whale, is over 20 times heavier than the heaviest creature on land, the African elephant.

Mass, weight and density

**Weight in men** *right*
A US male of average weight (162 lb) is here used as a unit for comparing the average weights of three animal heavyweights.
**a** Whale = 1895 men
**b** Elephant = 86.4 men
**c** Horse = 5.9 men

1,000,000 kg

100,000 lb

10,000 kg

10,000 lb

1000 kg

1000 lb

100 kg

100 lb

10 kg

10 lb

| | | |
|---|---|---|
| 1 Helena's hummingbird 0.07oz | 20 Cacomistle 4.5 lb | 39 Sheep 150 lb |
| 2 Pygmy shrew 0.16oz | 21 Ringtail monkey 6 lb | 40 Mountain lion 170 lb |
| 3 Hummingbird 0.39oz | 22 Chicken 7 lb | 41 Common seal 197.5 lb |
| 4 Mouse 0.79oz | 23 Domestic rabbit 8 lb | 42 Wild boar 302.5 lb |
| 5 Giant bat 1.9oz | 24 Otter 13 lb | 43 Llama 375 lb |
| 6 Weasel 2.38oz | 25 Armadillo 13.5 lb | 44 Red deer 390 lb |
| 7 Shrew 3.00oz | 26 Fox 14 lb | 45 Polar bear 715 lb |
| 8 Goliath beetle 3.00oz | 27 Cat 14 lb | 46 Moose 800 lb |
| 9 Mole 3.25oz | 28 Badger 17.5 lb | 47 Horse 950 lb |
| 10 Golden hamster 4.20oz | 29 Bobcat 17.5 lb | 48 Pilot whale 1500 lb |
| 11 Gerbil 4.41oz | 30 Raccoon 21 lb | 49 Cow 1800 lb |
| 12 Stoat 6.12oz | 31 Porcupine 27.5 lb | 50 Walrus 1.6 tons* |
| 13 Rat 16.05oz | 32 Ocelot 42.5 lb | 51 African elephant 7 tons* |
| 14 Chinchilla 1.5 lb | 33 Beaver 58.5 lb | 52 Sperm whale 37 tons* |
| 15 Marmoset 1.5 lb | 34 Coyote 75 lb | 53 *Brachiosaurus* 90 tons* |
| 16 Guinea pig 1.54 lb | 35 Porpoise 103 lb | 54 Blue whale 153.5 tons* |
| 17 Hedgehog 1.88 lb | 36 Cheetah 127.5 lb | |
| 18 Ferret 2.04 lb | 37 Alligator 150 lb | * Short tons |
| 19 Marten 3 lb. | 38 Chimpanzee 150 lb | |

©DIAGRAM

# HUMANS

People's individual weights vary within the limits set by our species. The heaviest person, for instance, was over nine times heavier than is average for a US adult, and over 12 times as heavy as a flyweight boxer. Here we present some usual and unusual aspects of weight within the human species.

**His and her weights** *below*
The diagram shows the average weights of US males and females at ages from birth to 65 years. The average weight for a US adult male is 162 lb and for an adult female 135 lb. Men reach their maximum weight, an average of around 173 lb,

between the ages of 35 and 54 years. Women reach their greatest weight, an average 152 lb, at around 55–60 years.

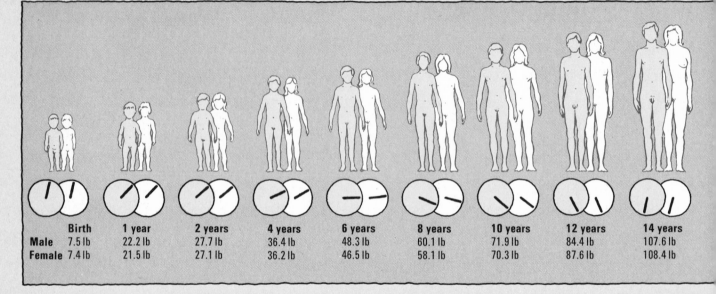

| | Birth | 1 year | 2 years | 4 years | 6 years | 8 years | 10 years | 12 years | 14 years |
|---|---|---|---|---|---|---|---|---|---|
| **Male** | 7.5 lb | 22.2 lb | 27.7 lb | 36.4 lb | 48.3 lb | 60.1 lb | 71.9 lb | 84.4 lb | 107.6 lb |
| **Female** | 7.4 lb | 21.5 lb | 27.1 lb | 36.2 lb | 46.5 lb | 58.1 lb | 70.3 lb | 87.6 lb | 108.4 lb |

**Boxing and wrestling** *right*
The narrow weight divisions of boxing and freestyle wrestling attempt to ensure that the contest is as fair as possible. The weights given here are the official weight limits for the AIBA (Amateur International Boxing Association), the WBC (World Boxing Council), and, *far right*, for Olympic wrestling. The weights for the AIBA and for Olympic wrestling are officially in kilograms. WBC weights are officially in pounds.

| Class | AIBA | | WBC | | Wrestling | |
|---|---|---|---|---|---|---|
| Light flyweight | 48kg (105.8 lb) | | 108 lb (49.0kg) | | 48kg (105.8 lb) | |
| Flyweight | 51kg (112.4 lb) | | 112 lb (50.8kg) | | 52kg (114.6 lb) | |
| Bantamweight | 54kg (119.0 lb) | | 118 lb (53.5kg) | | 57kg (125.7 lb) | |
| Super bantamweight | – | – | 122 lb (55.3kg) | | – | – |
| Featherweight | 57kg (125.7 lb) | | 126 lb (57.2kg) | | 62kg (136.7 lb) | |
| Junior lightweight | – | – | 130 lb (59.0kg) | | – | – |
| Lightweight | 60kg (132.3 lb) | | 135 lb (61.2kg) | | 68kg (149.9 lb) | |
| Light welterweight | 63.5kg (140.0 lb) | | 140 lb (63.5kg) | | – | – |
| Welterweight | 67kg (147.7 lb) | | 147 lb (66.7kg) | | 74 kg (163.1 lb) | |
| Light middleweight | 71kg (156.5 lb) | | 154 lb (69.9kg) | | – | – |
| Middleweight | 75kg (165.3 lb) | | 160 lb (72.6kg) | | 82kg (180.8 lb) | |
| Light heavyweight | 81kg (178.6 lb) | | 175 lb (79.4kg) | | 90kg (198.4 lb) | |
| Heavyweight | 81+kg (178.6+ lb) | | 175+ lb (79.4+ kg) | | 100kg (220.5 lb) | |
| Heavyweight plus | – | – | – | – | 100+ kg (220.5+ lb) | |

**Your weight in gold?**
*right* It is said that kings used to receive their tributes in an amount equal to their own weights. The average US man weighs 162 lb. Shown here are the volumes that would be taken up by the same weight of various solids and liquids.

| | | |
|---|---|---|
| 1 | Gold | 0.14ft³ |
| 2 | Copper | 0.29ft³ |
| 3 | Diamond | 0.74ft³ |
| 4 | Glass | 1.00ft³ |
| 5 | Sugar | 1.62ft³ |
| 6 | Coal | 1.92ft³ |
| 7 | Nylon | 2.33ft³ |
| 8 | Milk | 2.52ft³ |
| 9 | Sea water | 2.53ft³ |
| 10 | Gasoline | 3.86ft³ |

**Perhaps humans have an excuse for forgetting things— our brains weigh about 3lb, only one fifth as much as an elephant's brain.**

*A six-year-old child weighs roughly the same as the air in a furnished bedroom measuring 9 × 9 × 8ft.*

**An average man's weight is 21.6 times more than the average weight for a newborn boy baby. An average woman weighs 18.2 times the weight of an average newborn girl.**

**Heavyweight humans** *right*
The weights of the heaviest humans are here compared with average weights for US men and women, and with typical weights of selected animals.

**a** Jon Brower Minnoch (born 1941), man with the highest estimated weight.
**b** Robert Earl Hughes (1926–58), man with the highest undisputed weight.

**c** Ida Maitland (1898–1932), woman for whom the highest weight has been claimed.
**d** Mrs Percy P. Washington (1926–72), woman with the greatest weight registered on scales (800 lb); total weight estimated at 880 lb.

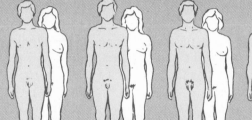

| **16 years** | **18 years** | **25 years** | **45 years** | **65 years** |
|---|---|---|---|---|
| 129.7 lb | 143.0 lb | 153.0 lb | 173.0 lb | 164.0 lb |
| 117.0 lb | 120.0 lb | 124.0 lb | 139.0 lb | 134.0 lb |

© DIAGRAM

**An average girl reaches 50% of her adult weight at age nine. An average boy does not reach 50% of his adult weight until he is eleven.**

1  2  3  4  5  6  7  8  9  10

kg    lb

650

Sea cow 1300 lb

● **a** Minnoch 1400 lb

1250

550

Saltwater crocodile 1100 lb

● **b** Hughes 1069 lb

450    1000

Horse 950 lb

● **c** Maitland 911 lb

● **d** Washington 880 lb

Polar bear 715 lb

350    750

250

Gorilla 450 lb

500

150

250

Chimpanzee 150 lb

● Average US man 162 lb
● Average US woman 135 lb

50

121

# WEIGHTS LIFTED

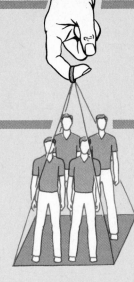

Individual strength depends on many personal factors such as size, weight and muscular development. Most normally healthy people should be able to lift about their own weight. Here some of the heavier weights lifted by men and women are translated into more easily understandable terms for us weaker mortals!

**Digital strength** *right*
Warren L. Travis is reported to have lifted 667 lb with one finger. This is equivalent to lifting four men of average weight (162 lb).

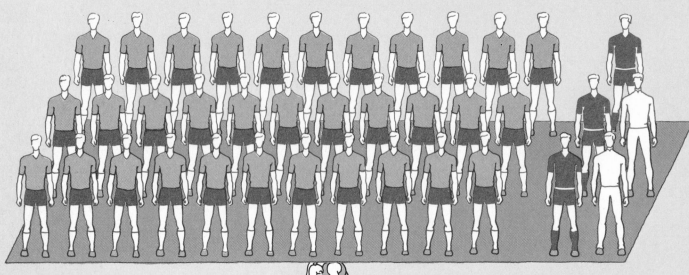

**Back to basics** *above*
The greatest weight ever lifted by a man was 6270 lb, in a backlift in 1957 by Olympic weightlifting champion Paul Anderson. The weight comprised a table on which there was a safe filled with lead and other pieces of heavy metal.

This is equivalent to lifting:
3 soccer teams;
1 referee;
2 linesmen; and
2 substitutes—
making a total of 38 men of average weight!

**Hip lady!** *left*
The heaviest weight ever lifted by a woman was 3564 lb, in a hip and harness lift by Josephine Blatt in 1895. This is equivalent to lifting 26 chorus girls the weight of an average US woman (135 lb).

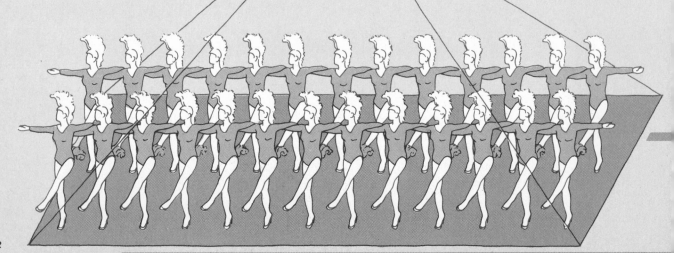

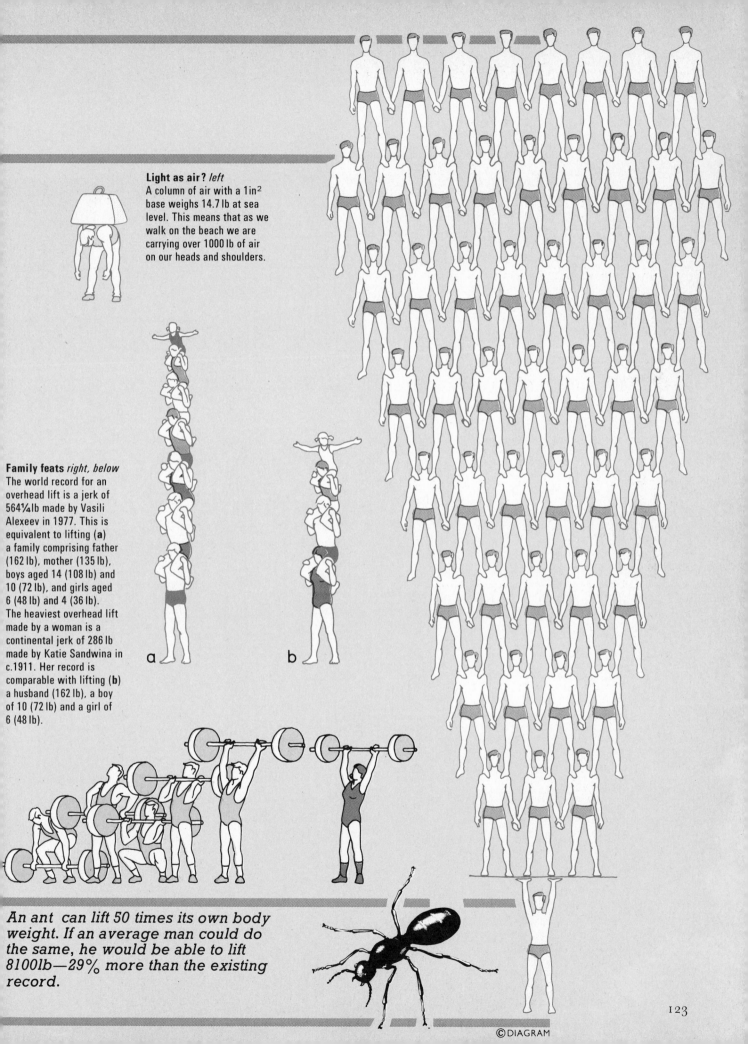

**Light as air?** *left*
A column of air with a 1in² base weighs 14.7 lb at sea level. This means that as we walk on the beach we are carrying over 1000 lb of air on our heads and shoulders.

**Family feats** *right, below*
The world record for an overhead lift is a jerk of 564¼lb made by Vasili Alexeev in 1977. This is equivalent to lifting (**a**) a family comprising father (162 lb), mother (135 lb), boys aged 14 (108 lb) and 10 (72 lb), and girls aged 6 (48 lb) and 4 (36 lb). The heaviest overhead lift made by a woman is a continental jerk of 286 lb made by Katie Sandwina in c.1911. Her record is comparable with lifting (**b**) a husband (162 lb), a boy of 10 (72 lb) and a girl of 6 (48 lb).

a

b

*An ant can lift 50 times its own body weight. If an average man could do the same, he would be able to lift 8100lb—29% more than the existing record.*

©DIAGRAM

# CHAPTER 6

This illustration from
Diderot's *Encyclopédie* of
1751 shows one man
working an enormous wine
press. Mechanical ingenuity
can be used to compensate
for a limited supply of power.

A steam-generating heavy
water reactor in Dorset,
England. Nuclear power may
solve the energy crisis, but
strict safety regulations
are vital (Photo: UK Atomic
Energy Authority).

# ENERGY

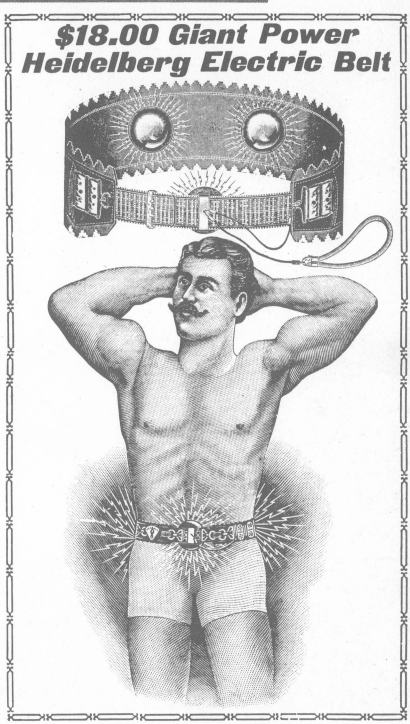

Illustration from the Sears Roebuck catalogue of 1902 showing an electric belt claimed as a cure for "disorders of the nerves, stomach, liver and kidneys," and for "weakness, diseased or debilitated condition of the sexual organs from any cause whatever..."

# MEASURING ENERGY

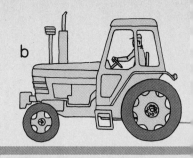
b

On these two pages we look at different ways of measuring energy, and on subsequent pages we consider some of the forms that energy takes. Energy is defined as the equivalent of or the capacity to do work. Power is a measure of the amount of energy spent over a certain period of time. (Temperature comparisons are in chapter 7.)

**The joule** (J) is the amount of energy needed to move a mass of one kilogram through one meter with an acceleration of one meter per second per second.
**The erg** is the amount of energy needed to move one gram through one centimeter with an acceleration of one centimeter per second per second.
**The calorie** (cal, or more specifically, $cal_{15}$) is the amount of energy needed to raise the temperature of one gram of water by one degree Celsius (or Centigrade) from 14.5°C to 15.5°C (58.1°F to 59.9°F).
**The British thermal unit** (Btu) is the energy needed to raise the temperature of one pound of water from 60°F to 61°F (15.5°C to 16.1°C).
**The watt** (W) is the power provided when one joule is used for one second. 1000 watts are known as a **kilowatt** (kW).
**The kilowatt hour** (kWh) is the energy expended when one kilowatt is available for one hour.
**The British horsepower** (hp) is the power needed to raise 550 lb one foot in one second.
**The metric horsepower** is the power needed to raise 75kg one meter in one second.

**Unit equivalents**
$1J = 10^7 erg$
$1erg = 10^{-7}J$
$1cal = 4.1855J$
$1000cal = 1$ kilocalorie, or 1 Calorie
$1Btu = 1054.5J$
$1W = 0.001341hp$
$1hp = 745.7W$
$1$ hp (metric) $= 735.5W$

**Energy and power units**
The table *right* defines the major units of energy and power in use today. As most countries measure their electricity in watts, we take the joule and the watt as our basic units. Equivalent values for units are listed in the small table *left*.

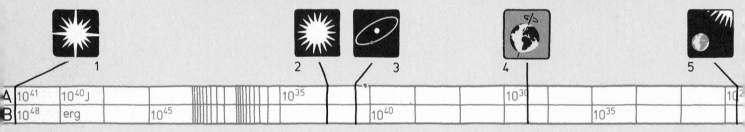

| A | $10^{41}$ | $10^{40}J$ | | | | $10^{35}$ | | | | $10^{30}$ | | | $10^{2}$ |
| B | $10^{48}$ | erg | | $10^{45}$ | | | $10^{40}$ | | | $10^{35}$ | | | |

1   2   3   4   5

| A | $10^7 J$ | $10^6$ | $10^5$ | $10^4$ | $10^3$ | $10^2$ | $10$ | $1$ | $10^{-}$ |
| B | erg | | | | $10^{10}$ | $10^9$ | $10^8$ | $10^7$ | $10^6$ |
| C | $10^7 cal$ | $10^6$ | $10^5$ | $10^4$ | $10^3$ | $10^2$ | $10$ | $1$ | D $10^{18}$ |

15   16   17   18   19   20

**Universal energy scales**
*above, right* Here joules and ergs appear on equivalent logarithmic scales that extend, left to right on two bars, from $10^{41}$ to $10^{-19}J$ (scale **A**), and from $10^{48}$ to $10^{-12}erg$ (scale **B**). These scales encompass the whole range of energy known to man. If we were to show the same energy range on a conventional scale with one erg equal to one millimeter, our scale bar would be some $10^{42}km$ long!

Included below our joule and erg scales are equivalent scales for calories (scale **C**) and electronvolts (scale **D**). These scales cover the energy ranges over which these units are normally used. The electronvolt (eV) is a very small unit used in atomic and subatomic physics. One electronvolt is equal to $1.602 \times 10^{-19}J$. The energy contents of selected phenomena are plotted on the scales and listed *right*.

**Energies compared** *above*
1 Supernova $10^{41}J$
2 Annual energy output of the Sun $10^{34}J$
3 Earth traveling in orbit around the Sun $2 \times 10^{33}J$
4 Earth spinning on its axis $3 \times 10^{29}J$
5 Earth's annual share of solar radiation $5.6 \times 10^{24}J$

6 Eruption (1883) of the volcano Krakatoa $6 \times 10^{18}J$
7 Very severe earthquake (Richter 8) $10^{18}J$
8 100Mt thermonuclear bomb $4.2 \times 10^{17}J$
9 Hurricane $4 \times 10^{15}J$
10 Atomic bomb dropped on Hiroshima $8.4 \times 10^{13}J$

11 Energy generated by Saturn V rocket $1.3 \times 10^{11}J$
12 Explosion of 1 short ton of TNT $4.2 \times 10^9 J$
13 A day's heavy manual labor $1.7 \times 10^7 J$
14 Energy content of 1 lb of good quality bituminous coal $1.5 \times 10^7 J$

**The energy in a slice of apple pie (350 Calories) is equivalent to the energy content of 11.2oz of TNT. A young man's 3000 Calories of food energy eaten daily is equivalent to the energy in 6 lb of TNT.**

The energy content of 1 lb of good quality bituminous coal is 3750 times the amount of energy used up by a burning match.

a

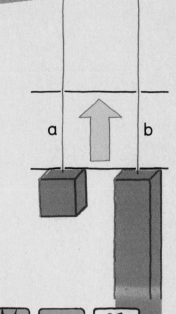

a                    b

| J | | cal | hp | | kW |
|---|---|---|---|---|---|
| 4.1855 | 1 | 0.2389 | 1.3410 | 1 | 0.7457 |
| 8.3710 | 2 | 0.4777 | 2.6820 | 2 | 1.4914 |
| 12.557 | 3 | 0.7165 | 4.0231 | 3 | 2.2371 |
| 16.742 | 4 | 0.9554 | 5.3641 | 4 | 2.9828 |
| 20.928 | 5 | 1.1942 | 6.7051 | 5 | 3.7285 |
| 25.113 | 6 | 1.4331 | 8.0461 | 6 | 4.4742 |
| 29.299 | 7 | 1.6719 | 9.3871 | 7 | 5.2199 |
| 33.484 | 8 | 1.9108 | 10.728 | 8 | 5.9656 |
| 37.670 | 9 | 2.1496 | 12.069 | 9 | 6.7113 |
| 62.783 | 15 | 3.5827 | 20.115 | 15 | 11.186 |
| 104.64 | 25 | 5.9712 | 33.526 | 25 | 18.643 |
| 146.49 | 35 | 8.3596 | 46.936 | 35 | 26.100 |
| 188.35 | 45 | 10.748 | 60.346 | 45 | 33.557 |
| 230.20 | 55 | 13.137 | 73.756 | 55 | 41.014 |
| 272.06 | 65 | 15.525 | 87.166 | 65 | 48.471 |
| 313.91 | 75 | 17.914 | 100.58 | 75 | 55.928 |
| 355.77 | 85 | 20.302 | 113.99 | 85 | 63.385 |
| 397.62 | 95 | 22.690 | 127.40 | 95 | 70.842 |

**Conversion tables** *left*
To convert joules to calories, horsepower to kilowatts, and vice versa, find the number of the unit you want to convert in the central column of the correct table and then read off its equivalent in the appropriate column.

**Horsepower comparison**
*right* The horsepower is the unit of power that James Watt (1736–1819) established as being the amount of energy needed to raise 33,000 lb one foot in one minute. It is now more usually defined as the energy needed to raise 550 lb one foot in one second. In our diagram we show a horse lifting a 550 lb weight one foot in one second (**a**) and compare it with a typical 75hp tractor, which could lift a weight of 41,250 lb (75 x 550 lb) the same distance in the same time (**b**).

6    7    8    9    10    11    12    13    14

$10^{20}$

$10^{15}$

$10^{10}$  $10^9$  $10^8$

$10^{30}$    $10^{25}$    $10^{20}$    $10^{15}$

$10^{-3}$ $10^{-4}$ $10^{-5}$ $10^{-6}$ $10^{-7}$ $10^{-8}$ $10^{-9}$ $10^{-10}$     $10^{-15}$

$10^4$ $10^3$ $10^2$ $10$ $1$ $10^{-1}$ $10^{-2}$ $10^{-3}$ $10^{-4}$ $10^{-5}$ $10^{-6}$ $10^{-7}$ $10^{-8}$ $10^{-9}$ $10^{-10}$

$10^{15}$    $10^{12}$    $10^9$    $10^6$    $10^3$ $10^2$ $10$  $1$

21    22    23    24    25    26    27    28

**15** Man running for 1 hour 2.5 x $10^6$J
**16** Woman running for 1 hour 1.8 x $10^6$J
**17** Energy in a slice of apple pie 1.5 x $10^6$J
**18** Burning match 4 x $10^3$J
**19** Lethal dose of X-rays 7 x $10^2$J

**20** Depressing key of a manual typewriter $10^{-1}$J
**21** Chirrup of a cricket 9 x $10^{-4}$J
**22** Wingbeat of a honeybee 8 x $10^{-4}$J
**23** Moonlight on a person's face for 1 second 8 x $10^{-5}$J

**24** Energy released by splitting one uranium atom 4 x $10^{-11}$J
**25** Energy released for each atom of helium formed by the fusion of two atoms of deuterium 4.3 x $10^{-12}$J
**26** Rest-mass energy of an electron 8.2 x $10^{-14}$J

**27** 0 dB of sound (minimum audibility) for 1 second on a person's eardrum $10^{-16}$J
**28** Energy of a photon within the visible range 2.5 x $10^{-19}$J to 5.1 x $10^{-19}$J

If the energy in sound waves could be converted into electrical power it would take the combined energy of 100,000,000,000,000,000 ($10^{17}$) mosquito buzzes to provide enough power to light a reading lamp.

© DIAGRAM

# ENERGY SOURCES

The total amount of energy potentially available each year at Earth's surface is more than 20 billion times greater than present energy consumption, but as yet man has learned to make little use of solar radiation, which makes up nearly all of this total. Instead he uses increasingly scarce, non-renewable sources such as oil.

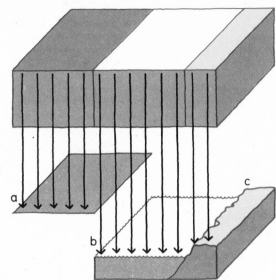

**Solar and non-solar** *left*
For this diagram we look only at energy that is potentially available at Earth's surface every year (as distinct from "non-renewable" sources such as oil). Of this annual total, the ratio of solar to non-solar energy is 2600:1.

**Solar radiation** *right*
An estimated $1.56 \times 10^{18}$kWh of solar energy ($1.95 \times 10^{14}$ tonnes of coal equivalent) annually reaches the outer limit of Earth's atmosphere. Of this: 40% is absorbed by the atmosphere (**a**); 44% reaches sea areas (**b**); 16% reaches land areas (**c**).

|   |             | 1968          | 1978           |
|---|-------------|---------------|----------------|
| 1 | Oil         | 2892 (42.0%)  | 4614 (46.0%)   |
| 2 | Coal        | 2330 (33.8%)  | 2717 (27.1%)   |
| 3 | Natural gas | 1233 (17.9%)  | 1861 (18.6%)   |
| 4 | Water power | 413 (6.0%)    | 606 (6.0%)     |
| 5 | Nuclear power | 20 (0.3%)   | 228 (2.3%)     |
|   | **Total** of above | 6888 (100%) | 10,026 (100%) |

Figures in million metric tonnes of coal equivalent

**Consumption comparisons**
The table *left* provides a comparison of the five most important sources of world primary energy consumption in 1968 and 1978 (based on information in the BP Statistical Review of the World Oil Industry, 1978). Consumption of energy from each of these sources increased from 1968 to 1978. Although there was no change in their order of importance, the percentage share of the annual total increased noticeably for oil and nuclear power and decreased for coal. 1978 percentages are shown *below*.

**Consumption increases**
*right* Levels of primary energy consumption from selected sources in 1978 are here shown as multiples of their 1968 equivalents.
**a** Total of five major sources (x 1.6)
**b** Nuclear power (x 11.4)
**c** Coal (x 1.2)

*The energy equivalent of 1 day's consumption of electricity in the United States would be sufficient to power an automobile 36,000 times around the world.*

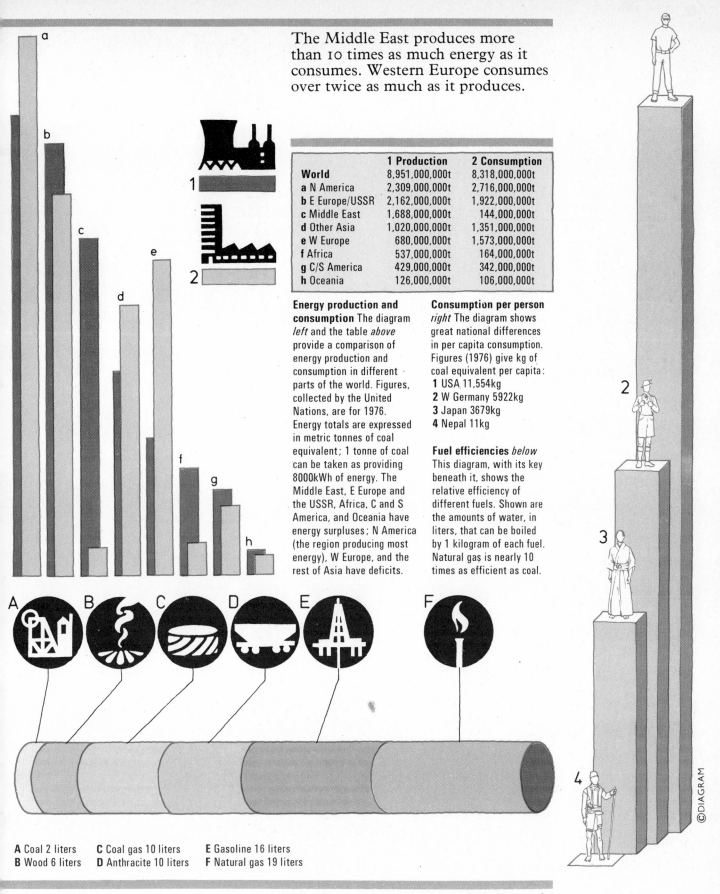

The Middle East produces more than 10 times as much energy as it consumes. Western Europe consumes over twice as much as it produces.

| | 1 Production | 2 Consumption |
|---|---|---|
| **World** | 8,951,000,000t | 8,318,000,000t |
| **a** N America | 2,309,000,000t | 2,716,000,000t |
| **b** E Europe/USSR | 2,162,000,000t | 1,922,000,000t |
| **c** Middle East | 1,688,000,000t | 144,000,000t |
| **d** Other Asia | 1,020,000,000t | 1,351,000,000t |
| **e** W Europe | 680,000,000t | 1,573,000,000t |
| **f** Africa | 537,000,000t | 164,000,000t |
| **g** C/S America | 429,000,000t | 342,000,000t |
| **h** Oceania | 126,000,000t | 106,000,000t |

**Energy production and consumption** The diagram *left* and the table *above* provide a comparison of energy production and consumption in different parts of the world. Figures, collected by the United Nations, are for 1976. Energy totals are expressed in metric tonnes of coal equivalent; 1 tonne of coal can be taken as providing 8000kWh of energy. The Middle East, E Europe and the USSR, Africa, C and S America, and Oceania have energy surpluses; N America (the region producing most energy), W Europe, and the rest of Asia have deficits.

**Consumption per person** *right* The diagram shows great national differences in per capita consumption. Figures (1976) give kg of coal equivalent per capita:
**1** USA 11,554kg
**2** W Germany 5922kg
**3** Japan 3679kg
**4** Nepal 11kg

**Fuel efficiencies** *below* This diagram, with its key beneath it, shows the relative efficiency of different fuels. Shown are the amounts of water, in liters, that can be boiled by 1 kilogram of each fuel. Natural gas is nearly 10 times as efficient as coal.

**A** Coal 2 liters
**B** Wood 6 liters
**C** Coal gas 10 liters
**D** Anthracite 10 liters
**E** Gasoline 16 liters
**F** Natural gas 19 liters

To exert power equivalent to the amount of electricity used by US manufacturing industry in a single week, one worker doing average manual labor would have to work for 145,193,740 years (working fifty 40-hour weeks per year).

©DIAGRAM

# VOLCANOES, BOMBS AND EARTHQUAKES

The greatest releases of energy on Earth occur during volcanic eruptions, earthquakes and nuclear explosions. The eruption of Tambora in 1815 is believed to have been over 100 times more powerful than the largest nuclear test. The latter, at Novaya Zemlya, was comparable to an earthquake of Richter magnitude 7 to 8.

**Scales of destruction**
*right, far right* Four scales are used here.
**Scale A** on both diagrams gives energy in joules.
**Scale B** shows short tons, kilotons (kt = 1000t), and megatons (Mt = 1,000,000t) of TNT equivalent, where one ton equals $4.2 \times 10^9$J.
**Scale C** is Richter's scale for measuring earthquakes.
**Scale D** is Mercalli's scale for measuring earthquakes.

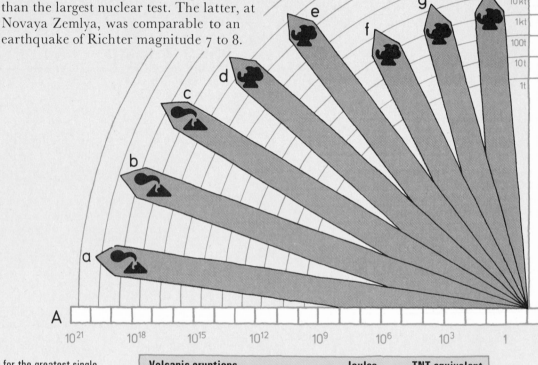

**Volcanoes and bombs**
*above, right* Shown here are estimates of energy from volcanoes and nuclear explosions. For Tambora (**a**), the greatest volcanic eruption known, we give the total release of energy. For Santorini (**b**) and for Krakatoa (**c**) we use figures for the greatest single explosions. The H-bomb tested at Novaya Zemlya (**d**) was the biggest to date; Eniwetok (**e**) was the first H-bomb test. The bomb tested at Alamogordo (**f**) and the bombs dropped on Hiroshima (**g**) and Nagasaki (**h**) were identical A-bombs.

| Volcanic eruptions | Joules | TNT equivalent |
|---|---|---|
| **a** Tambora, Indonesia (April 1815) | $8 \times 10^{19}$J | 20,000Mt |
| **b** Santorini, Greece (c. 1470BC) | $3 \times 10^{19}$J | 7500Mt |
| **c** Krakatoa, Indonesia (August 1883) | $6 \times 10^{18}$J | 1500Mt |
| **Nuclear explosions** | | |
| **d** Novaya Zemlya, USSR (October 1961) | $3 \times 10^{17}$J | 60Mt |
| **e** Eniwetok, US Pacific (November 1952) | $6 \times 10^{16}$J | 15Mt |
| **f** Alamogordo, USA (July 1945) | $8 \times 10^{13}$J | 20kt |
| **g** Hiroshima, Japan (August 1945) | $8 \times 10^{13}$J | 20kt |
| **h** Nagasaki, Japan (August 1945) | $8 \times 10^{13}$J | 20kt |

**A- and H-bombs compared**
*left* Nuclear bombs work in one of two ways. An atomic bomb functions by fission, using the energy released by the splitting of uranium and plutonium atoms. A hydrogen—or thermonuclear—bomb uses the energy released by the fusion of two hydrogen atoms into one helium atom. Our diagram compares the 80,000MW of power produced by one gram of fissioning uranium (**1**), with the 240,000MW of power that one gram of deuterium (an isotope of hydrogen) yields through fusion (**2**).

**The H-bomb tested at Novaya Zemlya in October 1961 was 3000 times as powerful as the A-bomb dropped on Hiroshima in August 1945.**

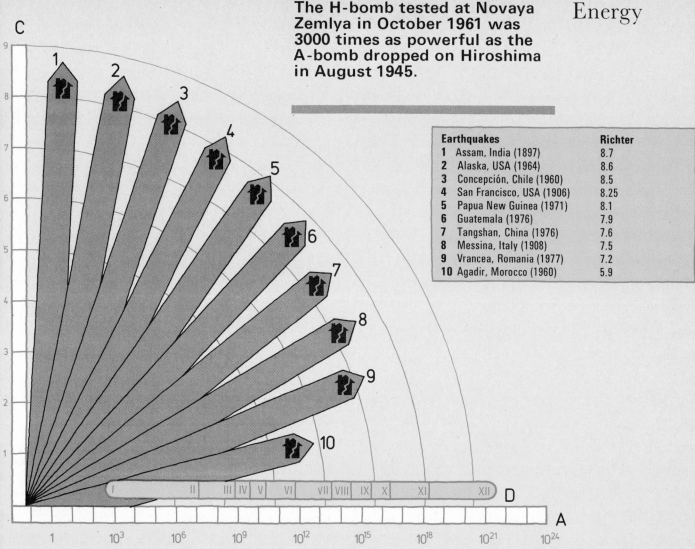

| Earthquakes | Richter |
|---|---|
| **1** Assam, India (1897) | 8.7 |
| **2** Alaska, USA (1964) | 8.6 |
| **3** Concepción, Chile (1960) | 8.5 |
| **4** San Francisco, USA (1906) | 8.25 |
| **5** Papua New Guinea (1971) | 8.1 |
| **6** Guatemala (1976) | 7.9 |
| **7** Tangshan, China (1976) | 7.6 |
| **8** Messina, Italy (1908) | 7.5 |
| **9** Vrancea, Romania (1977) | 7.2 |
| **10** Agadir, Morocco (1960) | 5.9 |

**Richter scale** *below*
This table gives joule equivalents for units of the Richter scale. This scale is used to record an earthquake's ''magnitude.'' It is a measure, based on seismograph readings and mathematical formulae, of the total energy released.

**Mercalli equivalents**
*below* The Mercalli scale measures earthquake intensity. Numbers refer to an earthquake's effects at some specific place on Earth's surface. Mercalli numbers and characteristics are listed here with Richter, joule and TNT equivalents.

**Earthquake magnitudes**
*above* Shown on the diagram and listed in the table beside it are the magnitudes of selected earthquakes in different parts of the world. We give the year of the earthquake, and then its magnitude on the Richter scale.

**Frequency of earthquakes**
Each year there are more than 300,000 earth tremors with Richter magnitudes of 2–2.9. An earthquake with a Richter magnitude of 8.5 or over occurs about every 5–10 years.

| Richter | Joules |
|---|---|
| 0 | $6.3 \times 10^{-2}$J |
| 1 | $1.6 \times 10$J |
| 2 | $4.0 \times 10^3$J |
| 3 | $1.0 \times 10^6$J |
| 4 | $2.5 \times 10^8$J |
| 5 | $6.3 \times 10^{10}$J |
| 6 | $1.6 \times 10^{13}$J |
| 7 | $4.0 \times 10^{15}$J |
| 8 | $1.0 \times 10^{18}$J |
| 9 | $2.5 \times 10^{20}$J |
| 10 | $6.3 \times 10^{22}$J |

| Mercalli number and characteristics | | Richter | Joules | TNT equivalent |
|---|---|---|---|---|
| I | Instrumental : detected only by seismographs | $<3.5$ | $<1.6 \times 10^7$J | $<7.6$ lb |
| II | Feeble : noticed only by some people at rest | 3.5 | $1.6 \times 10^7$J | 7.6 lb |
| III | Slight : similar to vibrations from a passing truck | 4.2 | $7.5 \times 10^8$J | 357 lb |
| IV | Moderate : felt generally indoors ; parked cars rock | 4.5 | $4.0 \times 10^9$J | 1905 lb |
| V | Rather strong : felt generally ; most sleepers wake | 4.8 | $2.1 \times 10^{10}$J | 5t |
| VI | Strong : trees sway ; furniture moves ; some damage | 5.4 | $5.7 \times 10^{11}$J | 136t |
| VII | Very strong : general alarm ; walls crack | 6.1 | $2.8 \times 10^{13}$J | 6.6kt |
| VIII | Destructive : weak structures damaged ; walls fall | 6.5 | $2.5 \times 10^{14}$J | 60kt |
| IX | Ruinous : some houses collapse as ground cracks | 6.9 | $2.3 \times 10^{15}$J | 550kt |
| X | Disastrous : many buildings destroyed ; rails bend | 7.3 | $2.1 \times 10^{16}$J | 5Mt |
| XI | Very disastrous : few buildings survive ; landslides | 8.1 | $1.7 \times 10^{18}$J | 405Mt |
| XII | Catastrophic : total destruction ; ground forms waves | $>8.1$ | $>1.7 \times 10^{18}$J | $>405$Mt |

© DIAGRAM

# SOUND

The term "sound" is used to refer both to a physical phenomenon (vibrations transmitted as compression waves through air or some other medium) and to a sensation in our minds (our brain's response to these vibrations after they reach our eardrums). Here we compare the physical characteristics of some different sounds.

**Wavelength and frequency**
*right* Sound waves are longitudinal pressure waves. Wavelength is the distance between successive peaks (**a**). Frequency is the number of waves that pass a given point in a given time; it is calculated by dividing wave speed by wavelength, and is measured in cycles per second or hertz (Hz). The shorter the length of a wave, the higher is its frequency. The longer the wave, the lower is the frequency. High-pitched tones are produced by high-frequency waves; low tones by low-frequency waves.

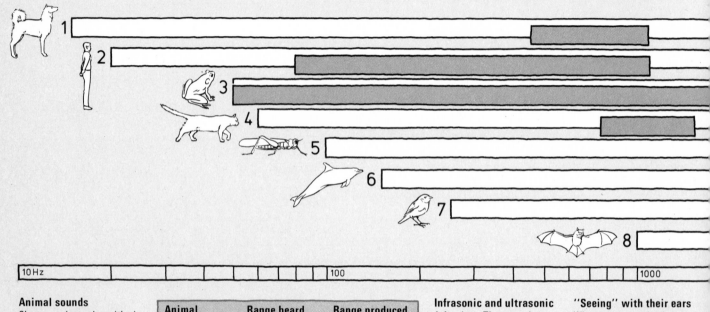

**Animal sounds**
Shown against a logarithmic hertz scale in the diagram *above* and listed in the table *right* are the sound frequency ranges that are heard (white bars) and produced (colored bars) by selected animals and man.

| Animal | Range heard | Range produced |
|---|---|---|
| 1 Dog | 15–50,000Hz | 452–1080Hz |
| 2 Man | 20–20,000Hz | 80–1100Hz |
| 3 Frog | 50–10,000Hz | 50–8000Hz |
| 4 Cat | 60–65,000Hz | 760–1520Hz |
| 5 Grasshopper | 100–15,000Hz | 7000–100,000Hz |
| 6 Dolphin | 150–150,000Hz | 7000–120,000Hz |
| 7 European robin | 250–21,000Hz | 2000–13,000Hz |
| 8 Bat | 1000–120,000Hz | 10,000–120,000Hz |

**Infrasonic and ultrasonic**
*left, above* The normal human ear is sensitive to sounds with frequencies between about 20Hz and 20,000Hz. Sounds with frequencies below 20Hz are described as "infrasonic," those above 20,000Hz as "ultrasonic."

**"Seeing" with their ears**
Whereas most animals locate objects visually, by seeing reflected light waves, a few animals, notably bats and dolphins, obtain such information via their ears, by picking up the reflected sound waves of their own high-pitched squeaks.

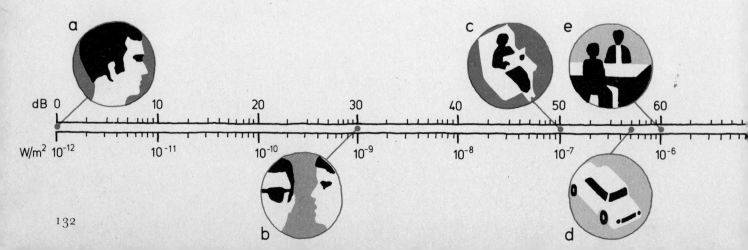

Most of the sounds made by bats are too high to be heard by humans, but the intensity of their squeaks is comparable with the sound of a four-engined jet aircraft only 1 mile away.

**Wave amplitude** *left*
Amplitude is the distance between a wave peak or trough and an intermediate line of equilibrium (**b**). The greater the amount of energy transmitted in a sound wave, the greater is the wave's amplitude and the louder the sound heard.

**Intensity and pressure**
The intensity, or energy content, of a sound wave is measured in watts per square meter ($W/m^2$) or, more usually, in arbitrary units termed decibels (dB). The pressure of a sound wave is measured in units called pascals (Pa).

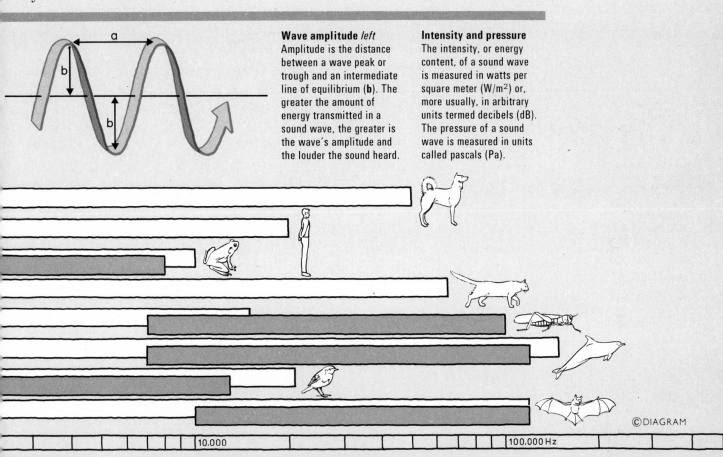

**A world of noise**
The diagram *below* and the table *right* show the relative intensities, in decibels (dB) and in Watts per square meter ($W/m^2$), of a range of familiar sounds. The minute energy content in any sound wave and the wide range of possible intensities make $W/m^2$ rather cumbersome units for sound. Decibels are easier to use, and correspond to our perception of "loudness." Starting with 0dB equal to an arbitrary $10^{-12} W/m^2$, we have an increase of 10dB of loudness for every tenfold increase in $W/m^2$ of power.

| a | Human minimum audibility level | 0dB | $10^{-12} W/m^2$ |
|---|---|---|---|
| b | Soft whisper at 5m | 30dB | $10^{-9} W/m^2$ |
| c | Interior of typical urban home | 50dB | $10^{-7} W/m^2$ |
| d | Light traffic at 15m | 55dB | $5 \times 10^{-7} W/m^2$ |
| e | Average conversation at 1m | 60dB | $10^{-6} W/m^2$ |
| f | Pneumatic drill at 15m | 85dB | $5 \times 10^{-4} W/m^2$ |
| g | Heavy traffic at 15m | 90dB | $10^{-3} W/m^2$ |
| h | Loud shout at 15m | 100dB | $10^{-2} W/m^2$ |
| i | Jet aircraft take-off at 600m | 105dB | $5 \times 10^{-2} W/m^2$ |
| j | Discotheque at full volume | 117dB | $7 \times 10^{-1} W/m^2$ |
| k | Jet aircraft take-off at 60m | 120dB | $1 W/m^2$ |
| l | Painful level for humans | 130dB | $10 W/m^2$ |
| m | Jet aircraft take-off at 30m | 140dB | $10^2 W/m^2$ |

**An ear for trouble** *left*
The quietest sounds heard by a person with normal hearing in two ears have an intensity of $10^{-12} W/m^2$ (0dB). Such a person experiences pain from sounds of $1-10 W/m^2$ (120–130dB), and is liable to permanent ear damage if sounds exceed $100 W/m^2$ (140dB).

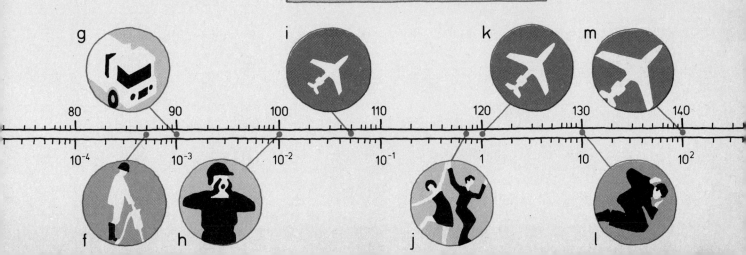

# MUSIC

In the sound phenomenon known as music, the most precisely controlled aspect is the pitch or frequency. Instruments are designed, and musicians are trained, to produce frequencies that conform to a basic set. This basic set is most easily seen in the piano, whose range of $7\frac{1}{4}$ octaves is divided into 88 equal steps.

**Orchestral instruments**
Listed *right* and shown on the diagram *below* are the normal ranges of the piano and some common orchestral instruments. The vertical black line at 440Hz indicates "concert A" ($A_4$), used as a tuning guide.

**All-encompassing piano**
The range of the piano encompasses the ranges of all Western orchestral instruments. The piano keys in our diagram correspond as closely as possible to the hertz scale labeled beneath them, and help to illustrate the ranges of tones produced by other instruments.

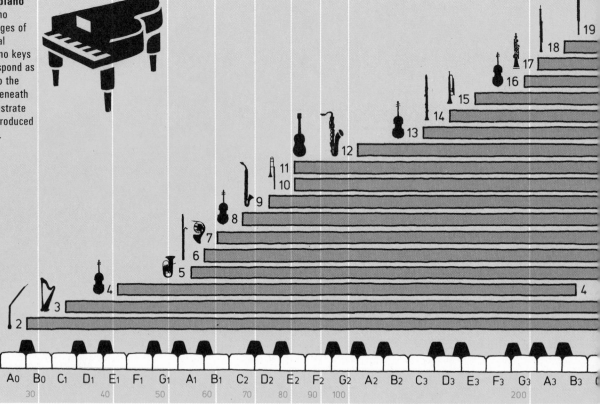

**Singing voices**
Listed *right* and shown *far right* against the same scale as our musical instrument ranges are the normal ranges for trained singing voices, from the bass's lowest note of $E_2$ (82.4Hz) to the soprano's highest $C_6$ (1046Hz).

| | | |
|---|---|---|
| **a** Soprano | $C_4$–$C_6$ | 262–1046Hz |
| **b** Alto | $G_3$–$F_5$ | 196–698Hz |
| **c** Tenor | $D_3$–$B\flat_4$ | 147–466Hz |
| **d** Baritone | $A_2$–$G_4$ | 110–392Hz |
| **e** Bass | $E_2$–$D_4$ | 82.4–294Hz |

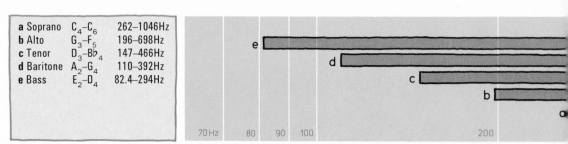

The normal range of the tenor trombone extends from the lowest note of a bass singer's normal range to the highest note for a tenor singer.

For tuning purposes the pitch of the A above middle C was in 1939 internationally agreed at 440Hz. Pitches formerly accepted for this same A include: 435Hz (Paris Academy 1859 and the Vienna conference of 1885); 415–425Hz (representative pitch standards in the early 18th century); 377Hz (Arnold Schlick "low organ" pitch of 1511).

| | | | |
|---|---|---|---|
| **1** Piano | $A_0$–$C_8$ | 27.5–4186Hz | |
| **2** Contrabassoon | $Bb_0$–$Eb_4$ | 29–311Hz | |
| **3** Harp | $C_1$–$G_7$ | 32.7–3136Hz | |
| **4** Double bass | $E_1$–$B_3$ | 41.2–247Hz | |
| **5** Eb bass tuba | $A_1$–$Eb_4$ | 55–311Hz | |
| **6** Bassoon | $Bb_1$–$Eb_5$ | 58.3–622Hz | |
| **7** French horn | $B_1$–$F_5$ | 61.7–698Hz | |
| **8** Violoncello | $C_2$–$E_5$ | 65.4–659Hz | |
| **9** Bass clarinet | $D_2$–$Eb_5$ | 73.4–622Hz | |
| **10** Tenor trombone | $E_2$–$Bb_4$ | 82.4–466Hz | |
| **11** Guitar | $E_2$–$F_5$ | 82.4–698Hz | |
| **12** Tenor saxophone | $Ab_2$–$Eb_5$ | 104–622Hz | |
| **13** Viola | $C_3$–$C_6$ | 131–1046Hz | |
| **14** Clarinet | $D_3$–$G_6$ | 147–1568Hz | |
| **15** Trumpet | $E_3$–$Bb_5$ | 165–932Hz | |
| **16** Violin | $G_3$–$C_7$ | 196–2093Hz | |
| **17** Soprano saxophone | $Ab_3$–$Eb_6$ | 208–1244Hz | |
| **18** Oboe | $Bb_3$–$F_6$ | 233–1397Hz | |
| **19** Flute | $C_4$–$C_7$ | 262–2093Hz | |
| **20** Piccolo | $D_5$–$Bb_7$ | 587–3729Hz | |

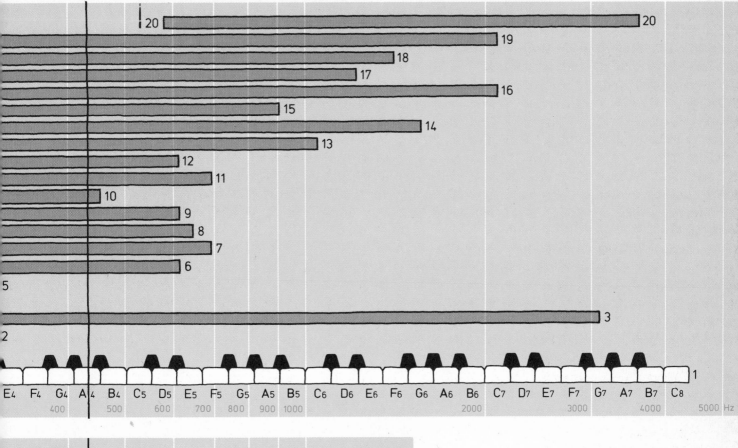

E₄ F₄ G₄ A₄ B₄ C₅ D₅ E₅ F₅ G₅ A₅ B₅ C₆ D₆ E₆ F₆ G₆ A₆ B₆ C₇ D₇ E₇ F₇ G₇ A₇ B₇ C₈

400 500 600 700 800 900 1000 2000 3000 4000 5000 Hz

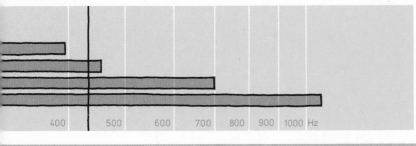

400 500 600 700 800 900 1000 Hz

**Heights and depths** *right*
Shown here are musicians playing the lowest and the highest sounding instruments of the orchestral woodwind and string families.

**A** Contrabassoon 29–311Hz
**B** Double bass 41.2–247Hz
**C** Violin 196–2093Hz
**D** Piccolo 587–3729Hz

©DIAGRAM

# ELECTROMAGNETIC WAVES

The energy of the Sun and of the local radio station are both transmitted by electromagnetic waves. Here we compare the characteristics of waves within different regions of the electromagnetic spectrum, and look at some of the practical applications that man has found for them in laboratories, homes and hospitals.

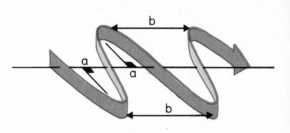

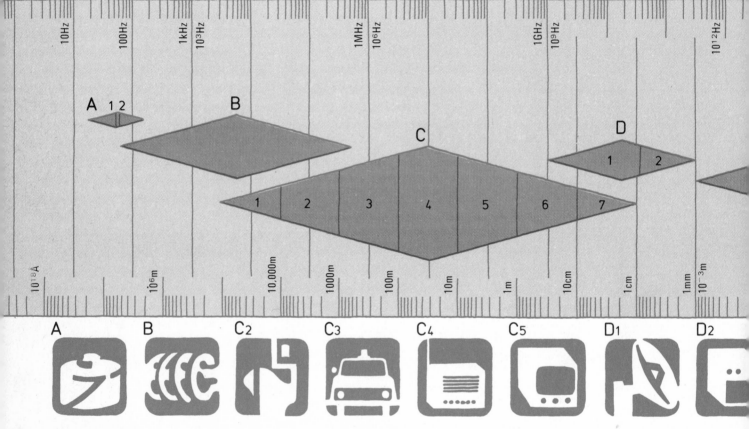

**Electromagnetic spectrum**
*above* The top logarithmic scale gives frequencies in hertz; the lower one gives equivalent wavelength measurements. The lower the frequency the longer is the wavelength; the higher the frequency the shorter the wavelength will be. Hertz measurements are used for low frequency waves, and wavelength measurements for higher frequency waves. Sections of the spectrum, described *right*, are located between the scales, and illustrated with examples indicating their use or character.

**A) Generated electricity**
The alternating current (AC) electricity used in some countries for domestic and commercial use is at the low frequency/long wavelength end of the spectrum, and ranges from 16.7–144Hz. Two lines (**1,2**) on diamond **A** indicate two common frequencies: 50Hz (Europe) and 60Hz (North America). These are heard as the "mains hum" from faulty domestic gadgetry, hi-fi systems, etc.

**B) Induction heating**
Waves in this frequency band are used to induce heat in metals. The metal is placed in the center of a series of wire coils through which current is passed, inducing electrical "eddy currents" in the metal, which raise its temperature. Commonly the frequency of the current supplied to the coil is in the range of 60–60,000Hz, but waves with frequencies up to 500,000Hz are used.

**C) Radio waves**
These are the waves used for radio and television transmission. They range from 3kHz to 30GHz and, as shown on diamond **C**, may be subdivided as follows.
**1** Very low frequency (vlf).
**2** Low frequency (lf) waves, used for ship radio signals.
**3** Medium frequency (mf), as used by police forces.
**4** High frequency (hf), used for "shortwave" radio.
**5** Very high frequency (vhf), used for radio and for television.
**6** Ultra high frequency (uhf).
**7** Super high frequency (shf).

**D) Microwaves**
Waves in this region are used in radar (**ra**dio **d**etecting **a**nd **r**anging), a method of detecting otherwise invisible objects by bouncing radio pulses off them. Such pulses are transmitted along a carrier wave in the range 1–35GHz (diamond **D**, region 1). The shorter wavelengths in the microwave region, down to 1mm (diamond **D**, region 2), have found application in cooking, greatly reducing cooking times.

Tests indicate that, according to average judgment, names for the pure spectral colors should be applied to light of the following wavelengths:

| | |
|---|---|
| Violet | 3900–4550Å |
| Blue | 4550–4920Å |
| Green | 4920–5770Å |
| Yellow | 5770–5970Å |
| Orange | 5970–6220Å |
| Red | 6220–7700Å |

## Wave characteristics
Electromagnetic waves are produced by rhythmic variations in electrical and magnetic fields. As shown in the diagram *left* they are "transverse" waves, vibrating in a plane at right angles (**a**) to the direction of flow.

## Measurement of waves
Electromagnetic waves are measured in two ways: by "wavelength" (the distance from one wave peak to another, **b** on the diagram *left*) and by "frequency" (the number of waves, or "cycles," per second). The table *right* gives units of measurement and methods of converting frequency measurements to wavelength measurements, and vice versa. All waves within the electromagnetic spectrum travel, or "propagate themselves," at a constant speed, the speed of light (approximately $3 \times 10^8$ m/s).

### Units of frequency
1000 hertz (Hz) = 1 kilohertz (kHz)
1000 kilohertz = 1 megahertz (MHz)
1000 megahertz = 1 gigahertz (GHz)
### Units of wavelength
1000 X-units (Xu) = 1 Ångstrom (Å) = $10^{-10}$ m
10,000 Ångstroms = 1 micron ($\mu$) = $10^{-6}$ m
1000 microns = 1 millimeter = $10^{-3}$ m
### Conversions
Wavelength (meters) = $3 \times 10^8$ m/s ÷ frequency (hertz)
Frequency (hertz) = $3 \times 10^8$ m/s ÷ wavelength (meters)

©DIAGRAM

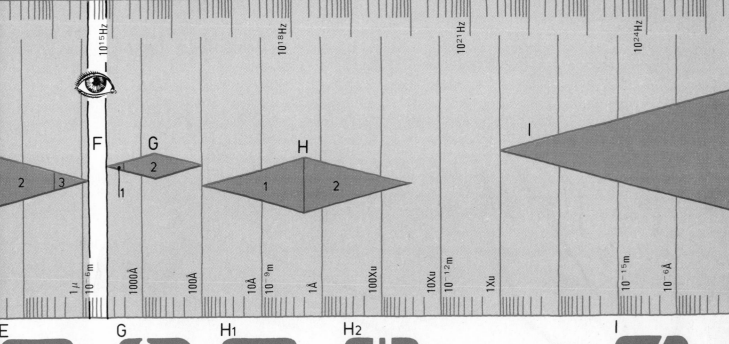

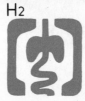

## E) Infrared waves
These are heat waves, with wavelengths between about 1mm and 7700Å. They are subdivided into far, middle, and near infrared (**1, 2, 3** on diamond **E**). Most of the energy radiated by hot objects (including the energy we receive from the Sun) lies chiefly in this range. Practical applications are in the areas of photography (plates that are sensitive to infrared radiation make it possible to take photographs in the dark), physical therapy, military reconnaissance, and astronomical research.

## F) Light waves
Although scientists use it more widely, the term "light" is most commonly taken to refer to the visible portion of the electromagnetic spectrum, ie to wavelengths of approximately 3900–7700Å. The color of an object is determined by the composition of its surface, which reflects certain wavelengths but not others. White objects reflect all wavelengths of the visible part of the spectrum; black objects reflect none of them.

## G) Ultraviolet light
This highly energetic radiation is invisible to the human eye, having wavelengths of about 3900–100Å. As indicated on diamond **G** it is subdivided into near (**1**) and far (**2**) regions. Earth's atmosphere absorbs much of this type of radiation from the Sun. Ultraviolet light causes sunburn, and helps in the formation of vitamin D within the body. It also causes some substances to fluoresce (invisible waves are absorbed and visible ones emitted).

## H) X-rays
These are even more energetic than ultraviolet light, with wavelengths of approximately 100Å to 30Xu. They have found wide application because of their ability to penetrate many substances. The science of X-ray spectroscopy uses the lower end of the X-ray frequency range (**1**). Higher frequency uses include the photographing of bones and the detection of flaws in metal objects (**2**).

## I) Gamma rays
These are produced when atomic nuclei pass from a higher to a lower energy level. They are received from distant nuclear explosions and from nuclear reactions in the universe, and are also produced by the interaction of so-called cosmic rays with particles in the atmosphere. Gamma rays have very high energy levels ($10^4$–$10^7$eV), and can pass through several centimeters of lead. The lowest frequencies of gamma rays have wavelengths of about 1Xu; in theory there is no top lim.

# FOOD

People, like other animals, obtain their energy from the food they eat. Here we compare the energy contents of different foods—from butter, with 1625 Calories per ½lb, to celery, with only 7 Calories in an 8 inch outer stalk. On the following pages we compare Calorie requirements for different people and for various activities.

**Calories and calories**
The energy content of food is measured in Calories (written with a capital C). One Calorie is equivalent to one kilocalorie and to 1000 calories (small c). For fuller definitions and for conversions into other energy units, see p. 126.

**A full table of food**
*right* Included here is a selection of different types of food, with the number of Calories contained in specified quantities of each. As far as possible, the quantities specified are for an ''average'' adult portion.

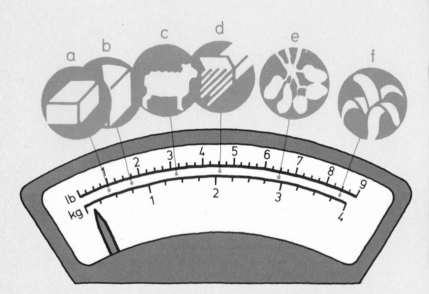

**Calorie food scale**
The diagram *above* and the list *right* show how much a young man would have to eat if he were to obtain his required daily intake of 3000 Calories (see p. 140) from eating only one type of food.

a Butter 15oz
b Cheddar cheese 1 lb 11oz
c Shoulder of lamb, roasted lean meat 3 lb 3oz
d Spaghetti, boiled 4 lb 9oz
e Potatoes, boiled or baked 6 lb 8oz
f Bananas 8 lb 8oz

Only 15oz of butter contains enough Calories to meet a young man's daily requirement of 3000 Calories. If he were to obtain the same number of Calories from lettuce, it would be necessary to eat 37lb 8oz of it.

| Meat | | |
|---|---|---:|
| | Sausages, pork, fried (4oz) | 543 |
| | Duck, roasted meat, no skin (4oz) | 352 |
| | Liver, calves', fried (4oz) | 296 |
| | Pork, loin, lean, roasted (4oz) | 288 |
| | Beef, rib, lean, roasted (4oz) | 273 |
| | Goose, roasted meat, no skin (4oz) | 266 |
| | Bacon, fried and drained (2oz) | 248 |
| | Lamb, shoulder, lean, roasted (4oz) | 233 |
| | Chicken, mixed meat, roasted (4oz) | 206 |
| **Fish** | Tuna, canned in oil (4oz) | 327 |
| | Mackerel, baked with butter (4oz) | 268 |
| | Herring, kippered (4oz) | 239 |
| | Salmon, baked with butter (4oz) | 207 |
| | Halibut, baked with butter (4oz) | 194 |
| | Cod, baked with butter (4oz) | 192 |
| | Lobster, cooked meat (4oz) | 108 |
| | Mussels, raw meat (4oz) | 108 |
| | Shrimps, shelled, raw (4oz) | 103 |
| **Dairy products** | Butter (8oz) | 1625 |
| | Cream, whipping (½ cup) | 358 |
| | Ice cream, rich (½ cup) | 165 |
| | Milk, cow's (1 cup) | 159 |
| | Yoghurt, plain (1 cup) | 152 |
| | Cheese, Cheddar (1 oz) | 113 |
| | Egg, chicken's, raw, 1 large (2oz) | 90 |
| | Cheese, Camembert (1oz) | 85 |
| | Cottage cheese, plain (1oz) | 24 |
| **Fruit and vegetables** | Avocado, ½ (3⅛in diameter) | 185 |
| | Potatoes, boiled/baked (4oz) | 115 |
| | Banana, 1 (7¾in long) | 81 |
| | Orange, 1 navel (2⅞in diameter) | 71 |
| | Grapes, European-type (4oz) | 68 |
| | Apple, 1 (2½in diameter) | 61 |
| | Carrots, cooked (4oz) | 20 |
| | Cabbage, cooked (4oz) | 16 |
| | Lettuce, 1 portion (2oz) | 10 |
| | Celery, raw, 1 outer stalk (8in) | 7 |
| **Bread and cereals** | Rice, boiled (4oz) | 400 |
| | Spaghetti, boiled (4oz) | 165 |
| | Oatflakes (1 cup) | 132 |
| | Wheatflakes (1 cup) | 106 |
| | Cornflakes (1 cup) | 97 |
| | Pumpernickel (1 slice) | 79 |
| | Bread, white, firm crumb (1 slice) | 63 |
| | Bread, rye (1 slice) | 56 |
| | Bread, wholewheat (1 slice) | 56 |
| **Sundries** | Apple pie, 2-crusted (1 slice) | 350 |
| | Peanuts (2oz) | 330 |
| | Milk chocolate (2oz) | 294 |
| | Brazil nuts (2oz) | 185 |
| | Potato chips/crisps (1oz) | 162 |
| | Doughnut, plain | 150 |
| | Jams and preserves (1oz) | 77 |
| | Chocolate chip cookie | 50 |
| | Sugar, granulated (1 US teaspoon) | 15 |

Calories

**A large egg contains 90 Calories
if it is served boiled or poached,
108 Calories if it is fried, and
120 Calories if it is scrambled.**

**Calories by the quarter**
*left* This diagram gives
a visual comparison of
the number of Calories
contained in 4oz of a
selection of foods from the
table on the previous page.
A Butter 812.5
B Peanuts 660
C Milk chocolate 588
D Pork sausages (fried) 543
E Rice (boiled) 400
F Beef (roast, lean rib) 273
G Cod (buttered, baked) 192
H Potatoes (boiled) 115
I Apple 68
J Cabbage (boiled) 16

**Energy in eggs**
*right* Here we express the
Calorie contents of 4oz of
different types of meat and
fish in terms of the number
of large boiled eggs that
would have to be eaten to
provide the same number of
Calories. (Cuts and cooking
methods are the same as
those in the main table.)
a Cod 2.1
b Chicken 2.3
c Lamb 2.6
d Mackerel 3.0
e Beef 3.0
f Pork 3.2
g Duck 3.9
h Bacon 5.5
i Pork sausages 6

**A drink or two or more**
The diagram *below* and the
list *right* provide a
comparison of the Calorie
contents of various drinks.
Shown are the number of
glasses (4 US fl.oz) of each
drink that would have to be
drunk to provide 1200
Calories, the number of
Calories in a US pint bottle
of 90° proof distilled spirits.

1 Southern Comfort 2.5
2 Distilled spirits (90°) 4
3 Sweet vermouth 6.7
4 Beaujolais 12.5
5 Reisling wine 13.3

6 Stout 17
7 Fresh orange juice 20
8 Lager 23.1
9 Cola 25
10 Tonic water 31.6

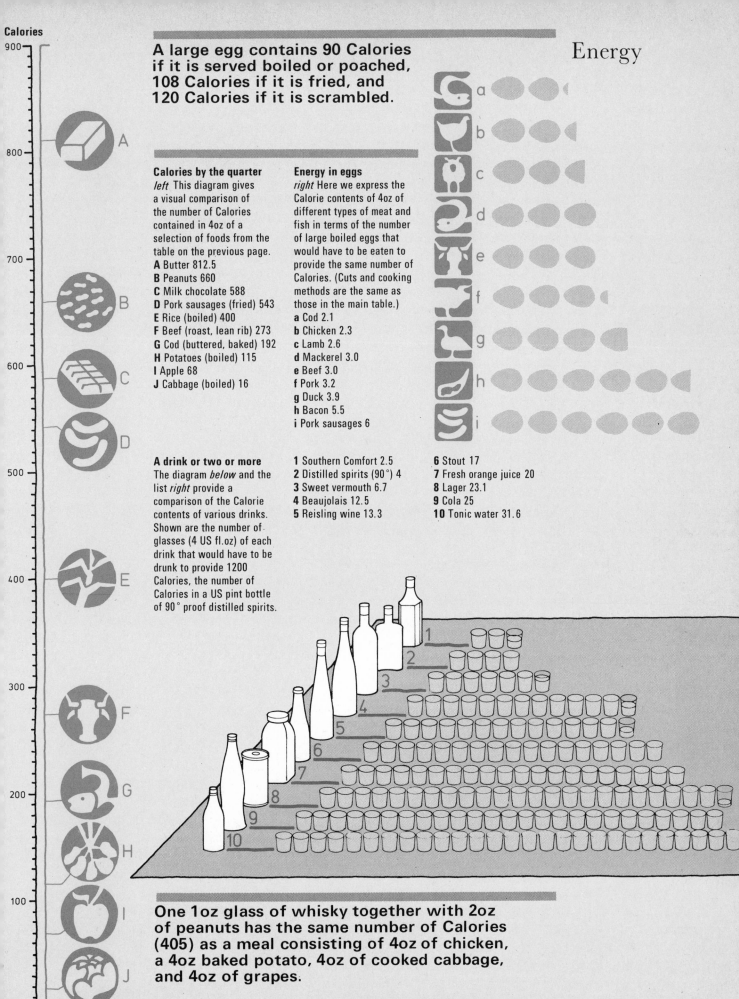

**One 1oz glass of whisky together with 2oz
of peanuts has the same number of Calories
(405) as a meal consisting of 4oz of chicken,
a 4oz baked potato, 4oz of cooked cabbage,
and 4oz of grapes.**

139

©DIAGRAM

# FOOD AND WORK

On the previous two pages we compared the energy contents of foods. Here we compare daily food energy needs of males and females of different ages, and make comparisons of Calorie use during different activities. Maintaining basic body processes burns up about two thirds of an average adult's Calorie intake.

**Calories per day**
The diagram *right* and the table *far right* show estimated daily Calorie (kilocalorie) needs for males and females of different ages. Sex and age are the most important factors affecting Calorie needs, but size, physical activity, and climate are also important. Male and female needs are similar until puberty, thereafter males typically need more Calories than females of similar age. Children use up a lot of Calories for their size, because energy is needed for growth.

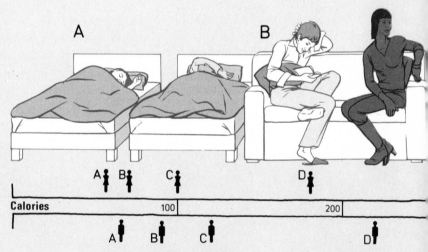

Years   0        10        20        30

| Activity | Calories used per hour | |
|---|---|---|
| | Males | Females |
| A Sleeping | 65 | 55 |
| B Sitting | 90 | 70 |
| C Standing | 120 | 100 |
| D Walking | 220 | 180 |
| E Walking uphill | 440 | 360 |
| F Running | 600 | 420 |

**Use of Calories**
The table *above* and the diagram *right* give estimates of the number of Calories needed by average men and women to perform particular activities for one hour. Obviously the amount of effort any individual puts into an activity affects results, but a general pattern of Calorie use is evident. Men use more Calories than women for all activities, because men have more weight to carry around and because women usually have more body fat and so need less energy to retain body heat.

A        B

A♀ B♀    C♀                    D♀
Calories                100              200
A♂    B♂    C♂                         D♂

**The body machine** *left*
Efficiency is the ratio of output (work) to input (fuel/food). Here we compare the efficiency of the human body with that of four other machines. An unfit person's normal 16–27% can be raised to 56% with training.

1 Electric motor 80%
2 Steam turbine 40%
3 Petrol motor 20–30%
4 Steam engine 10–15%
5 Human body 16–56%

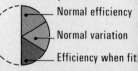
Normal efficiency
Normal variation
Efficiency when fit

1        2        3        4        5

**An 18-year-old male's 3000 Calories a day is equivalent to the energy contained in 13oz of good quality bituminous coal. An 18-year-old female's 2300 Calories is equivalent to 10oz of the same grade of coal.**

**A grandfather aged 75 requires the same number of Calories per day as his grandson aged 8. A grandmother aged 75 has the same daily Calorie needs as her 6-year-old granddaughter.**

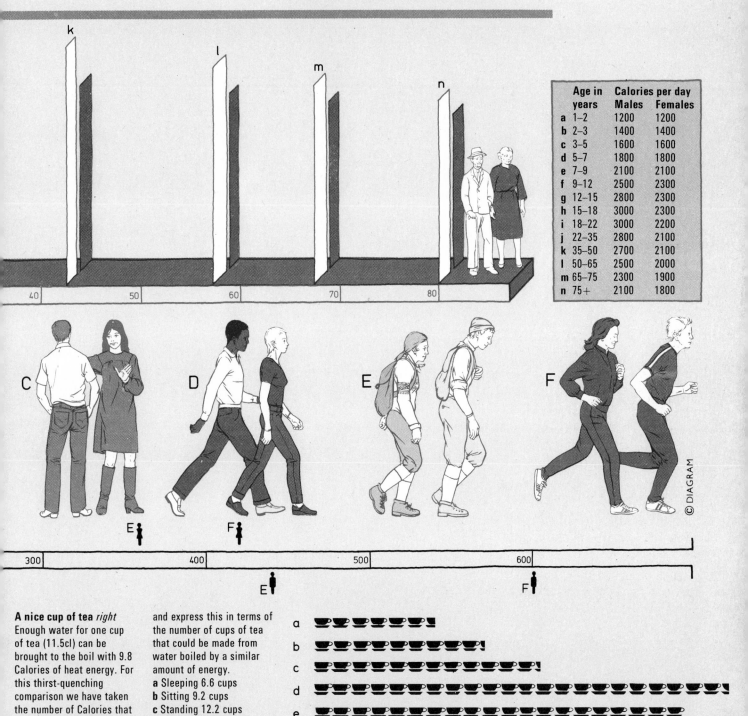

| | Age in years | Calories per day Males | Females |
|---|---|---|---|
| a | 1–2 | 1200 | 1200 |
| b | 2–3 | 1400 | 1400 |
| c | 3–5 | 1600 | 1600 |
| d | 5–7 | 1800 | 1800 |
| e | 7–9 | 2100 | 2100 |
| f | 9–12 | 2500 | 2300 |
| g | 12–15 | 2800 | 2300 |
| h | 15–18 | 3000 | 2300 |
| i | 18–22 | 3000 | 2200 |
| j | 22–35 | 2800 | 2100 |
| k | 35–50 | 2700 | 2100 |
| l | 50–65 | 2500 | 2000 |
| m | 65–75 | 2300 | 1900 |
| n | 75+ | 2100 | 1800 |

© DIAGRAM

**A nice cup of tea** *right*
Enough water for one cup of tea (11.5cl) can be brought to the boil with 9.8 Calories of heat energy. For this thirst-quenching comparison we have taken the number of Calories that a man uses in one hour spent at different activities, and express this in terms of the number of cups of tea that could be made from water boiled by a similar amount of energy.
**a** Sleeping 6.6 cups
**b** Sitting 9.2 cups
**c** Standing 12.2 cups
**d** Walking 22.4 cups
**e** Running 61.2 cups

During 8 hours of sleep a man uses the same number of Calories as if he had walked for 2 hours and 22 minutes or run for 52 minutes.

# CHAPTER 7

LES GRANDES DUNES D'EL BAB.

Photograph from a book published in 1912 showing a nomad and his camel traversing the Libyan Sahara, where the world's highest air temperatures are recorded.

Mount Erebus—a 12,200ft active volcano—towers above the icy wastes of Antarctica in this painting by Edward Wilson, who went with Scott in 1901–04 (Abbot Hall Art Gallery, Kendal, England).

# TEMPERATURE

An engraving showing an experiment by the 18th-century French scientist Antoine-Laurent Lavoisier in which he used two large lenses to focus the heat energy of the Sun in order to ignite alcohol in a container (Science Museum, London).

# MEASURING TEMPERATURE

Temperature is a measurement of heat energy made on one of the scales devised for this purpose. Fahrenheit, Réaumur and Celsius based their scales on the boiling and freezing points of water. The scales of Kelvin and Rankine were based on "absolute zero," the theoretical point at which there is no temperature or pressure.

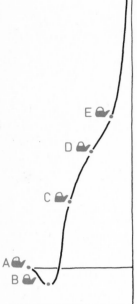

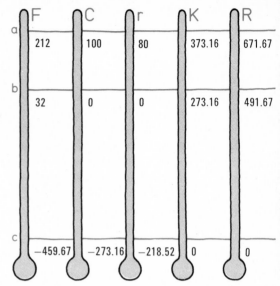

| | F | C | r | K | R |
|---|---|---|---|---|---|
| a | 212 | 100 | 80 | 373.16 | 671.67 |
| b | 32 | 0 | 0 | 273.16 | 491.67 |
| c | −459.67 | −273.16 | −218.52 | 0 | 0 |

**High tea?** The diagram *left* and the table *below* show the boiling point of water at different altitudes. Differences occur because atmospheric pressure falls as altitude increases, and the lower the pressure, the lower the boiling point of water (and vice versa).

**Temperature scales** *right* This diagram shows the values of the boiling (**a**) and freezing (**b**) points of water and of absolute zero (**c**) on five temperature scales. Below this are the formulae for converting one to another. The Fahrenheit, Celsius and Réaumur (now obsolete) scales divide the distance between the melting and boiling points of water arbitrarily into 180 °F, 100 °C and 80 °r. The Kelvin and Rankine scales begin at "absolute zero." The Kelvin unit (K) equals the Celsius degree, and the Rankine degree (°R) equals the Fahrenheit degree.

| Place | Altitude | Water boils | |
|---|---|---|---|
| **A** London, England | Sea level | 212.0 °F | 100 °C |
| **B** Dead Sea | −1296ft | 213.8 °F | 101 °C |
| **C** Denver, Colorado | 5280ft | 203.0 °F | 95 °C |
| **D** Quito, Ecuador | 9350ft | 194.0 °F | 90 °C |
| **E** Lhasa, Tibet | 12,087ft | 188.6 °F | 87 °C |
| **F** Mt Everest (top) | 29,002ft | 159.8 °F | 71 °C |

| From | To | Formulae |
|---|---|---|
| Fahrenheit | Celsius | $(°F − 32) ÷ 1.8$ |
| Celsius | Fahrenheit | $(°C × 1.8) + 32$ |
| Fahrenheit | Kelvin | $(°F + 459.67) ÷ 1.8$ |
| Celsius | Kelvin | $°C + 273.16$ |
| Réaumur | Kelvin | $(°r × 1.25) + 273.16$ |
| Rankine | Kelvin | $°R ÷ 1.8$ |
| Kelvin | Fahrenheit | $(K × 1.8) − 459.67$ |
| Kelvin | Celsius | $K − 273.16$ |

**Universal temperatures** *below* Scale **A**, extending the full width of these pages, is a logarithmic Kelvin temperature scale. It runs, left to right, from very high temperatures ($10^{10}$K) to very low ones (below 0.0001K). Drawn in their equivalent positions alongside the Kelvin scale are a Celsius ( also called Centigrade) scale (**B**) and a Fahrenheit scale (**C**). The Kelvin scale measures absolute temperatures and because of this makes an ideal universal scale; the Celsius and Fahrenheit scales, being based on the boiling and freezing points of water, are rarely used to express the greatest extremes.

**Very high temperatures** Selected high-temperature phenomena are included in the list *right*—with temperatures expressed in Kelvins. The same examples have also been plotted on the universal temperature scale *below*, and then illustrated beneath it.

1 Supernova $3.5 × 10^9$K
2 Interior of hottest stars, in excess of $10^9$K
3 Thermonuclear explosion $10^8$K
4 Sun's interior $2 × 10^7$K
5 Sun's corona $10^6$K
6 Molecules break down into atoms 5000K
7 Temperature of a lamp's tungsten filament 4000K
8 Heat of domestic coal gas flame 2500K
9 Temperature of molten lava 2000K

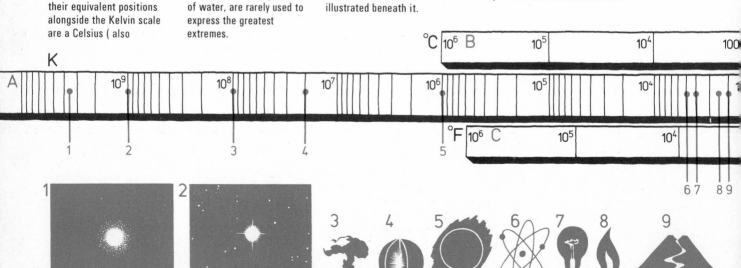

*The highest man-made temperatures, at the center of thermonuclear bombs, are in the order of $3 \times 10^8$ K. The lowest temperature ever reached in experiments is $5 \times 10^{-7}$ K.*

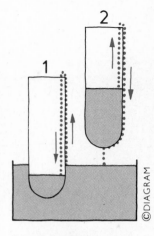

**Fahrenheit and Celsius**
*right* In the first two pairs of columns we give the Celsius equivalents for every five degrees Fahrenheit from −40°F to 220°F. In the third pair of columns we give the Fahrenheit equivalents for every five Celsius degrees from −40°C to 100°C.
One Fahrenheit degree is equivalent to 0.5 recurring (taken as 0.56) of a Celsius degree. One Celsius degree is equivalent to 1.8 Fahrenheit degrees. To find the equivalents for the figures between those listed, add or subtract the appropriate amount from the nearest figure given.

| °F | °C | °F | °C | °C | °F |
|---|---|---|---|---|---|
| −40 = | −40.00 | 100 = | 37.78 | −40 = | −40 |
| −35 = | −37.23 | 105 = | 40.56 | −35 = | −31 |
| −30 = | −34.45 | 110 = | 43.34 | −30 = | −22 |
| −25 = | −31.67 | 115 = | 46.11 | −25 = | −13 |
| −20 = | −28.89 | 120 = | 48.89 | −20 = | −4 |
| −15 = | −26.12 | 125 = | 51.66 | −15 = | 5 |
| −10 = | −23.34 | 130 = | 54.45 | −10 = | 14 |
| −5 = | −20.56 | 135 = | 57.23 | −5 = | 23 |
| 0 = | −17.78 | 140 = | 60.00 | 0 = | 32 |
| 5 = | −15.00 | 145 = | 62.78 | 5 = | 41 |
| 10 = | −12.23 | 150 = | 65.56 | 10 = | 50 |
| 15 = | −9.45 | 155 = | 68.34 | 15 = | 59 |
| 20 = | −6.67 | 160 = | 71.12 | 20 = | 68 |
| 25 = | −3.89 | 165 = | 73.89 | 25 = | 77 |
| 30 = | −1.11 | 170 = | 76.67 | 30 = | 86 |
| 35 = | 1.67 | 175 = | 79.45 | 35 = | 95 |
| 40 = | 4.45 | 180 = | 82.23 | 40 = | 104 |
| 45 = | 7.23 | 185 = | 85.00 | 45 = | 113 |
| 50 = | 10.00 | 190 = | 87.78 | 50 = | 122 |
| 55 = | 12.78 | 195 = | 90.56 | 55 = | 131 |
| 60 = | 15.56 | 200 = | 93.34 | 60 = | 140 |
| 65 = | 18.34 | 205 = | 96.11 | 65 = | 149 |
| 70 = | 21.11 | 210 = | 98.89 | 70 = | 158 |
| 75 = | 23.89 | 215 = | 101.67 | 75 = | 167 |
| 80 = | 26.67 | 220 = | 104.44 | 80 = | 176 |
| 85 = | 29.45 | | | 85 = | 185 |
| 90 = | 32.23 | | | 90 = | 194 |
| 95 = | 35.00 | | | 95 = | 203 |
| | | | | 100 = | 212 |

**Superfluid helium** *above*
Helium liquefies at 4.2K; at 2.2K it becomes "superfluid." If an empty tube is lowered into superfluid helium the helium creeps up the sides of the tube (**1**) to fill it to the level of the helium outside. If the tube is then removed from the liquid in the container, the helium in the tube climbs back out and down the sides of the tube (**2**)!

**Everyday temperatures**
The thermometer *left* is an enlargement of that over the main scale *below* and shows the temperature range with which we are most familiar. Examples falling within this range are plotted on the thermometer, showing °C and °F, and listed *right*.

**a** Water boils 212°F/100°C (373K)
**b** Some bacteria survive 158°F/70°C (343K)
**c** Highest recorded shade temperature 136.4°F/58°C (331K)
**d** Sparrow's mean body temperature 106°F/41°C (314K)
**e** Normal body temperature for humans 98.6°F/37°C (310K)
**f** Butter melts 87°F/30.6°C (304K)
**g** Comfortable room temperature 68°F/20°C (293K)
**h** Pure water freezes 32°F/0°C (273K)
**i** Temperature of Arctic seawater 30°F/−1.1°C (272K)
**j** Mercury freezes −38.0°F/−38.87°C (234.29K)

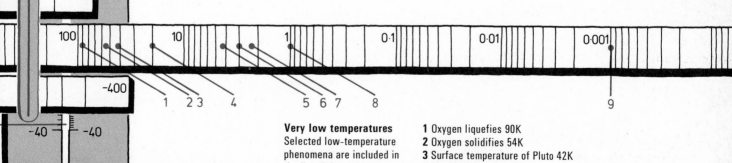

**Very low temperatures**
Selected low-temperature phenomena are included in the list *right*—with temperatures expressed in Kelvins—and also plotted on the Kelvin scale *above*.

**1** Oxygen liquefies 90K
**2** Oxygen solidifies 54K
**3** Surface temperature of Pluto 42K
**4** Hydrogen liquefies 20K
**5** Helium liquefies 4.2K
**6** Temperature of outer space 3K
**7** Helium becomes "superfluid" 2.2K
**8** Temperature reached by evaporating helium 1K
**9** Temperature reached by magnetized atomic nuclei 0.001K

©DIAGRAM

# FREEZING, MELTING AND BOILING POINTS

All matter can exist in three states: as a solid, a liquid or a gas. The particular state of matter at a given time depends on the amount of energy it contains, which is measured by its temperature. Here we compare the freezing/melting and boiling points of selected elements, with one another and with other temperature phenomena.

**In different states** *below, right* Shown here are the temperatures at which water and selected elements pass from one state to another (see key beneath the first diagram). In the lists beside the diagrams the first figure is the freezing/melting point and the second the boiling point; Celsius temperatures are given in accordance with scientific practice. The range of temperatures through which water is liquid is marked as a band (**A**) in the middle of the first diagram and at the left of the second.

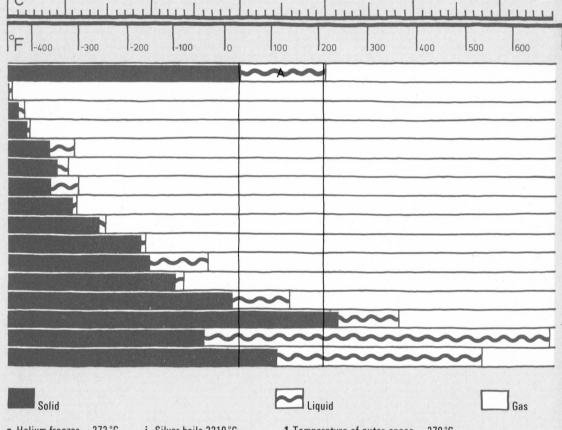

Water 0/100 °C
Helium − 272/− 269 °C
Hydrogen − 259/− 253 °C
Neon − 249/− 246 °C
Fluorine − 220/− 188 °C
Nitrogen − 210/− 196 °C
Oxygen − 219/− 183 °C
Argon − 189/− 186 °C
Krypton − 157/− 152 °C
Xenon − 112/− 107 °C
Chlorine − 101/− 35 °C
Radon − 71/− 62 °C
Bromine − 7/59 °C
Iodine 114/184 °C
Mercury − 39/357 °C
Phosphorus 44/280 °C

Solid       Liquid       Gas

**Temperatures compared**
Plotted *below* and listed *right* are freezing/melting and boiling points of elements and water (**a–p**). Other temperature phenomena (**1–8**) are also included for comparison.

**a** Helium freezes − 272 °C
**b** Water freezes 0 °C
**c** Water boils 100 °C
**d** Lead melts 328 °C
**e** Silver melts 962 °C
**f** Gold melts 1064 °C
**g** Iron melts 1536 °C
**h** Platinum melts 1772 °C

**i** Silver boils 2210 °C
**j** Gold boils 2900 °C
**k** Plutonium boils 3360 °C
**l** Carbon melts 3550 °C
**m** Platinum boils 3825 °C
**n** Molybdenum boils 4700 °C
**o** Carbon boils 4825 °C
**p** Tungsten boils 5660 °C

**1** Temperature of outer space − 270 °C
**2** Normal human body temperature 37 °C
**3** Surface temperature of Venus 480 °C
**4** Temperature of molten lava 1730 °C
**5** Surface temperature of a red star 2530 °C
**6** Surface temperature of an orange star 3860 °C
**7** Molecules break down into atoms 4730 °C
**8** Surface temperature of the Sun 5330 °C

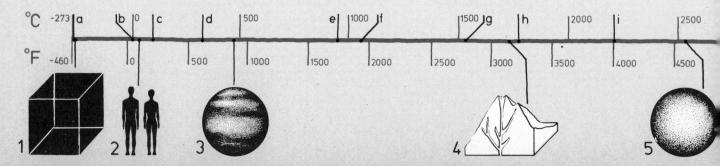

Mercury, which freezes at −39°C, is unsuitable for thermometers to be used in the coldest regions of the world. Thermometers containing pure alcohol, with a freezing point of −114°C, will record all but the very lowest freak temperatures.

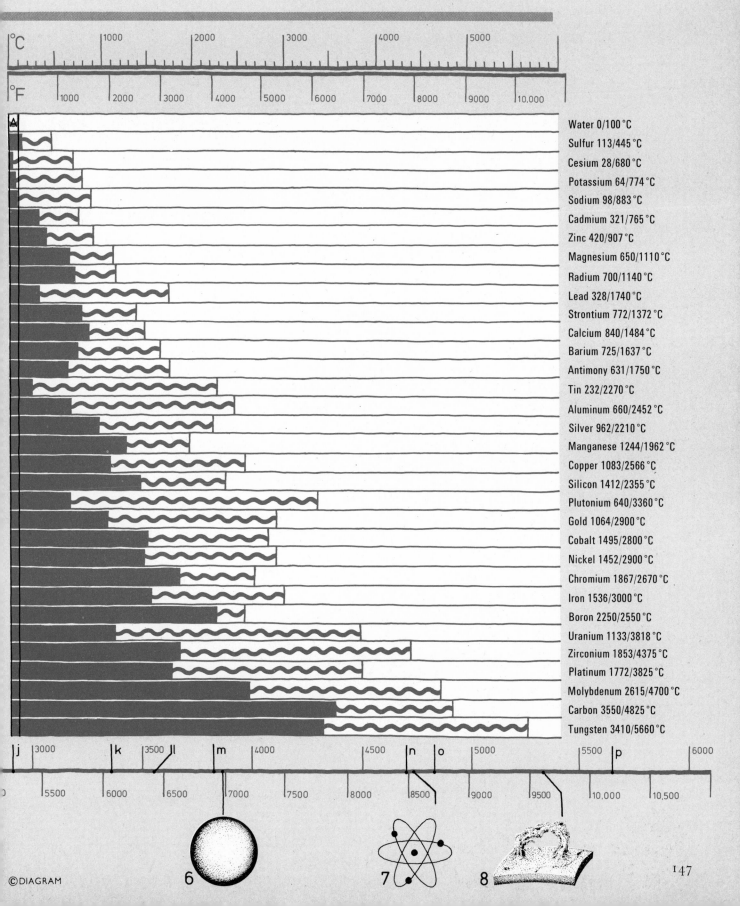

°C 1000 2000 3000 4000 5000

°F 1000 2000 3000 4000 5000 6000 7000 8000 9000 10,000

Water 0/100°C
Sulfur 113/445°C
Cesium 28/680°C
Potassium 64/774°C
Sodium 98/883°C
Cadmium 321/765°C
Zinc 420/907°C
Magnesium 650/1110°C
Radium 700/1140°C
Lead 328/1740°C
Strontium 772/1372°C
Calcium 840/1484°C
Barium 725/1637°C
Antimony 631/1750°C
Tin 232/2270°C
Aluminum 660/2452°C
Silver 962/2210°C
Manganese 1244/1962°C
Copper 1083/2566°C
Silicon 1412/2355°C
Plutonium 640/3360°C
Gold 1064/2900°C
Cobalt 1495/2800°C
Nickel 1452/2900°C
Chromium 1867/2670°C
Iron 1536/3000°C
Boron 2250/2550°C
Uranium 1133/3818°C
Zirconium 1853/4375°C
Platinum 1772/3825°C
Molybdenum 2615/4700°C
Carbon 3550/4825°C
Tungsten 3410/5660°C

j 3000 k 3500 ll m 4000 4500 n o 5000 5500 p 6000

5500 6000 6500 7000 7500 8000 8500 9000 9500 10,000 10,500

6    7    8

©DIAGRAM

# STARS AND PLANETS

Temperatures in the universe range from an estimated 3,500,000,000K for a supernova to only 3K for the temperature of outer space. Here we look at estimated surface temperatures of stars, the Sun, the planets and of our Moon. Also compared are estimated interior temperatures of the Sun, Earth and Jupiter.

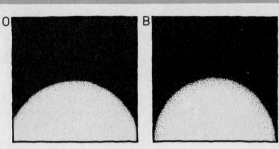

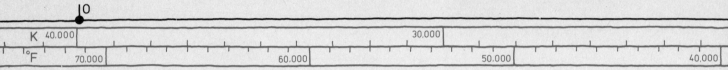

**Temperatures of stars**
Illustrated *top* are examples of different types of star, identified by letters relating to their classification by color. Plotted on the scale *above* and listed in the table *right* are calculated "surface" temperatures for typical stars of each class.

There is a clear relationship between a star's color and its surface temperature; blue-white stars are very much hotter than stars with a maximum emission at the orange-red end of the color spectrum. Our Sun is a class G yellow star.

| Class | Color | Effective surface temperature | |
|-------|-------|---------|---------|
| O | Blue-white | 40,000K | 71,500 °F |
| B | Blue-white | 15,500K | 27,400 °F |
| A | White | 8500K | 14,800 °F |
| F | Yellow-white | 6580K | 11,380 °F |
| G | Yellow | 5520K | 9480 °F |
| K | Orange | 4130K | 6970 °F |
| M | Red | 2800K | 4580 °F |

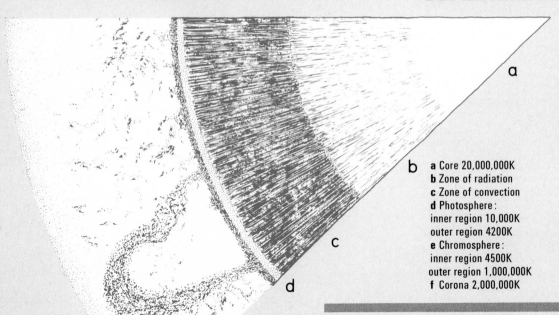

a Core 20,000,000K
b Zone of radiation
c Zone of convection
d Photosphere:
inner region 10,000K
outer region 4200K
e Chromosphere:
inner region 4500K
outer region 1,000,000K
f Corona 2,000,000K

**Solar temperatures** *left*
This section diagram shows the zones produced as energy travels outward from the Sun's core (**a**). The list beside the diagram identifies the different zones and gives estimated temperatures in Kelvins. The chromosphere (**e**) and the corona (**f**) have higher temperatures than some zones nearer to the Sun's core, a consequence of the frictional action and high velocity of particles within these outer zones. The temperature of the Sun's "surface" (within the photosphere) is usually taken as 5600K (9620 °F).

*The Sun, a class G yellow star, has an estimated surface temperature of 5600K. This makes it twice as hot as a typical class M red star, but only just over one seventh as hot as a typical class O, blue-white star.*

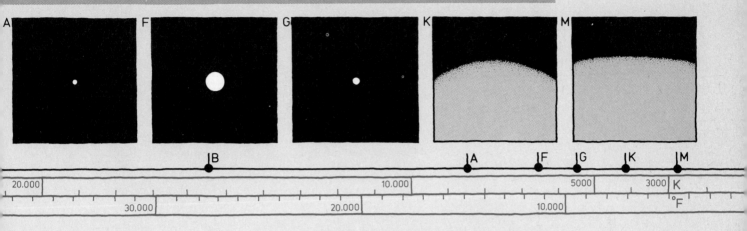

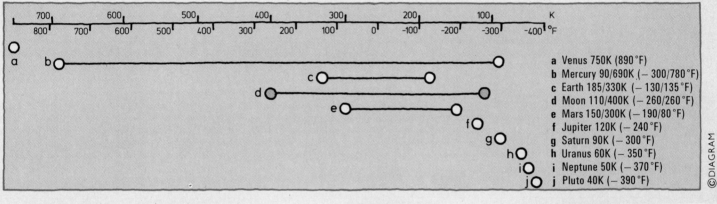

**a** Venus 750K (890 °F)
**b** Mercury 90/690K (− 300/780 °F)
**c** Earth 185/330K (− 130/135 °F)
**d** Moon 110/400K (− 260/260 °F)
**e** Mars 150/300K (− 190/80 °F)
**f** Jupiter 120K (− 240 °F)
**g** Saturn 90K (− 300 °F)
**h** Uranus 60K (− 350 °F)
**i** Neptune 50K (− 370 °F)
**j** Pluto 40K (− 390 °F)

©DIAGRAM

**Hot and cold planets**
*above* Compared here are estimated surface temperatures of the planets and of our Moon. For the four dense inner planets and Moon (**a–e**) we give temperatures for the solid surface. For the four huge low-density outer planets (**f–i**) and for distant Pluto (**j**), the generally accepted cloud "surface" temperatures are given.

**Inside stories** *right*
Here we compare estimated temperatures for Earth (**1**) and Jupiter (**2**). The core of Jupiter is believed to be over six times hotter than Earth's core, whereas its "surface" is more than twice as cold as Earth's.
**1 Earth temperature**
**a** Core 4500K (7600 °F)
**b** Base of mantle 3300K (5500 °F)
**c** Surface (average) 295K (70 °F)
**2 Jupiter temperature**
**a** Core 30,000K (53,500 °F)
**b** Top of inner layer of liquid hydrogen 11,000K (19,300 °F)
**c** Surface 120K (− 240 °F)

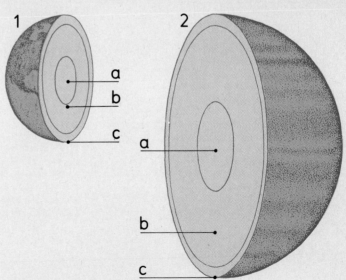

The rock temperature at the bottom of the deepest (12,600ft) mine on Earth, the Western Deep Levels Mine in S Africa's Transvaal, is 328K (131 °F). The hole temperature at the bottom of the 31,441ft-deep drilling in Washita County, Oklahoma, USA is 519K (475 °F).

# EARTH 1

On these pages we compare temperatures at different heights within Earth's atmosphere and look at general patterns of world temperature distribution. Also included for comparison are some of the hottest and coldest temperatures ever recorded on Earth, ranging from 136.4°F (58°C) to −126.9°F (−88.3°C).

**Lofty temperatures** *right*
Indicated on this diagram are the temperature characteristics of regions within Earth's atmosphere. In the lowest region, the troposphere, temperature drops about 3°F (1.7°C) for every 1000ft (305m) of altitude. Temperature then rises in the stratosphere, falls in the mesosphere and rises again in the thermosphere. The wide range of temperature at the thermopause is accounted for by differences in solar activity, at night and during the day.

**Curve and effect** *left*
This diagram shows how temperature is affected by the curve of Earth's surface. In Polar regions the Sun's rays (**a,c**) are diffused over a greater area—and are therefore less effective— than they are near the Equator (**b**).

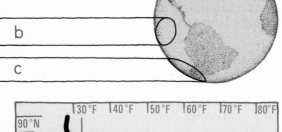

**Ocean temperatures** *left*
This diagram allows us to compare average annual mid-ocean surface temperatures at different latitudes. The curve of Earth's surface results in a general decrease in temperature toward the Poles (see diagram *above*), but other factors—such as the distribution of large land masses—modify the general pattern. Thus the highest temperatures are at 10°N and not at the Equator, and the decrease of temperature toward the Poles does not occur at a constant rate.

The East Sahara is the sunniest place on Earth, with an annual average of over 97% sunshine in daylight hours. The least sunny place is the North Pole, where no sun is recorded for winter stretches lasting 186 days.

**Exosphere**
Normal idea of temperature no longer applies

**Thermopau**
630–2700°F (330–1500°C

**Thermosphere**
Temperature rises with altitude

**Mesosphere**
Temperature falls with altitude

**Mesopause**
−171°F (113

**Stratosphere**
Temperature rises with altitude

**Stratopause**
32°F (0°C)

**Troposphere**
Temperature falls

**Tropopause**
−90°F (−68

km
500

mi
300

400

200

300

200

100

100

*The hottest place on Earth is Dallol in Ethiopia, with an annual average temperature of 94°F (34.4°C). The coldest place is Polus Nedostupnosti in Antarctica, with an annual average of −72°F (−57.8°C).*

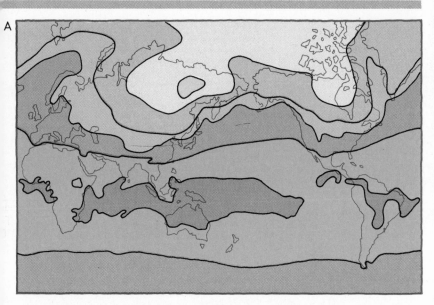

A

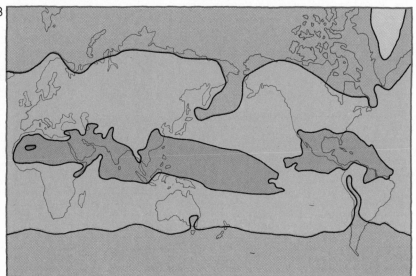

B

**136.4°F (58°C)**
The hottest temperature ever recorded on Earth, at Al'Aziziyah, Libya.

**134.0°F (56.7°C)**
N. America's hottest recorded temperature, in Death Valley, California.

**127.6°F (53.1°C)**
Australia's hottest recorded temperature, at Cloncurry, Queensland.

**114.8°F (46°C)**
The hottest recorded temperature in Europe (excluding the USSR), at Cordoba, Spain.

**−49°F (−45°C)**
The coldest recorded temperature in Europe (excluding the USSR), at Sodankylä, Finland.

**−72.9°F (−58.3°C)**
N. America's coldest recorded temperature, at Floeberg Bay, Ellesmere Island, Canada.

**−90.4°F (−68.0°C)**
The coldest recorded temperature outside Antarctica, at Oymyakon, Siberia, USSR.

**−126.9°F (−88.3°C)**
The coldest temperature ever recorded on Earth, at Vostok, Antarctica.

**Worldwide temperatures**
*above* These maps show the areas of the world that have similar mean air temperatures (see the thermometer key *right*) for the months of January (map **A**) and July (map **B**). Notice how the distribution of land masses and oceans distorts the general pattern of temperature decrease toward the Poles. Differences between winter and summer temperatures are less marked over the oceans than over large land masses; compare, for example, the S Pacific with the Eurasian land mass.

**Temperature thermometer**
*right* The colored bars on this Celsius/Fahrenheit thermometer serve as a key to the temperature maps *above*. Indicated to the *right* of the thermometer are some of the hottest and coldest temperatures ever recorded on Earth.

**The hottest shade temperature ever recorded, at Al'Aziziyah, Libya is some 263°F (146°C) hotter than the coldest screen temperature ever recorded, at Vostok, Antarctica.**

©DIAGRAM

# EARTH 2

A city's annual temperature pattern depends first on latitude, and then on modifying factors such as its distance from the moderating influence of the sea and its altitude. Here we compare the monthly average temperatures and annual temperature ranges of representative cities from each continent.

**City temperatures** *below*
The graphs show monthly averages of maximum daily temperatures for selected cities in each continent. The cities are listed at the bottom of the page, where their latitudes are given to the nearest degree. Maps above the graphs show the

cities' locations. Our selection illustrates the temperature patterns found in each continent. Mid- or high-latitude cities in the heart of large continents show the most pronounced temperature curves. Cities in low latitudes show the smallest monthly variations.

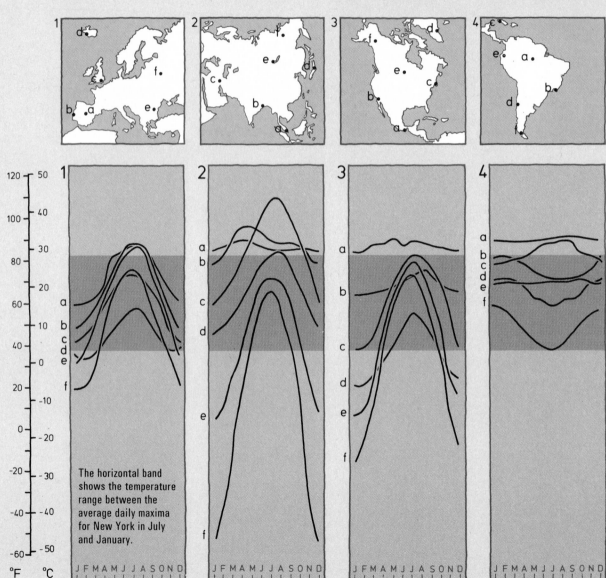

The horizontal band shows the temperature range between the average daily maxima for New York in July and January.

**1 Europe**
**a** Madrid, Spain 40°N
**b** Lisbon, Portugal 38°N
**c** London, England 51°N
**d** Reykjavik, Iceland 64°N
**e** Bucharest, Romania 44°N
**f** Moscow, USSR 55°N

**2 Asia**
**a** Singapore 1°N
**b** Calcutta, India 22°N
**c** Baghdad, Iraq 33°N
**d** Tokyo, Japan 35°N
**e** Irkutsk, USSR 52°N
**f** Verkhoyansk, USSR 67°N

**3 North America**
**a** Salina Cruz, Mexico 16°N
**b** San Diego, USA 32°N
**c** New York, USA 40°N
**d** Angmagssalik, Greenland 65°N
**e** Winnipeg, Canada 50°N
**f** Dawson City, Canada 64°N

**4 South America**
**a** Manaus, Brazil 3°S
**b** Rio de Janeiro, Brazil 23°S
**c** Havana, Cuba 23°N
**d** Valparaiso, Chile 33°S
**e** Quito, Ecuador 0°
**f** Punta Arenas, Chile 53°S

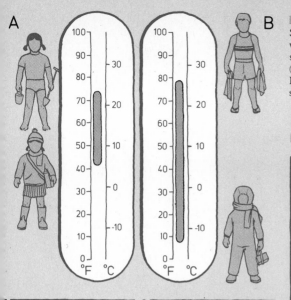

**A**  **B**

Similar clothing can be worn on a typical summer's day in London (**A**) and in Winnipeg (**B**). But winter clothing suitable for London would be totally inadequate to cope with Winnipeg's average daily maximum temperatures in winter, even though the two cities are on similar latitudes.

# Temperature

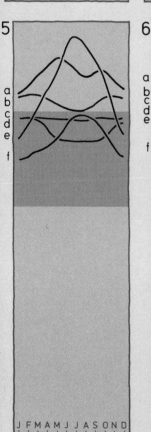

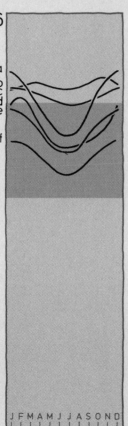

| City | Temperatures | | Range | |
|------|----------|-----------|---------|---------|
| **2f** Verkhoyansk | −54/65 °F | −47/18 °C | 119 °F | 65 °C |
| **3f** Dawson City | −16/72 °F | −27/22 °C | 88 °F | 49 °C |
| **3e** Winnipeg | 7/78 °F | −14/26 °C | 71 °F | 40 °C |
| **1f** Moscow | 20/75 °F | −7/24 °C | 55 °F | 31 °C |
| **5e** Ain Salah | 69/117 °F | 21/47 °C | 48 °F | 26 °C |
| **3c** New York | 38/82 °F | 3/28 °C | 44 °F | 25 °C |
| **6a** Alice Springs | 67/98 °F | 19/37 °C | 31 °F | 18 °C |
| **1c** London | 42/73 °F | 6/23 °C | 31 °F | 17 °C |
| **1d** Reykjavik | 34/57 °F | 1/14 °C | 23 °F | 13 °C |
| **4f** Punta Arenas | 37/59 °F | 3/15 °C | 22 °F | 12 °C |
| **6e** Sydney | 59/79 °F | 15/26 °C | 20 °F | 11 °C |
| **2b** Calcutta | 78/96 °F | 26/36 °C | 18 °F | 10 °C |
| **5a** Khartoum | 89/107 °F | 32/42 °C | 18 °F | 10 °C |
| **6f** Dunedin | 48/65 °F | 9/18 °C | 17 °F | 9 °C |
| **5d** Cape Town | 68/80 °F | 20/27 °C | 12 °F | 7 °C |
| **4b** Rio de Janeiro | 72/82 °F | 22/28 °C | 10 °F | 6 °C |
| **5b** Freetown | 83/91 °F | 28/33 °C | 8 °F | 5 °C |
| **2a** Singapore | 85/89 °F | 29/32 °C | 4 °F | 3 °C |
| **4e** Quito | 68/71 °F | 20/22 °C | 3 °F | 2 °C |

**Great and small ranges**
The table *left* and the bar diagram *below left* show the annual temperature ranges of some of our cities, here ranked according to their size of range. The top of each bar marks the average daily maximum temperature for the hottest month; the bottom of each bar marks the same for the coldest month. Verkhoyansk has a much greater range (119 °F, 65 °C) than any other major weather station in any continent. Asia, S America and Africa all have stations with very small ranges (less than 5 °F / 3 °C).

**5**  **6**

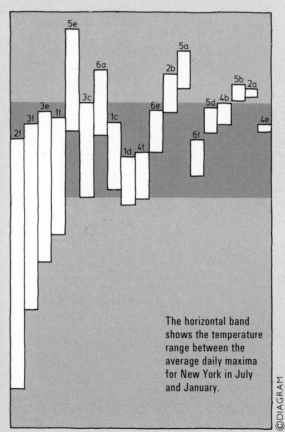

The horizontal band shows the temperature range between the average daily maxima for New York in July and January.

J F M A M J J A S O N D   J F M A M J J A S O N D

©DIAGRAM

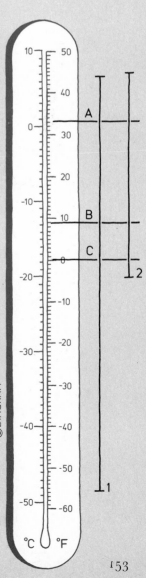

**5 Africa**
**a** Khartoum, Sudan 15 °N
**b** Freetown, Sierra Leone 8 °N
**c** Entebbe, Uganda 0°
**d** Cape Town, South Africa 33 °S
**e** Ain Salah, Algeria 27 °N
**f** Algiers, Algeria 36 °N

**6 Oceania**
**a** Alice Springs, Australia 23 °S
**b** Darwin, Australia 12 °S
**c** Port Moresby, Papua New Guinea 9 °S
**d** Perth, Australia 32 °S
**e** Sydney, Australia 34 °S
**f** Dunedin, New Zealand 46 °S

**Extreme days** *right*
Record movements of temperature are compared here with daily average temperatures for January.
**1** At Browning, Montana, USA on January 23–24, 1916, the temperature fell 100 °F (55.5 °C), from 44 °F (6.7 °C) to −56 °F (−48.8 °C).

**2** At Spearfish, S Dakota, USA, on January 22, 1943, the temperature rose 49 °F (27.2 °C) in 2 minutes, from −4 °F (−20 °C) to 45 °F (7.2 °C).

**A** New York 33.3 °F (0.7 °C).
**B** Moscow 9 °F (−12.7 °C).
**C** Winnipeg 0.1 °F (−17.7 °C).

153

# BODY TEMPERATURES

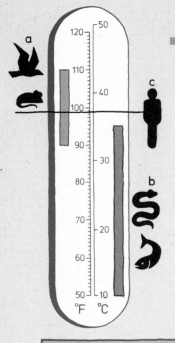

All animals need heat to keep their bodies alive. But some need or tolerate higher temperatures than others. Certain desert lizards can scamper over sun-baked rocks hot enough to fry an egg on. Built-in antifreeze enables the Antarctic ice fish to swim happily in water cold enough to turn ordinary blood to ice.

**Temperature ranges** *left*
The body temperatures of most warm-blooded animals fall within a fairly narrow range (**a**). The range of ideal temperatures for most cold-blooded animals is both wider and lower (**b**). The horizontal line marks man's normal temperature (**c**).

**In a class of their own**
Plotted *right* on the thermometers and listed in the tables are normal body temperatures of some warm-blooded animals (mammals **A**, birds **B**), and also ideal temperatures of some cold-blooded ones (reptiles **C**, amphibians and fish **D**).

| A) Mammals | | |
|---|---|---|
| **1** Goat | 103.8°F | 39.9°C |
| **2** Domestic rabbit | 101.3°F | 38.5°C |
| **3** Northern fur seal | 99.9°F | 37.7°C |
| **4** Polar bear | 99.1°F | 37.3°C |
| **5** Man | 98.6°F | 37.0°C |
| **6** African elephant | 97.5°F | 36.4°C |
| **7** Blue whale | 95.9°F | 35.5°C |
| **8** Three-toed sloth | 91.7°F | 33.2°C |
| **9** Spiny anteater | 73.9°F | 23.3°C |

| B) Birds | | |
|---|---|---|
| **10** Western pewee | 112.6°F | 44.8°C |
| **11** Canada jay | 109.4°F | 43.0°C |
| **12** House sparrow | 105.8°F | 41.0°C |
| **13** Wandering albatross | 105.3°F | 40.7°C |
| **14** Owl | 104.4°F | 40.2°C |
| **15** Hummingbird | 104.2°F | 40.1°C |
| **16** Ostrich | 102.6°F | 39.2°C |
| **17** King penguin | 99.9°F | 37.7°C |
| **18** Arctic gull | 93.2°F | 34.0°C |

**A) Mammals** *left*
Mammals have "thermostats" that help keep their bodies at a constant temperature. Heat produced by "burning" food is kept inside the body by fur. Surplus heat is lost by sweating, panting, or by convection, conduction, or radiation from the skin.

**B) Birds** *left*
Birds "burn" food fast to provide energy for flying, so their temperatures tend to be higher than mammals'. Of both sets of warm-blooded creatures listed, only one flying bird (**18**) is cooler than (**1**), the hottest-blooded mammal indicated.

**Hibernation** *left*
Shown are falls in body temperature survived by five warm-blooded creatures hibernating in cold weather. (Low body temperatures save energy and may prolong life when food is scarce.)
**a** Poor-will 104–64°F
**b** Dormouse 98.6–35.6°F
**c** Opossum 95–50.9°F
**d** Common hamster 110–43°F
**e** Marmot 107–50°F
Hibernating mammals can raise their temperatures to avoid freezing. But hibernating amphibians seem immune to frostbite.

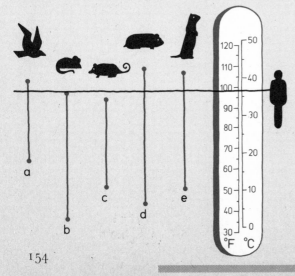

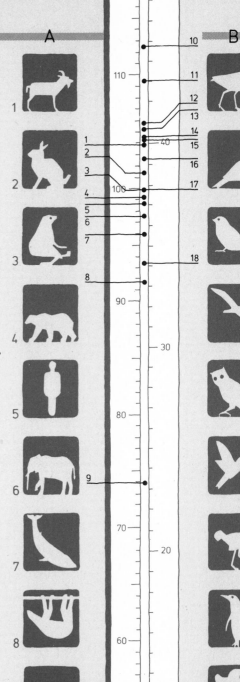

A    B

**Temperature ranges** *right*
Shown is the range of body temperature survived by six kinds of animal. Man's normal body temperature is included—as a horizontal line—for comparison.
**a** Crocodile 73.4–84.2 °F
**b** Catfish 42.8–93.2 °F
**c** Ascaphus frog 39.9–60.3 °F
**d** Horned lizard 77–113 °F
**e** Salamander 42.4–79.7 °F
**f** Garter snake 39.6–102 °F
Crocodiles tolerate only a small temperature change. Catfish and garter snakes survive the greatest fluctuations. The Ascaphus frog dies of overheating at temperatures that can kill a man with cold.

**C) Reptiles** *right*
Many of these reptiles are most active when their body temperatures exceed 90 °F. But cold-blooded animals lack internal temperature controls. To keep an even temperature they must bask as the Sun rises, then hide in shade to cool down.

**D) Amphibians/fish** *right*
Most amphibians and fish are active at lower body temperatures than most reptiles. This applies especially to coldwater fish and to amphibians from cool climates. Most listed species thrive at below the given temperatures.

**Environments** *right*
**a** 104 °F (40 °C) desert habitat of rattlesnake.
**b** 93.9 °F (34.4 °C) Dallol, Ethiopia, the hottest town.
**c** 84.2 °F (29 °C) grassland habitat of red kangaroo.
**d** 69.8 °F (21 °C) lowest water temperature survived by coral-building polyps.
**e** 28.4 °F (−2 °C) average heat of Antarctic ocean surface, home of penguins.
**f** −58 °F (−50 °C) winter survived by arctic fox.
**g** −94 °F (−70 °C) winter survived by musk ox.
**h** −96 °F (−71.1 °C) record low at Oymyakon, USSR, coldest permanent town.

**Man's temperature range**
*above* Compared are man's normal body temperature (horizontal line) and the survived extremes of 112 °F and 60.8 °F (**g**). To survive such extremes is very rare; most individuals would die of hyperthermia (overheating) or hypothermia (overcooling).

| C) Reptiles | | |
|---|---|---|
| **19** Spiny lizard | 98.4 °F | 36.9 °C |
| **20** Ornate lizard | 96.8 °F | 36.0 °C |
| **21** Horned lizard | 95.0 °F | 35.0 °C |
| **22** Australian bearded lizard | 94.6 °F | 34.8 °C |
| **23** Nocturnal Saharan viper | 91.4 °F | 33.0 °C |
| **24** Australian shingle-back skink | 90.9 °F | 32.7 °C |
| **25** Indian python | 83.5 °F | 28.6 °C |
| **26** Crocodile | 78.1 °F | 25.6 °C |
| **27** Common garter snake | 70.9 °F | 21.6 °C |

| D) Amphibians/fish | | |
|---|---|---|
| **28** Mozambique rain frog | 79.7 °F | 26.5 °C |
| **29** North American bullfrog | 76.5 °F | 24.7 °C |
| **30** Large-mouthed black bass | 75.2 °F | 24.0 °C |
| **31** Goldfish | 74.3 °F | 23.5 °C |
| **32** Catfish | 68.0 °F | 20.0 °C |
| **33** Mole salamander | 62.6 °F | 17.0 °C |
| **34** Yellow perch | 60.8 °F | 16.0 °C |
| **35** Lungless salamander | 58.6 °F | 14.8 °C |
| **36** Ascaphus frog | 50.0 °F | 10.1 °C |

©DIAGRAM

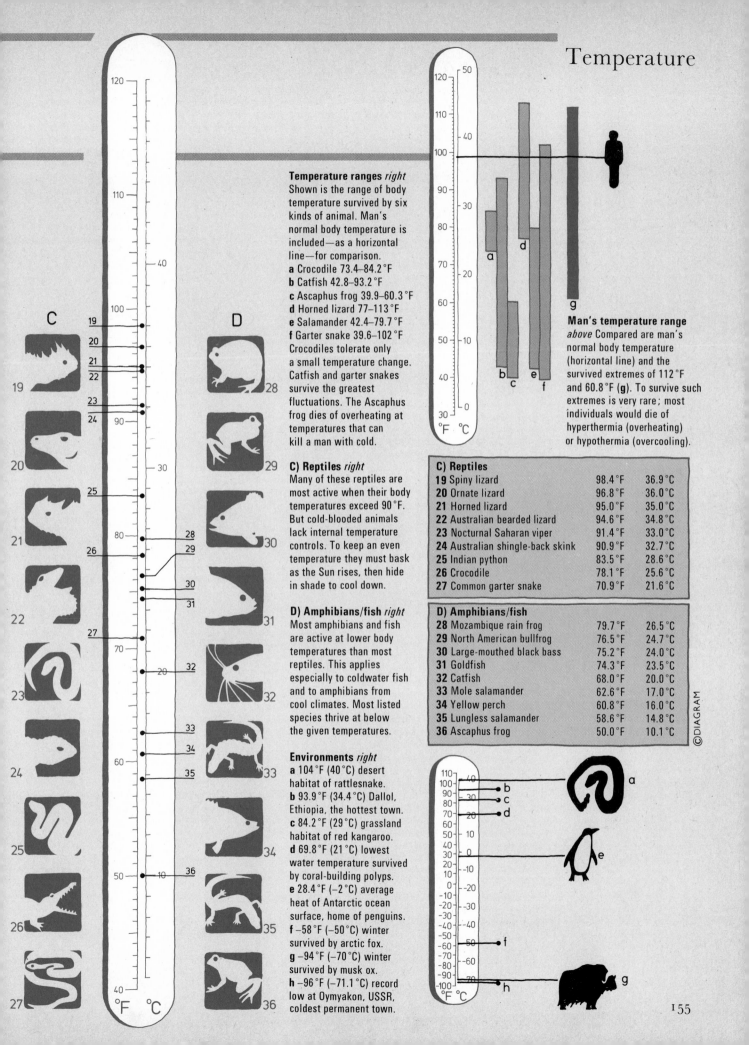

# CHAPTER 8

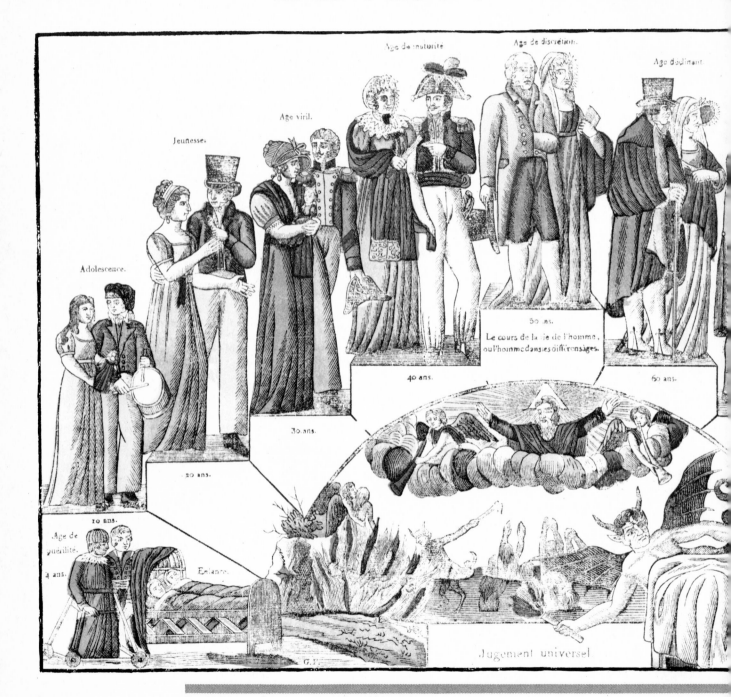

This 19th-century French popular print uses a staircase to demonstrate the stages in a couple's life. From infancy, they ascend through childhood, adolescence, youth, virility and maturity to reach a peak at the age of discretion. Thereafter they go into decline, to pass through decadence, frailty and decrepitude before returning again to infancy.

# TIME

ES.

de décadence.

Age caduc.

Age de décrépitude

80 ans.

90 ans.

100 ans.
Age d'imbécilité
ou d'enfance.

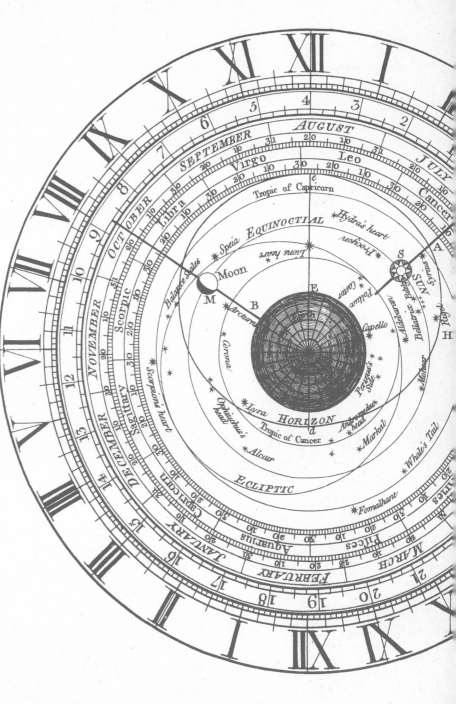

An illustration of an
elaborate clock face from
the second edition (1778)
of *Mechanical Exercises*,
an important work on
horology by the British
inventor James Ferguson.

# MEASURING TIME 1

Time can be measured by motion, and it was the motion of Earth, Moon, Sun and stars that provided man with his first means of measuring time. Accurate lengths for the basic units of day, month and year were known thousands of years ago, even though the astronomical factors on which they were based were improperly understood.

| Sidereal year | 365.25636556 days | (365d 6h 9m 10s) |
|---|---|---|
| Anomalistic year | 365.25964134 days | (365d 6h 13m 53s) |
| Tropical year | 365.242198781 days | (365d 5h 48m 45s) |
| | | |
| Sidereal month | 27.32166 days | (27d 7h 43m 11s) |
| Tropical month | 27.32158 days | (27d 7h 43m 5s) |
| Synodic month | 29.53059 days | (29d 12h 44m 3s) |
| | | |
| Mean solar day | 1 day | (24h) |
| Sidereal day | 0.997269 day | (23h 56m 4s) |

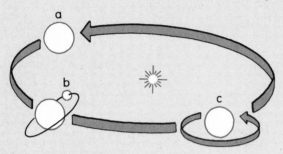

**Years, months, days** *left*
In simple terms, a year is the time it takes Earth to orbit once around the Sun (**a**), a month is the time it takes the Moon to make one orbit of Earth (**b**), and a day is the time it takes Earth to rotate once on its axis (**c**).

**Complex timetable** *above*
Different techniques of measurement give differing lengths for years, months and days. Sidereal times are calculated with reference to fixed stars. An anomalistic year requires Earth's orbit to be measured from the perihelion or aphelion (p. 29).

Tropical measurements refer to the apparent passage of the Sun and the actual passage of the Moon across Earth's equatorial plane. A synodic month is based on the phases of the Moon. A mean solar day relates to periods of darkness and light averaged over a year.

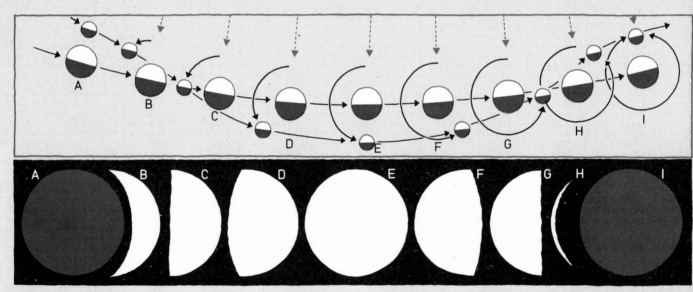

**Synodic month** *above*
Observation of the phases of the Moon has given man the time unit known as a synodic month. One full cycle of the Moon's phases takes approximately 29½ days. We illustrate how the Moon appears to us on selected nights within a month (**A–I**), and link this to a diagram showing the relative positions of Moon and Earth at different times in the month. The Moon always presents the same face to Earth, but the amount visible depends on how much of it is facing—and thus lit by—the Sun.

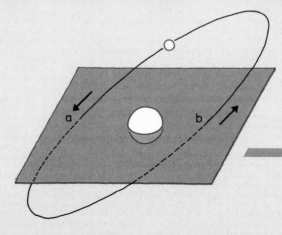

**Tropical month** *left*
The period of time known as a tropical month is approximately 27⅓ days long (compared to the 29½ days of a synodic month). As shown in the diagram, a tropical month is the period of time from when the orbiting Moon once passes through the plane of Earth's Equator to the next time that it passes through that plane in the same direction (**a** to **a** or **b** to **b**). It is measured with reference to the Moon's position in the sky, and is very close in length to a sidereal month.

**There is a difference of more than two days between the length of a month measured by observing the phases of the Moon (a synodic month, 29½ days) and a month measured by noting the return of the Moon to a certain point in the sky (a tropical month, 27⅓ days).**

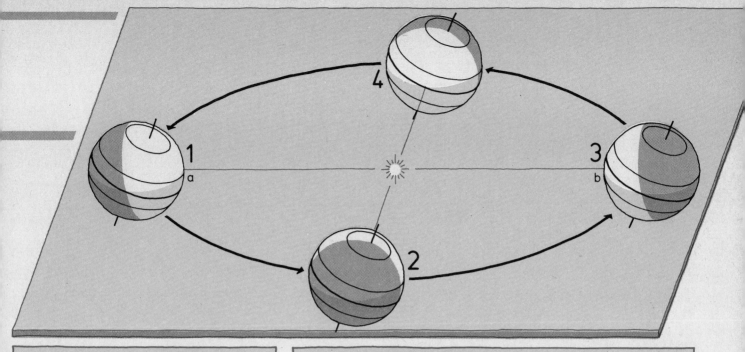

| | Date | Northern hemisphere | Southern hemisphere |
|---|---|---|---|
| 1 | June 21 | Summer solstice | Winter solstice |
| 2 | September 23 | Autumn equinox | Vernal (spring) equinox |
| 3 | December 22 | Winter solstice | Summer solstice |
| 4 | March 21 | Vernal (spring) equinox | Autumn equinox |

©DIAGRAM

**Years and seasons** *above*
The period of approximately
365¼ days that we know as
a year was discovered by
careful observation of the
Sun's apparent path through
the sky. Our diagram shows
Earth at four points in its
orbit, corresponding to the
seasons (see left-hand table).

Seasonal variations in
insolation result from the
inclination (23° 27') of
Earth's axis to its plane of
rotation around the Sun.
Parts of the globe tilted
away from the Sun receive
less radiant energy per unit
area than those receiving
rays more directly (p. 150).

**Equinox and solstice**
*above* The inclination of
Earth to its plane of rotation
around the Sun also
produces variations in the
relative lengths of "day"
and "night" at different
times of the year. The
right-hand table beneath
the diagram gives the dates

at which Earth is in the
positions shown, and lists
the solstices and equinoxes
that occur on the different
dates. Solstices are when
the Sun appears to be
overhead at midday at the
maximum distance North
and South of the Equator,
currently on the two Tropics

(**a**, **b**). Days are longest
and nights are shortest at
the summer solstice, and
vice versa at the winter
solstice. At the equinoxes—
when day and night are
everywhere equal—the Sun
appears directly overhead
at midday at the Equator.

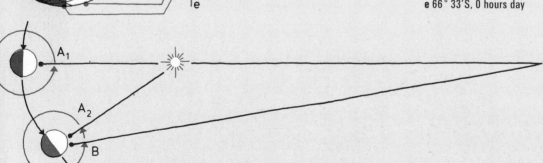

a 66° 33'N, 24 hours day
b 49° 3'N, 16 hours day
c Equator (0°), 12 hours day
d 49° 3'S, 8 hours day
e 66° 33'S, 0 hours day

**Longest and shortest days**
*left* Here we compare day
lengths at different latitudes
on June 21. On this date,
places in the Northern
hemisphere have their
maximum, and places in the
Southern hemisphere their
minimum, number of hours
of daylight.

**Day by day** *left*
A day measured by the Sun
(ie the time between the
Sun being at the same point
overhead on two successive
days, $A_1$–$A_2$) is longer than
a sidereal day (the time
between a distant star being
at the same point on two
successive days, $A_1$–$B$).

*It could be said that the North and South Poles have
only one "day" a year—made up of six months of
daylight and six months of darkness.*

# MEASURING TIME 2

On the preceding two pages we looked at the astronomically based units of the day, the month and the year. Here we turn to "man-made" units, starting with multiples of years and days and going on to the various subdivisions of a day that have developed with the invention of increasingly accurate instruments for measuring time.

| | |
|---|---|
| 1 day (d) = | 24 hours (h, hr) |
| 1 day = | 1440 minutes (m, min, ') |
| 1 day = | 86,400 seconds (s, sec, '') |
| 1 hour = | 0.0417 of a day |
| 1 hour = | 60 minutes |
| 1 hour = | 3600 seconds |
| 1 minute = | 0.0006944 of a day |
| 1 minute = | 60 seconds |
| 1 second = | 0.0000115 of a day |

| | |
|---|---|
| Millennium | 1000yr |
| Half-millennium | 500yr |
| Century | 100yr |
| Half-century | 50yr |
| Decade | 10yr |
| Half-decade | 5yr |

**Years and years** *left*
Listed here are some widely used names for periods of more than one year. Decade is derived from the Greek *deka* and the Latin *decem* meaning 10, century comes from the Latin *centuria*, whereas *millennium* is itself a Latin word for 1000 years.

**Short and long weeks** *right*
**a** 4-day intervals were formerly used in W Africa.
**b** The ancient Assyrians had weeks of 6 days.
**c** The 7-day week came to us from the ancient Babylonians and Jews.
**d** The French Revolutionary calendar had a 10-day week.

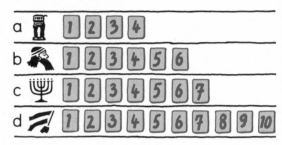

**Hours in a day** *left*
To measure the 24 hours in a day the hour hand of a conventional clock must make two full revolutions. Our diagram also shows the two systems of counting the hours, giving 24-hour clock equivalents for the morning and afternoon hours.

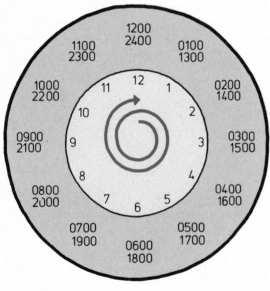

**Minutes and seconds** *right*
Here we use two dials to show the division of clock faces into the 60 sections used to measure minutes and seconds. The minute hand (**a**) makes one revolution in an hour, and the second hand (**b**) makes one in a minute and thus 60 in an hour.

**Toward improved precision** *right* Some important inventions in the history of time-keeping devices are listed here with their dates and then plotted against a logarithmic scale showing their average error in seconds or parts of a second per day.

**a** Mechanical clock c. 1280
**b** Pendulum clock c. 1650
**c** Mercury vial pendulum clock c. 1720
**d** Clocks with barometric compensation c. 1810
**e** Free-swinging pendulum clock c. 1910
**f** Quartz crystal clock 1929
**g** Cesium clock 1952

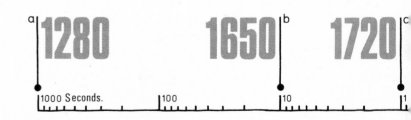

A medieval cook could get into a lot of trouble if he followed a modern recipe requiring him to cook a dish for an hour—for until the development of the mechanical clock, an "hour" was longer in summer than it was in winter. Whatever the relative length of daylight and darkness, the day was divided into 12 daytime and 12 nighttime hours.

**A stopped clock shows the correct time on two occasions per day. This record is beaten only by a clock whose hands turn very much too quickly.**

**Units and equivalents** *left*
This table gives the basic subdivisions of a day, with abbreviations in brackets the first time each unit appears. (The abbreviations h, m and s are officially preferred except where m might be confused for meters.)

| | | |
|---|---|---|
| 1 terasecond (Ts) | = $10^{12}$s | = 31689 years |
| 1 gigasecond (Gs) | = $10^9$s | = 31.7 years |
| 1 megasecond (Ms) | = $10^6$s | = 11.6 days |
| 1 kilosecond (ks) | = $10^3$s | = 16.67 minutes |
| 1 millisecond (ms) | = $10^{-3}$s | = 0.001s |
| 1 microsecond ($\mu$s) | = $10^{-6}$s | = 0.000001s |
| 1 nanosecond (ns) | = $10^{-9}$s | = 0.000000001s |
| 1 picosecond (ps) | = $10^{-12}$s | = 0.000000000001s |
| 1 femtosecond (fs) | = $10^{-15}$s | = 0.000000000000001s |
| 1 attosecond (as) | = $10^{-18}$s | = 0.000000000000000001s |

**Seconds of various lengths**
If seconds are defined in terms of the length of a day (1/86400), then they are subject to the same variations as the day (see p. 158). Thus, for example, one sidereal second is approximately 0.997269 of a mean solar second.

**A standard second** *right*
The International System (SI) now takes the second as its base unit for time, defining it as 9,192,631,770 oscillations of a Cesium-133 atom. Here we give the equivalents of an SI second in mean solar seconds (**a**) and sidereal seconds (**b**).

a $1 = 1.000001$

b $1 = 1.00274$

**Table of seconds** *left*
As this table indicates, a consequence of greater precision in the measuring of seconds has been the application to them of offical metric suffixes. Names are here followed by their abbreviations and equivalents.

**A decimal clock** *right*
Here we show an unusual clock face (**1**) devised to measure time according to a decimalized time system. Although unlikely to catch on, it does provide some interesting comparisons. The clock has three hands.
**A** The deciday hand makes one revolution each day, marking off 10 decidays (each equal to 2.4 hours).
**B** The centiday hand makes 10 revolutions in a day, each of them marking off 10 centidays (each 14.4 minutes) and 100 millidays.
**C** The fastest hand makes 1000 revolutions a day, one each milliday (86.4 seconds).

**Two-timing** *left*
The hands on these two clock faces show the same time of day. The decimal clock (**1**) expresses it as 2 decidays 3 centidays and 5 millidays (see explanation to *left* of the clock faces). The hands on the conventional clock (**2**) show the equivalent time of 05h 38m 24s.

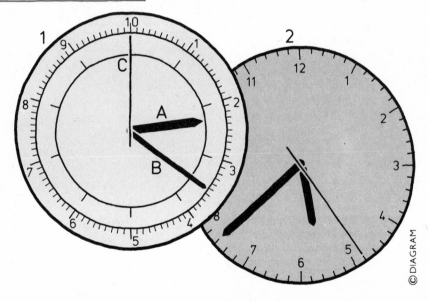

©DIAGRAM

**1810** d    **1910** e    **1929** f    **1952** g

0·1    0·01    0·001    0·0001    0·00001    0·000001

*A clock that is losing 30 minutes a day will show the correct time once every 24 days, but a clock that is losing only one-thousandth of a second per day will be correct only once every 118,275 years.*

# CALENDARS

Most calendars represent an attempt to measure easily the days and parts of days counted in observations of the changing positions in the sky of the Sun or Moon (see pages 158–159). Here we make comparisons between different calendars and also look at some of the events used as starting points when counting years.

| | | |
|---|---|---|
| **A** | Jewish religion's date for the Creation | 3761BC |
| **B** | Starting point for the Mayan "Long Count" | 3111BC |
| **C** | Era named for Kali, consort of the god Siva | 3102BC |
| **D** | Introduction of current Chinese year system | c.1600BC |
| **E** | Date for the founding of the city of Rome | 753BC |
| **F** | Date taken to be that of the Buddha's birth | 544BC |
| **G** | Date adopted as that of the birth of Christ | 1AD |
| **H** | Traditional date for the flight of Mohammed | 622AD |
| **I** | Declaration of the 1st French Republic | 1792AD |

**The beginnings of time**
The table *above* and the diagram *below* show years—reckoned in Christian or Common Era terms—that have been taken as starting points for the counting of years. Most are dates of religious significance, but others (**D, E, I**) have secular origins. Some are still in use (**A, D, F, G, H**), but others lost favor (**C, E, I**), or died with a civilization (**B**).

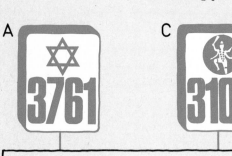

**Year upon year** *left*
Comparisons for 1980–81AD.
**a** 1980AD, starts January 1, lasts 366 days.
**b** Chinese year, starts our February 16, lasts 355 days.
**c** Jewish year, starts our September 11, lasts 383 days.
**d** Muslim year, starts our November 9, lasts 355 days.

**Year of Our Lord 1980**
*right* English names for the months are followed here by the number of days that they contain in 1980, a 366-day "leap" year. The calendar system described here is now more widely used than any other. Known as the Gregorian calendar, it is a 16th-century adaptation of the Julian calendar devised in the 1st century BC. By it:
a) years whose number is not divisible by 4 have 365 days;
b) centennial years, eg 1900, have 365 days unless the figures before the noughts are exactly divisible by 4;
c) other years have 366 days.

## ✝ 1980

| | |
|---|---|
| January | (31) |
| February | (29)† |
| March | (31) |
| April | (30) |
| May | (31) |
| June | (30) |
| July | (31) |
| August | (31) |
| September | (30) |
| October | (31) |
| November | (30) |
| December | (31) |

† 28 days except in leap years

**Jewish and Muslim years**
*right* Here we list in order the names of the months (with numbers of days in brackets) for the Jewish year 5741 and the Muslim year 1401, both of which start during 1980AD. A Jewish year has 13 not 12 months if its number, when divided by 19, leaves 0, 3, 6, 8, 11, 14 or 17. Its precise number of days is fixed with reference to particular festivals that must not fall on certain days of the week. A Muslim year has 355 not 354 days if its number, when divided by 30, leaves 2, 5, 7, 10, 13, 16, 18, 21, 24, 26 or 29.

*The Gregorian calendar, devised in the 16th century, is considerably more accurate than its predecessor, the Julian calendar. Over a 4000-year period, the Gregorian calendar loses only 1 day 4 hours and 55 minutes when compared to the tropical year. The Julian calendar loses 31 days 4 hours and 13 minutes over a similar period.*

a

365  366

b

354  355

c

353  354  355  383  384  385

**Years short and long** *right*
Here we show how the number of days in a year varies among cultures and from year to year.
**a** Years with 365 or 366 days derive from the solar year (see p. 158), which lasts roughly 365¼ days.
**b** The Muslim year, based on 12 lunar cycles each of approximately 29½ days, has a total of 354 or 355 days.
**c** The Jewish year is also lunar, but to keep broadly in line with the solar cycle some years have 12 months (353, 354 or 355 days) and others have 13 months (383, 384 or 385 days).

E

G
**1**

I
**1792**

BC                    1000 AD

F

H

✡ 5741

| Tishri | (30) |
| Heshvan | (29)▽ |
| Kislev | (29)▽ |
| Tevet | (29) |
| Shevat | (30) |
| Adar | (30) |
| ve-Adar* | (29) |
| Nisan | (30) |
| Iyyar | (29) |
| Sivan | (30) |
| Tammuz | (29) |
| Av | (30) |
| Elul | (29) |

☾★ 1401

| Muharram | (30) |
| Safar | (29) |
| Rabī' I | (30) |
| Rabī' II | (29) |
| Jumādā I | (30) |
| Jumādā II | (29) |
| Rajab | (30) |
| Sha 'bān | (29) |
| Ramadān | (30) |
| Shawwāl | (29) |
| Dhū al-Qa 'dah | (30) |
| Dhū al-Hijjah | (30)† |

▽30 days in some years
*Not in 12-month years

† 29 days in some years

**The zodiacal year**
The table *right* lists the signs of the zodiac, their meanings or equivalents in English, and the dates that astrologers ascribe to each sign. During the course of a year, Earth's orbit around the Sun makes the Sun appear to pass through each of the 12 zodiacal constellations in turn. The actual dates of passage, however, no longer correspond exactly to the dates used by astrologers. On January 1, for example, the Sun is in Sagittarius not in Capricorn. Included *below* is the traditional symbol for each sign.

| | | |
|---|---|---|
| **1** Aries | Ram | March 21–April 20 |
| **2** Taurus | Bull | April 21–May 20 |
| **3** Gemini | Twins | May 21–June 20 |
| **4** Cancer | Crab | June 21–July 21 |
| **5** Leo | Lion | July 22–August 21 |
| **6** Virgo | Virgin | August 22–September 21 |
| **7** Libra | Balance | September 22–October 22 |
| **8** Scorpio | Scorpion | October 23–November 21 |
| **9** Sagittarius | Archer | November 22–December 20 |
| **10** Capricorn | Goat | December 21–January 19 |
| **11** Aquarius | Water-bearer | January 20–February 18 |
| **12** Pisces | Fish | February 19–March 20 |

©DIAGRAM

6        7        8        9        10        11        12

# PLANETARY TIMES

We on Earth are very accustomed to our day of approximately 24 hours and our year of approximately 365 days. A look at the days and years of other planets, however, shows that they keep very different time. Venus, for example, has a day longer than its year, whereas a single year on Neptune consists of over 90,000 of its days.

| Planet | Rotation period | Sidereal period |
|---|---|---|
| A Mercury | 59 days | 88 days |
| B Venus | 243 days (retrograde) | 224.7 days |
| C Earth | 23h 56m 4s | 365.256 days |
| D Mars | 24h 37m 23s | 687 days |
| E Jupiter | 9h 50m 30s | 11.86 years |
| F Saturn | 10h 14m | 29.46 years |
| G Uranus | 11h (retrograde) | 84.01 years |
| H Neptune | 16h | 164.8 years |
| I Pluto | 6 days 9h | 247.7 years |

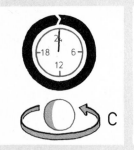

**Days and years** *left*
The diagram shows a planet's day (**a**) and year (**b**). A planet's day—properly called its rotation period—is the time taken by the planet to rotate once on its axis. Its year—or sidereal period—is the time it takes to orbit the Sun once.

**All the planets** *above*
Listed are the rotation period (day) and sidereal period (year) for each of the planets, in distance order from the Sun. Times are in sidereal Earth days and years (see p. 158). Retrograde means rotating E–W relative to fixed stars.

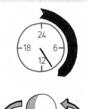

C

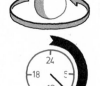

E

F

G

H

**Shorter days** *above, right*
Here we use 24h-clock faces to compare the length of day on Earth (**C**) with the lengths of days on planets with shorter days:
Jupiter (**E**) 9h 50m 30s
Saturn (**F**) 10h 14m
Uranus (**G**) 11h
Neptune (**H**) 16h

D

I

A

B

**Longer days** *right*
Clock faces and calendar pages show the lengths of days on planets with days that are longer than an Earth day:
Mars (**D**) 24h 37m 23s
Pluto (**I**) 6 days 9h
Mercury (**A**) 59 days
Venus (**B**) 243 days

**1**

**6**

**59**

**243**

**Earth (a) rotates on its axis 25.38 times for every once that the Sun (b) rotates on its own axis. Thus it could be argued that only one in 25.38 Earth days is truly a "Sun-day."**

A child on Pluto would have to wait
247 Earth years for his first birthday.
A child on Mercury, however,
would have a much better deal—
four birthdays in a single Earth year!

**Years and years and years**
*right* This diagram provides
a visual comparison of year
lengths on the planets (as
listed *left*). Thick lines on
the diagram indicate how
many of their own years—
or what portion of them—
the various planets experience
for every Earth year (**C**).

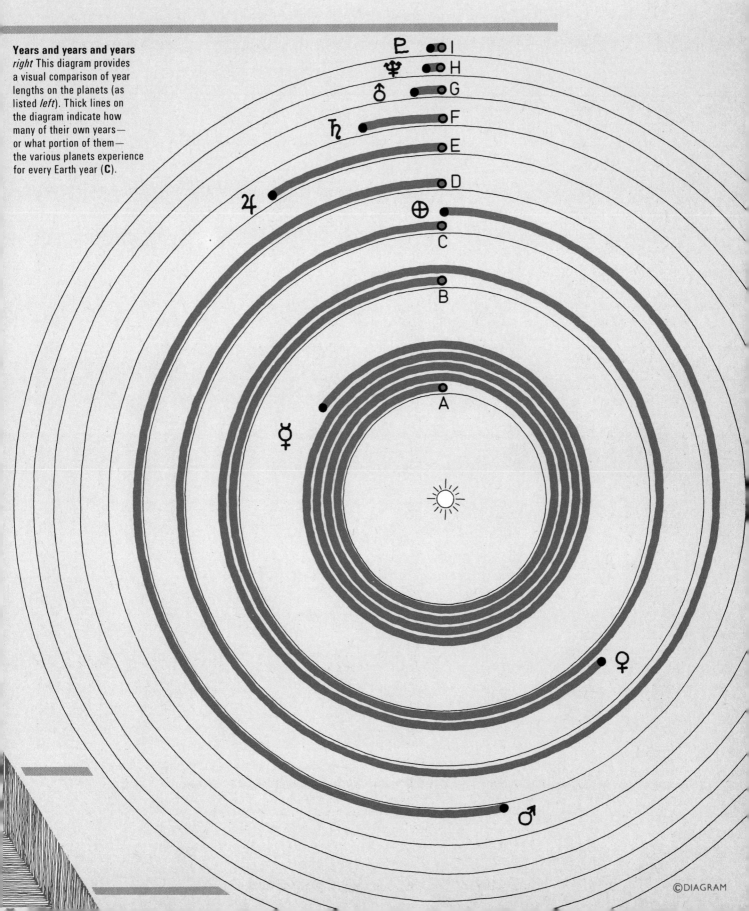

©DIAGRAM

# TIME ZONES

True noon at any place is when the Sun is at its highest point in the sky. If time were reckoned solely by the Sun, it would be necessary to turn the clock forward by 4 minutes for every degree of latitude traveled east. In practice, however, it has been more convenient to develop a system of internationally recognized time zones.

**More time for summer**
In order to benefit from more daylight in summer some countries in higher latitudes adopt Daylight Saving Time. Clocks are advanced, usually 1 hour, in spring and put back in the fall. (Our map ignores these adjustments.)

**World time zones** *right*
The map shows standard times, relative to Greenwich Mean Time (GMT). Each country chooses the standard time, or times, most convenient to it, so modifying the basic pattern whereby the globe is divided into time zones each 15° of longitude wide. In principle, successive zones to the east of the Greenwich zone (centered on the Greenwich Meridian, marked **A** on the map) are 1 hour in advance of GMT, and successive zones west of it are 1 hour behind GMT. The International Date Line is marked **B** on the map.

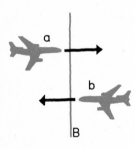

**Making a date** *above*
If two aircraft, one of them flying east (**a**) and the other west (**b**), were to set off from the Greenwich Meridian (0° longitude) and then fly on to see each other at the other side of the world (180° longitude), passengers in aircraft **a** would have gained 12 hours whereas those in aircraft **b** would have lost 12 hours. In theory there would be a whole day between them. In practice, however, the problem is solved by the International Date Line, where the date officially changes (**B** on the map *right*).

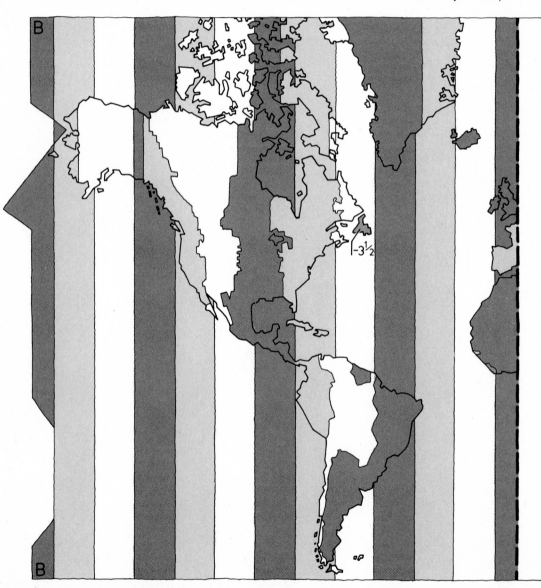

**When New Yorkers are eating breakfast (8 a.m. local time), Londoners are eating lunch (1 p.m.), Muscovites are taking tea (4 p.m.), Djakartans are eating dinner (8 p.m.), while in Wellington it is time for a bedtime drink (midnight).**

In the USSR all trains and airplanes keep Moscow time (GMT +3). Thus the station clock at Nakhodka, the Eastern terminus of the Trans-Siberian Railway, shows a time seven hours in advance of local time (GMT +10).

**London to L.A. in 1 hour !**
*right* The regular flying time between London and Los Angeles is 9 hours, but if we consider only local times passengers arrive 1 hour after take-off. The explanation lies in the 8-hour difference between the cities' standard times.

1 London local time :
a Take-off 1 p.m.
b Arrival 10 p.m.
2 Los Angeles local time :
a Take-off 5 a.m.
b Arrival 2 p.m.

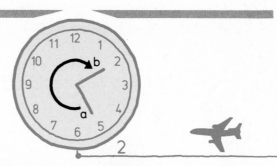

**Hours compared to GMT**

|  |  |
|---|---|
| Accra | GMT |
| London | GMT |
| Rabat | GMT |
| Reykjavik | GMT |
| Brazzaville | +1 |
| Brussels | +1 |
| Lagos | +1 |
| Madrid | +1 |
| Rome | +1 |
| Stockholm | +1 |
| Tunis | +1 |
| Warsaw | +1 |
| Athens | +2 |
| Beirut | +2 |
| Cairo | +2 |
| Lusaka | +2 |
| Pretoria | +2 |
| Tel Aviv | +2 |
| Ankara | +3 |
| Baghdad | +3 |
| Kampala | +3 |
| Moscow | +3 |
| Tehran | +3½ |
| Colombo | +5½ |
| New Delhi | +5½ |
| Dacca | +6 |
| Djakarta | +7 |
| Kuala Lumpur | +7½ |
| Manila | +8 |
| Peking | +8 |
| Tokyo | +9 |
| Canberra | +10 |
| Wellington | +12 |
| Brasilia | −3 |
| Buenos Aires | −3 |
| Caracas | −4 |
| Valparaiso | −4 |
| New York | −5 |
| Ottawa | −5 |
| Chicago | −6 |
| Mexico City | −6 |
| Los Angeles | −8 |

*Concorde flies from London to New York in an amazing three hours, allowing a London businessman to arrive in New York some two hours earlier than the time he set off!*

©DIAGRAM

# GEOLOGICAL TIME

The relative ages of Earth's rocks can be determined from fossils within them and from the relative positions of distinctive rock layers. But only with the development of techniques based on the rate of decay of radioactive substances did it become possible to give reasonably accurate dates for the various geological time divisions.

**Geological eras** *right*
This scale diagram shows the comparative durations and approximate dates of the four geological eras.
**A** Precambrian (4600 million to 570 million years ago). It contains two periods:
**1** Archean (4600 million to 2600 million years ago);

**2** Proterozoic (2600 million to 570 million years ago).
**B** Paleozoic (570 million to 230 million years ago).
**C** Mesozoic (230 million to 65 million years ago).
**D** Cenozoic (65 million years ago to the present).

| Era | Period | Epoch |
|---|---|---|
| **A Precambrian** | **1** Archean | |
| | **2** Proterozoic | |
| | | |
| **B Paleozoic** | **3** Cambrian | |
| | **4** Ordovician | |
| | **5** Silurian | |
| | **6** Devonian | |
| | **7** Carboniferous* | |
| | **8** Permian | |
| | | |
| **C Mesozoic** | **9** Triassic | |
| | **10** Jurassic | |
| | **11** Cretaceous | |
| | | |
| **D Cenozoic** | **12** Paleogene | **a** Paleocene |
| | | **b** Eocene |
| | | **c** Oligocene |
| | **13** Neogene | **d** Miocene |
| | | **e** Pliocene |
| | **14** Quaternary | **f** Pleistocene |
| | | **g** Holocene |

*Equivalents in
N America are:
**7i** Mississippian
**7ii** Pennsylvanian

**Geological time divisions**
The table *above* shows the division of geological time into eras, periods and epochs. The spiral diagram *top right* shows the initial division into eras (**A, B, C, D**). The three diagrams *right*, drawn to different scales, illustrate the approximate duration and dates of subdivisions within the three most recent eras. Period divisions (**1–14**) are keyed on the side of the bars; epoch divisions (**a–g**) are keyed on the top. The pictures above the bars are of animals that lived when those rocks were laid down.

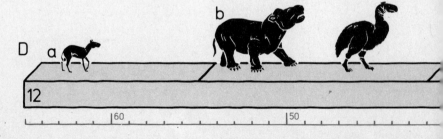

**"The moving creature that hath life"** was, according to the account in Genesis, created on the fifth day of the Creation. Scientists consider that the first primitive organisms appeared some 3500 million years ago, 1100 million years after the formation of our planet.

The Precambrian era
spans some 4030
million years, seven
times longer than the
time spanned by the
other three geological
eras together.

The present geological epoch, the
Holocene, began approximately
10,000 years ago. It therefore
accounts for a mere 0.00021%
of our geological time scale.

©DIAGRAM

# EVOLUTION

Here we show some of the creatures that lived in the three most recent eras of geological time. The boxes contain a selection of animals that illustrate the evolution of animal life from primitive arthropods to the appearance of early man. As on the previous two pages all dates given are for millions of years ago.

**Evolution in a year** *right*
The diagram shows Earth's evolution in terms of one 365-day year. Man's time on Earth is seen to be relatively short—ape-man appeared at 18.17 on December 31 and Christ was born only 14 seconds before the year end.

**a** Jan 1, Earth formed
**b** Mar 29, life begins
**c** Nov 16, trilobites common
**d** Nov 27, first fish
**e** Dec 4, first amphibians
**f** Dec 15, first dinosaurs
**g** Dec 26, dinosaurs die out
**h** Dec 28, mammals diversify
**i** Dec 31, first ape-man
**j** Dec 31, birth of Christ

**Creatures of the past**
Illustrated *right* and listed *below* is a representative selection of animals from the three most recent eras of geological time.

**A) Paleozoic era** (570–230)
Traces of life are present in older Precambrian rocks, but an abundance of fossils is first found in the Paleozoic era. Trilobites were especially numerous throughout this era, dying out only in the Permian period (280).

**B) Mesozoic era** (230–65)
The first mammal and the first bird appeared during the Mesozoic era. There was a great increase in the number of reptiles and land animals. Dinosaurs were dominant until the end of the Cretaceous period (65).

**C) Cenozoic era** (65–0)
Throughout the Cenozoic era mammals diversified and developed rapidly. Animal life in general began to assume the forms we recognize today. Primitive man first appeared only in the last three million years of this era.

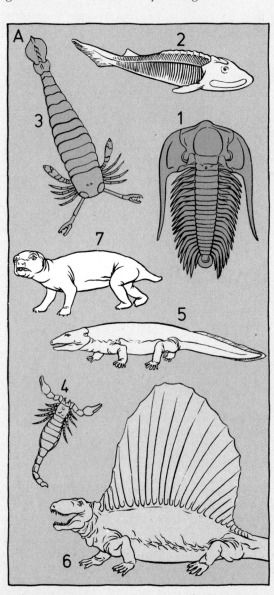

**A) Paleozoic era**
**1** Trilobite, arthropod, common in Cambrian period 570–500
**2** Ostracoderm, jawless fish of Ordovician period 500–436
**3** Eurypterid, sea scorpion of Silurian period 436–396
**4** Scorpion, early land animal of Silurian period 436–396
**5** Icthyostega, early amphibian of Devonian period 396–346
**6** Dimetrodon, reptile of early Permian period 280–225
**7** Thrinaxodon, Permian mammal-like reptile 280–225

**B) Mesozoic era**
**a** Pantothere, the first mammal, Triassic period 230–195
**b** Ammonite, cephalopod, common from Triassic to late Cretaceous period 230–65
**c** Archaeopteryx, the first bird, Jurassic period 195–141
**d** Stegosaurus, armored, herbivorous dinosaur, Jurassic period 195–141

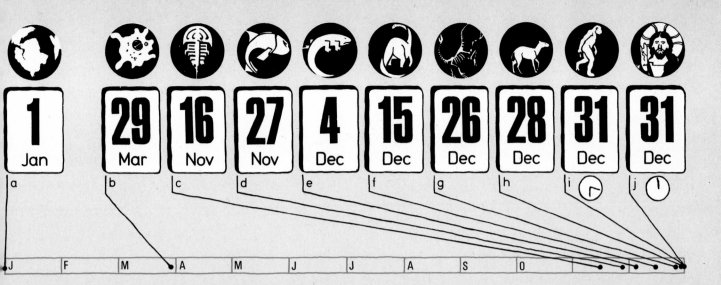

| | | | | | | | | | | |
|---|---|---|---|---|---|---|---|---|---|---|
| **1** Jan | **29** Mar | **16** Nov | **27** Nov | **4** Dec | **15** Dec | **26** Dec | **28** Dec | **31** Dec | **31** Dec |
| a | b | c | d | e | f | g | h | i | j |

J F M A M J J A S O

e Plesiosaur, marine reptile, common from Jurassic to Cretaceous period 195–65
f Pteranodon, flying reptile of Cretaceous period 141–65
g Tyrannosaurus, carnivorous dinosaur of Cretaceous period 141–65
h Triceratops, heavily armored, three-horned dinosaur of late Cretaceous period 100–65

**C) Cenozoic era**
1 Eohippus, ancestor of horse, Eocene epoch 55–42
2 Diatryma, flightless bird of Eocene epoch 55–42
3 Mesohippus, ancestor of horse, Oligocene epoch 42–22.5
4 Paleomastodon, ancestor of elephant, Oligocene epoch 42–22.5
5 Australopithecus, ape-man of Pliocene epoch, c. 3.0
6 Smilodon, saber-toothed tiger, Pleistocene epoch 1.8–0.01
7 Woolly mammoth of Pleistocene epoch 1.8–0.01

©DIAGRAM

171

# GESTATION AND INCUBATION

From the fertilization of an egg cell to birth or hatching takes hours or many months, according to the species involved. An elephant's possible 730 days' gestation is 61 times longer than the shortest known opossum pregnancy. A fertilized new-laid tortoise egg needs up to 114 days to hatch, a fruit fly's less than 1 day.

**Mammals** *right*
Shown are average pregnancy times for 10 mammals. Most small kinds, and all whose young are born tiny and undeveloped, have short pregnancies. Pregnancy is longest in big mammals like the rhinoceros, which bears large well-formed young.

1 Common opossum 13 days
2 House mouse 19 days
3 Dog 63 days
4 Goat 151 days
5 Chimpanzee 237 days
6 Man 265 days
7 Camel 406 days
8 Giraffe 410 days
9 Rhinoceros 560 days
10 Indian elephant 624 days

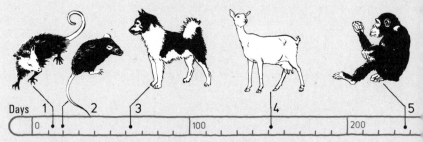

**Birds** *right*
This diagram shows average incubation periods for 10 birds. Eggs are fertilized and start developing in the body, but once laid they stop developing until incubation begins. Some birds sit on their eggs seven times as long as others.

A Finch 12 days
B Thrush 14 days
C Wren 16 days
D Pheasant 21.5 days
E Falcon 28.5 days
F Swan 30 days
G Ostrich 42 days
H Hawk 44 days
I Emperor penguin 63 days
J Royal albatross 79 days

**Reptiles** *right*
Shown are incubation and gestation periods for 10 reptiles. Some skinks and snakes bear living young*, but most reptiles lay eggs incubated by the Sun—the period depending on heat received and development, if any, before eggs are laid.

1 Australian skink 30 days
2 Grass lizard 42 days
3 Marine turtle 55 days
4 Hog-nosed snake 60 days
5 Alligator 61 days
6 Python 61.5 days
7 Spiny lizard 63 days
8 Box turtle 87 days
9 Viviparous lizard 90 days*
10 Tortoise 105 days

**Insect metamorphosis**
*right* This diagram shows average numbers of days spent by four insects in different developmental stages from new-laid egg to becoming adults. Most have three stages (egg, larva, pupa), but some have only two (egg, larva).

A Honeybee (worker): egg 3, larva 7, pupa 11 days
B Fruit fly: egg less than 1, larva 7, pupa 5 days
C Silkmoth: egg 10, larva 23, pupa 17 days
D Louse: egg 13, larva 8 days, no pupal stage

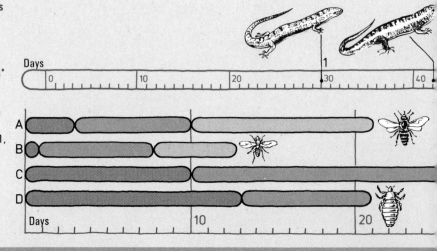

A rattlesnake father would have quite a problem if he wanted to be present at the hatching of his offspring—for incubation takes anything from 140 to 295 days.

The typical gestation period for
an Indian elephant is 624 days
—33 times as long as that for a
house mouse, and 48 times as long
as that for a common opossum.

**Fast developers** *left*
Given here are examples of
very brief incubation periods
or pregnancy terms among
insects, birds, mammals
and reptiles.
**a** Fruit fly less than 1 day
**b** Some finches 10 days
**c** Common opossum 13 days
**d** Some skinks 30 days

**Slow developers** *right*
This diagram shows some of
the longest-known periods
of incubation or pregnancy
among birds, insects,
reptiles and mammals.
**a** Royal albatross 81 days
**b** Some butterflies 270 days
**c** Tuatara 425 days
**d** Indian elephant 730 days

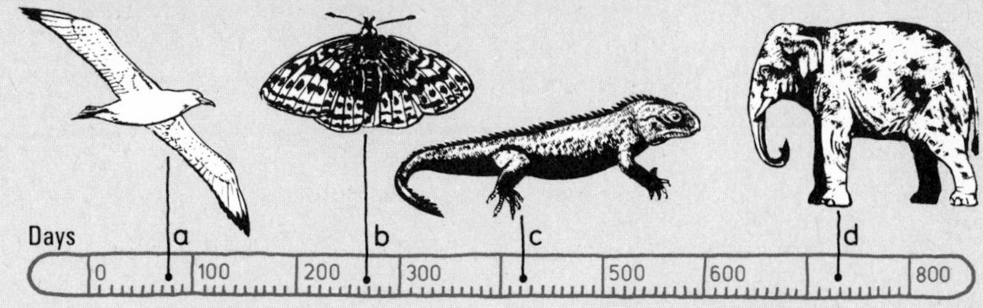

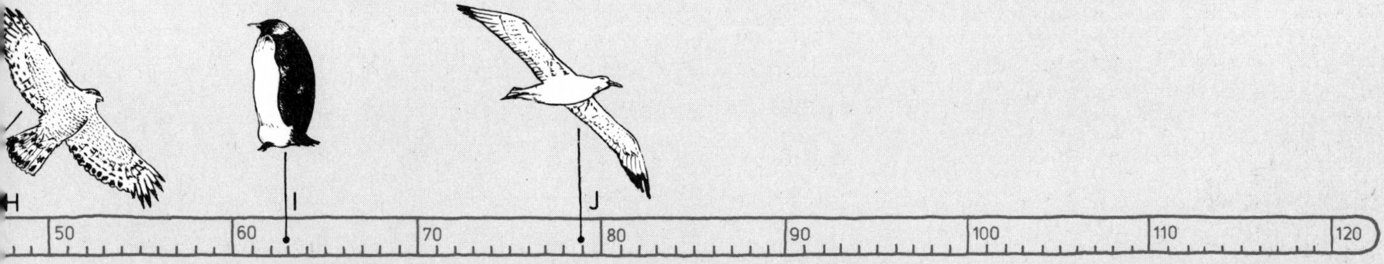

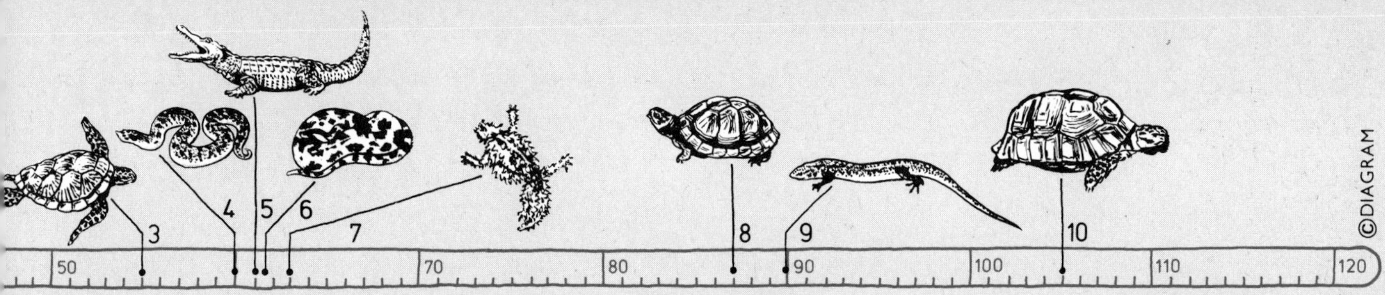

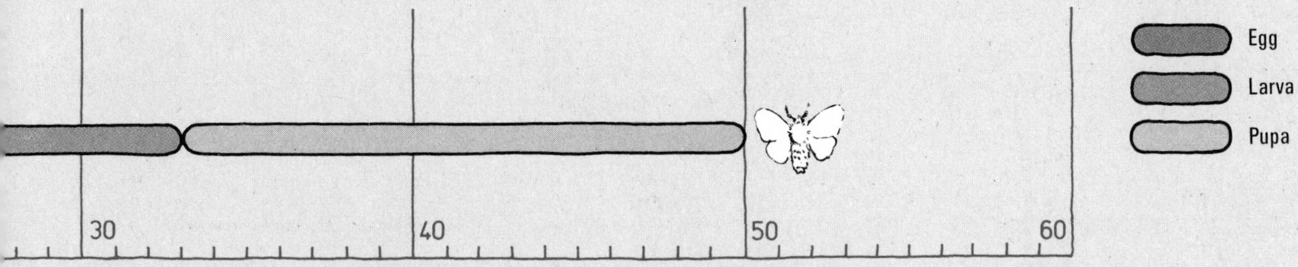

Days

a     b     c          d

0   100   200   300   500   600   800

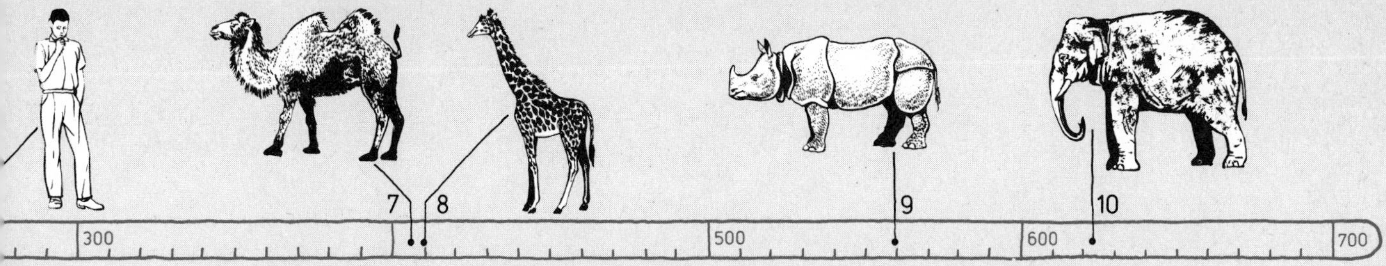

300   7 8   500   9   600   10   700

50   60   70   80   90   100   110   120

H   I   J

50   3   4 5 6   7   70   80   8 9   90   10   100   110   120

Egg

Larva

Pupa

30   40   50   60

*Kangaroos grow up to be heavier
than humans, but a kangaroo
pregnancy lasts less than one sixth
as long as a woman's—40 days
compared with 265 days.*

# LIFE EXPECTANCIES

Man is often acutely aware of the span of his own existence, and yet he has one of the longest life spans of all animals. Medical advances now allow more people to live to an old age, so increasing average life expectancies at birth. Women have a greater natural life expectancy than men, but to offset this more males than females are born.

**Animals and man** *below*
Only bacteria live longer than the tortoise, for which a life span of 100 years is nothing out of the ordinary. Man's average life expectancy of around 70 years in developed countries exceeds even record figures for most other animals.

Some typical life spans are indicated on this diagram and listed *right*.

**a** Mayfly (imago) 1 day
**b** Mouse 2–3yr
**c** Trout 5–10yr
**d** Squirrel 11yr
**e** Rabbit 12yr
**f** Sheep 10–15yr
**g** Cat 13–17yr
**h** Rattlesnake 18yr
**i** Owl 24yr
**j** Lion 25yr
**k** Horse 30yr
**l** Hippopotamus 40yr
**m** Pelican 45yr
**n** Ostrich 50yr
**o** Alligator 55yr
**p** African elephant 60yr
**q** Macaw 63yr
**r** Dolphin 65yr
**s** Raven 69yr
**t** Rhinoceros 70yr
**u** Man 68yr, woman 76yr (USA)
**v** Tortoise 100yr

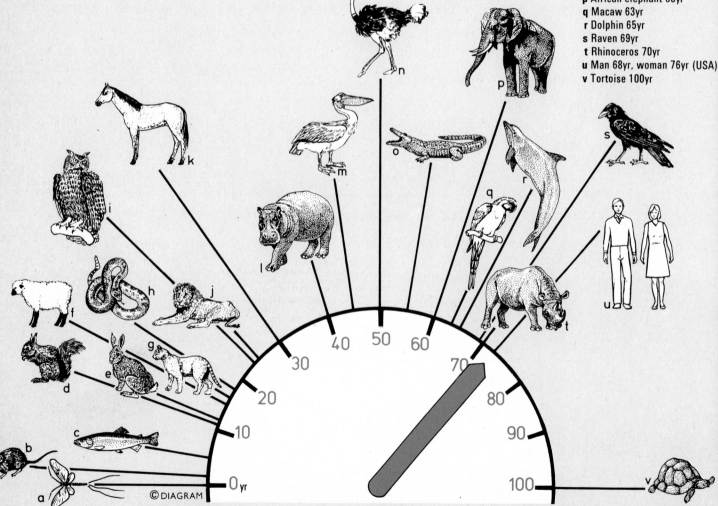

© DIAGRAM

**If the fox hadn't got him first, the old gray goose might have lived to be 31 years old.**

*"And all the days of Methuselah were nine hundred sixty and nine years: and he died."* (Genesis V 27)

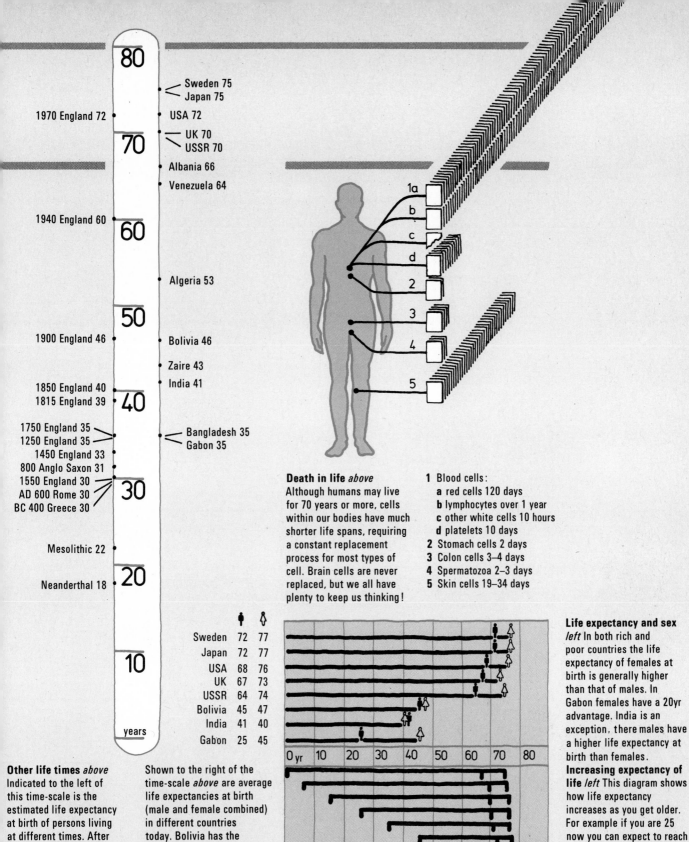

## Time-scale (years)

80

Sweden 75
Japan 75

1970 England 72

USA 72

70

UK 70
USSR 70

Albania 66

Venezuela 64

1940 England 60

60

Algeria 53

50

1900 England 46

Bolivia 46

Zaire 43

1850 England 40

India 41

1815 England 39

40

1750 England 35
1250 England 35
1450 England 33
800 Anglo Saxon 31
1550 England 30
AD 600 Rome 30
BC 400 Greece 30

Bangladesh 35
Gabon 35

30

Mesolithic 22

Neanderthal 18

20

10

years

**Death in life** *above*
Although humans may live for 70 years or more, cells within our bodies have much shorter life spans, requiring a constant replacement process for most types of cell. Brain cells are never replaced, but we all have plenty to keep us thinking!

1 Blood cells:
  a red cells 120 days
  b lymphocytes over 1 year
  c other white cells 10 hours
  d platelets 10 days
2 Stomach cells 2 days
3 Colon cells 3–4 days
4 Spermatozoa 2–3 days
5 Skin cells 19–34 days

| | ♂ | ♀ |
|---|---|---|
| Sweden | 72 | 77 |
| Japan | 72 | 77 |
| USA | 68 | 76 |
| UK | 67 | 73 |
| USSR | 64 | 74 |
| Bolivia | 45 | 47 |
| India | 41 | 40 |
| Gabon | 25 | 45 |

0 yr  10  20  30  40  50  60  70  80

**Life expectancy and sex**
*left* In both rich and poor countries the life expectancy of females at birth is generally higher than that of males. In Gabon females have a 20yr advantage. India is an exception, there males have a higher life expectancy at birth than females.

**Increasing expectancy of life** *left* This diagram shows how life expectancy increases as you get older. For example if you are 25 now you can expect to reach 70 if you are male and 77 if female. If you are 65 now your life expectancy has increased to 78 for men and 82 for women. Another major factor affecting your life expectancy is the age at which your parents died.

**Other life times** *above*
Indicated to the left of this time-scale is the estimated life expectancy at birth of persons living at different times. After centuries of fluctuating between 30 and 40, life expectancy has shot up as medicine has advanced.

Shown to the right of the time-scale *above* are average life expectancies at birth (male and female combined) in different countries today. Bolivia has the lowest life expectancy in South America, but many African and Asian countries fall below its figure.

**Delina Filkins of the USA was born in May 1815, the year of the Battle of Waterloo. She was 45 at the start of the American Civil War and 101 when America joined World War I. She died in December 1928, aged 113 years 214 days.**

# AGES OF MAN

Growth, maturation and aging take up various proportions of life in different people. But a life span of 70 years from the time of conception might consist roughly of the following: 1% pre-birth development and growth; 3% infancy; 14% childhood; 9% adolescence; 31% prime of life; 29% middle age; 13% old age.

**A** (Day 1) Sperm fertilizes ovum released into mother's oviduct.
**B** (Day 7) Fertilized ovum has formed a blastocyst embedded in the uterus.
**C** (Day 13) The blastocyst has produced a yolk sac and embryonic disk.
**D** (Day 23) Embryo now has the makings of heart, brain and spinal cord.
**E** (Day 29) Embryo now plainly has a head, and buds that will be arms and legs.
**F** (Week 5) Embryo about 0.5in (1.3cm); eyes, ears, vital organs taking shape.
**G** (Week 9) Embryo about 2in (5cm) long and weighs about 0.35oz (10gm).
**H** (Week 14) Embryonic development has given way to fetal growth. The fetus is 7in (18cm) and weighs 4oz (113gm).
**I** (Week 26) At 15in (38cm) and 2lb (907gm) fetus may survive if born.
**J** (Week 38) Baby born, measuring 20in (51cm) and weighing 7lb (3.18kg).
**K** (1 year old) Infant says first words, crawls, and can almost stand and walk.
**L** (3 years) Child knows own age in years, walks erect, easily climbs stairs.
**M** (5 years) Runs on toes, does useful chores, begins to read and write.
**N** (7 years) Learns to ride a bicycle, tell the time, draw a man side-face.
**O** (8 years) Solves simple mathematical problems; enjoys reading.
**P** (10 years) Solves problems in less concrete situations than before.
**Q** (13 years) Puberty has arrived, also early adolescent growth spurt.
**R** (18 years) Adolescence ending and early adulthood beginning.
**S** (40 years) The slow decline of faculties called middle age sets in.
**T** (60 years) Increasing adverse bodily changes mark the onset of old age.
**U** (75 years) Advanced old age sees over 50% loss of certain basic faculties.

**The days of our years are threescore years and ten (Psalm 90).**

*And one man in his time plays many parts, His acts being seven ages (William Shakespeare, "As You Like It").*

# Development accounts for only the first 14 weeks (36%) of a typical 38-week pregnancy.

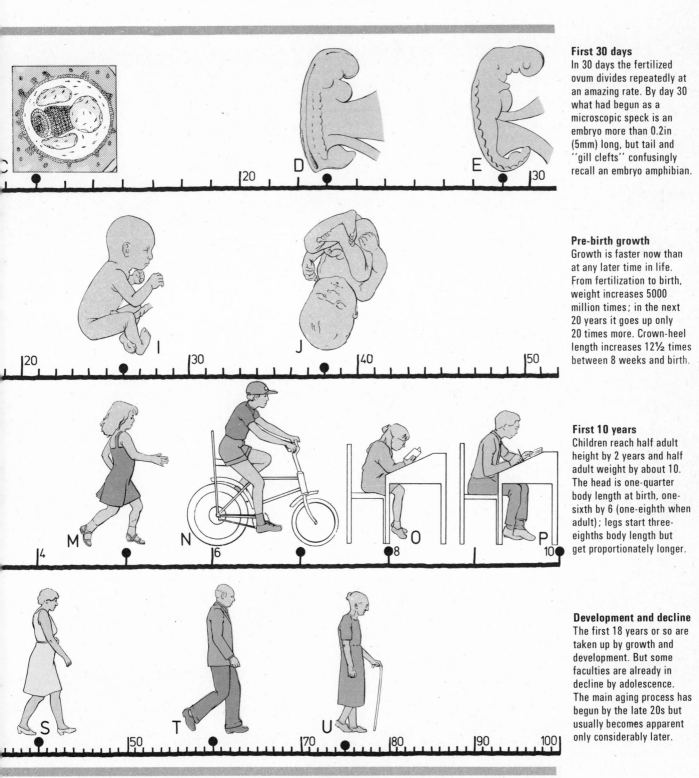

**First 30 days**
In 30 days the fertilized ovum divides repeatedly at an amazing rate. By day 30 what had begun as a microscopic speck is an embryo more than 0.2in (5mm) long, but tail and "gill clefts" confusingly recall an embryo amphibian.

**Pre-birth growth**
Growth is faster now than at any later time in life. From fertilization to birth, weight increases 5000 million times; in the next 20 years it goes up only 20 times more. Crown-heel length increases 12½ times between 8 weeks and birth.

**First 10 years**
Children reach half adult height by 2 years and half adult weight by about 10. The head is one-quarter body length at birth, one-sixth by 6 (one-eighth when adult); legs start three-eighths body length but get proportionately longer.

**Development and decline**
The first 18 years or so are taken up by growth and development. But some faculties are already in decline by adolescence. The main aging process has begun by the late 20s but usually becomes apparent only considerably later.

If age 60 is taken as the starting point for old age, then Japan's Shigechiyo Izumi—114 last birthday—has been "old" for 48% of his life. A typical person's life span of 70 years includes only 13% old age.

©DIAGRAM

# FAMOUS LIVES

The length of a person's life does not necessarily affect the measure of his achievement. Some famous persons have had comparatively short lives, others have lived for a long time but been active or · in positions of power for only a small portion of their total life span.

| | | |
|---|---|---|
| **A** | John Keats, English romantic poet (1795–1821) | 25 |
| **B** | Wilfred Owen, English war poet (1893–1918) | 25 |
| **C** | Georges Seurat, French artist (1859–91) | 31 |
| **D** | Franz Schubert, Austrian composer (1797–1828) | 31 |
| **E** | W.A. Mozart, Austrian composer (1756–91) | 35 |

**Short and long lives**
Plotted on the time scale *right* are the ages at which some famous writers, artists and composers died. Those with short lives are listed in the table *above* the scale, and those with long lives in the table *below* it.

**Lives of Presidents** *right*
Here we give dates of life and term of office, age on taking office (**a**) and on death (**b**) of US Presidents: longest lived (**1**), oldest into office (**2**), first (**3**), youngest to die of natural causes (**4**), and youngest elected and to die (**5**).

**Lives of monarchs**
Shown in the diagram *right* are the life spans and reigns of some short- and long-lived monarchs. The tables *below* the diagram list each monarch's dates of life and reign, length of reign (**a**), and age at death (**b**). John I of France, the posthumous son of Louis X, was born a King but survived only a few days. Edward V, one of the Princes in the Tower, was King of England for only 77 days. Excepting unreliably documented claims, Louis XIV had the longest reign of any monarch.

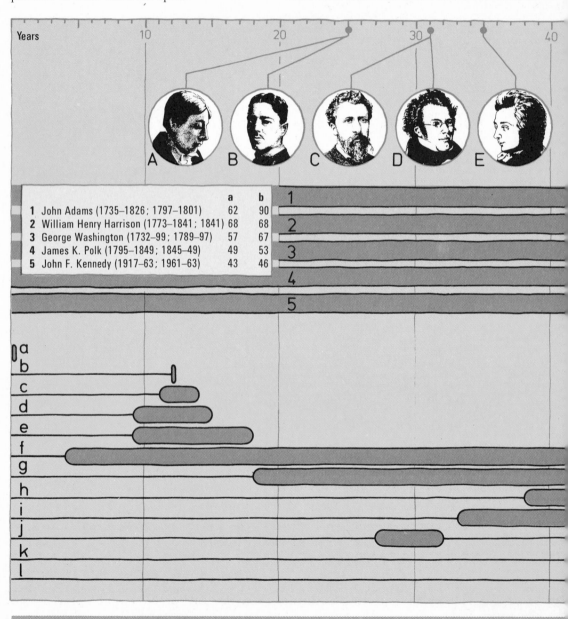

| | | a | b |
|---|---|---|---|
| **1** | John Adams (1735–1826; 1797–1801) | 62 | 90 |
| **2** | William Henry Harrison (1773–1841; 1841) | 68 | 68 |
| **3** | George Washington (1732–99; 1789–97) | 57 | 67 |
| **4** | James K. Polk (1795–1849; 1845–49) | 49 | 53 |
| **5** | John F. Kennedy (1917–63; 1961–63) | 43 | 46 |

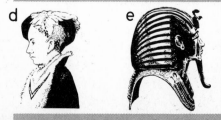

| | | a | b |
|---|---|---|---|
| **a** | John I of France (1316; 1316) | 0.01 | 0.01 |
| **b** | Edward V of England (1470–83; 1483) | 0.21 | 12 |
| **c** | Peter II of Russia (1715–30; 1727–30) | 3 | 14 |
| **d** | Edward VI of England (1537–53; 1547–53) | 6 | 15 |
| **e** | Tutankhamun of Egypt (c.1370–52BC; c.1361–52BC) | 9 | 18 |

Louis XIV was King of France for 95% of his lifetime, reigning for 72 out of his 76 years. Stanislaus I of Poland lived to be 12 years older than Louis XIV, but of his total of 88 years he was King for only 5 years, a mere 6% of his lifetime.

# Time

**Short but famous lives**
*left* Listed here, with the dates between which they lived and the ages at which they died, are people who, despite the shortness of their lives, made major contributions as writers, artists or composers.

**Long and memorable lives**
*below* Included in this table, with their dates and the ages at which they died, is a selection of famous writers, artists and composers who are also noteworthy for their exceptionally long lives.

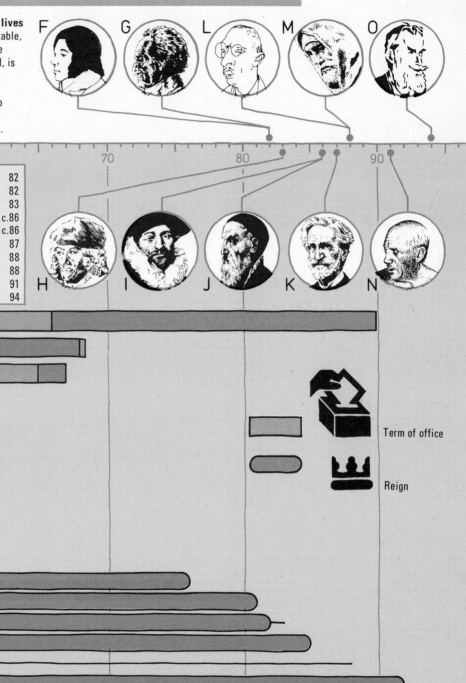

| | | |
|---|---|---|
| **F** | Francisco de Goya, Spanish artist (1746–1828) | 82 |
| **G** | J.W. von Goëthe, German writer (1749–1832) | 82 |
| **H** | François Voltaire, French writer (1694–1778) | 83 |
| **I** | Frans Hals, Flemish artist (c.1580–1666) | c.86 |
| **J** | Titian, Italian painter (c.1490–1576) | c.86 |
| **K** | Giuseppe Verdi, Italian composer (1813–1901) | 87 |
| **L** | Igor Stravinsky, Russian composer (1882–1971) | 88 |
| **M** | Michelangelo, Italian artist (1475–1564) | 88 |
| **N** | Pablo Picasso, Spanish artist (1881–1973) | 91 |
| **O** | G.B. Shaw, Irish playwright (1856–1950) | 94 |

Term of office

Reign

© DIAGRAM

| | | a | b |
|---|---|---|---|
| **f** | Louis XIV of France (1638–1715 ; 1643–1715) | 72 | 76 |
| **g** | Victoria of England (1819–1901 ; 1837–1901) | 63 | 81 |
| **h** | Haile Selassie of Ethiopia (1892–1975 ; 1930–36, 1942–74) | 38 | 83 |
| **i** | Haakon VII of Norway (1872–1957 ; 1905–57) | 51 | 85 |
| **j** | Stanislaus I of Poland (1677–1766 ; 1704–09) | 5 | 88 |
| **k** | Gustav V of Sweden (1858–1950 ; 1907–50) | 42 | 92 |
| **l** | Pope Leo XIII (1810–1903 ; 1878–1903) | 25 | 93 |

# EVENTS IN HISTORY

3000 BC

2000

1000

From the start of the Bronze Age in the Middle East through to the present day is a period of approximately 5000 years. Here we use a visual presentation of selected dates within this period to show the relationships in time between one important event and another and between these same events and the present day.

| a | Bronze Age in Syria and Palestine | c.3000BC | 4980 |
|---|---|---|---|
| b | Sumerian Classical Age begins | c.2850BC | 4830 |
| c | Egyptian Old Kingdom begins | c.2615BC | 4595 |
| d | Harappa culture in Indus Valley | c.2000BC | 3980 |
| e | Height of Minoan civilization | c.1600BC | 3580 |
| f | Shang dynasty in China | c.1400BC | 3380 |
| g | Israelites ruled by King David | 1000BC | 2980 |
| h | Golden Age of Athens | c.450BC | 2430 |
| i | Rome defeats Carthage | 146BC | 2126 |
| * | Birth of Christ | | c.1980 |

**Ancient civilizations**
Indicated on the time scale *left* and listed in the table *above* are key dates from civilizations that pre-dated the birth of Christ. The final column in the table shows the number of years between each event and 1980.

**Traveling back in time**
The time spiral *right* takes us back in time from the year 2000AD to the birth of Christ. Major events and famous reigns are indicated on the spiral, and listed *below* together with their dates and number of years back from 1980.

| A | First men on the Moon | 1969 | 11 |
|---|---|---|---|
| B | World War 2 | 1939–45 | 35 |
| C | World War 1 | 1914–18 | 62 |
| D | American Civil War | 1861–65 | 115 |
| E | Latin American revolutions | 1806–25 | 155 |
| F | Napoleon, ruler of France | 1799–1815 | 165 |
| G | French Revolution | 1789 | 191 |
| H | American independence | 1776 | 204 |
| I | Frederick the Great of Prussia | 1740–86 | 194 |
| J | Louis XIV of France | 1643–1715 | 265 |
| K | Thirty Years' War | 1618–48 | 332 |
| L | Pilgrims arrive at Cape Cod | 1620 | 360 |
| M | Queen Elizabeth I of England | 1558–1603 | 377 |
| N | Reformation started by Luther | 1517 | 463 |
| O | Columbus crosses the Atlantic | 1492 | 488 |
| P | Lorenzo de' Medici (of Florence) | 1478–92 | 488 |
| Q | Black Death in Europe | 1348–50 | 630 |
| R | Genghis Khan | 1206–27 | 753 |
| S | Third Crusade | 1189–92 | 788 |
| T | Norman Conquest of England | 1066 | 914 |
| U | Important Viking expeditions | 840–885 | 1095 |
| V | Emperor Charlemagne | 771–814 | 1166 |
| W | Traditional start of Islam | 622 | 1358 |
| X | Pope Gregory the Great | 590–604 | 1376 |
| Y | End of Roman Empire in West | 476 | 1504 |
| Z | Roman Empire at maximum extent | 117 | 1863 |
| * | Birth of Christ | | c.1980 |

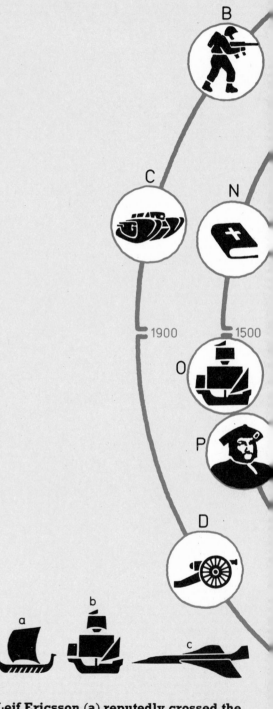

Leif Ericsson (a) reputedly crossed the Atlantic in c. 1000AD, roughly 500 years before Columbus's first crossing (b) in 1492. A similar time span separates Columbus's voyage from the first transatlantic passenger flight of Concorde (c) in 1977.

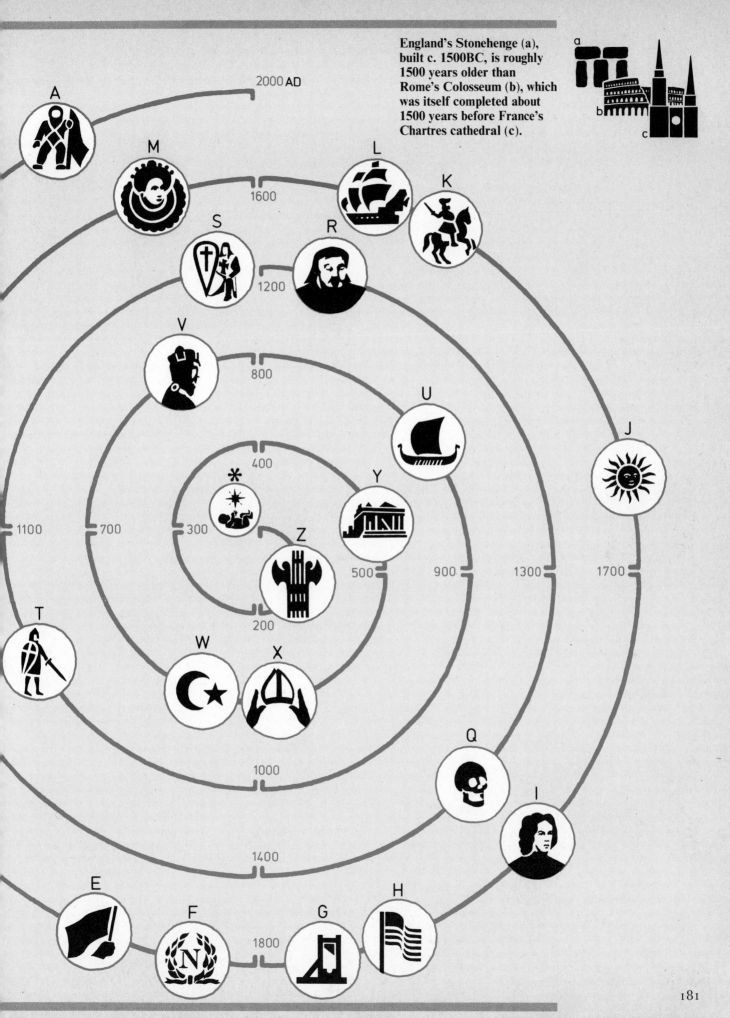

England's Stonehenge (a), built c. 1500BC, is roughly 1500 years older than Rome's Colosseum (b), which was itself completed about 1500 years before France's Chartres cathedral (c).

2000 AD

1600

1200

800

400

300

200

500    900    1300    1700

700

1100

1000

1400

1800

©DIAGRAM

# CHAPTER 9

Like father, like son—
Sir Malcolm Campbell and
his son Donald are here
photographed in 1933 with
the record-breaking car
*Bluebird*. Campbell senior
raised the world land-
speed record nine times in
1924–35. His son took the
land-speed record once, in
1964, and the water-speed
record seven times before
his death in 1967 (BBC
Hulton Picture Library).

# SPEED

The running action of a dog is shown in this sequence of photographs from Eadweard Muybridge's *Animal Locomotion*, published in 1887 (Kingston-upon-Thames Museum and Art Gallery).

Flying through the air on a cannonball—just one of the fabulous exploits described in R. E. Raspe's *Baron Münchhausen's Narrative of His Marvellous Travels and Campaigns in Russia*, first published in 1785 (The Mansell Collection).

# MEASURING SPEED

In this chapter we look at comparisons of speed, concentrating on its definition as the amount of time taken to travel a particular distance. Speed is calculated by dividing a distance measurement by a time measurement, and is expressed in units that combine both these factors, as for example in kilometers per hour.

| 1 mile per hour (mph) | = 1.6093 kilometers per hour |
|---|---|
| 1 yard per minute (yd/min) | = 0.9144 meters per minute |
| 1 foot per second (ft/s) | = 0.3048 meters per minute |
| 1 inch per second (in/s) | = 2.5400 centimeters per second |
| 1 kilometer per hour (km/h) | = 0.6214 miles per hour |
| 1 meter per minute (m/min) | = 1.0936 yards per minute |
| 1 meter per minute (m/min) | = 3.2808 feet per minute |
| 1 centimeter per second (cm/s) | = 0.3937 inches per second |
| 1 mile per hour | = 1.4667 feet per second |
| 1 kilometer per hour | = 0.2778 meters per second |

A          B C                    D

$10^{-10}$      $10^{-9}$        $10^{-8}$        $10^{-7}$      $10^{-6}$

km/h

**Universal speed scales**
Here we use consecutive logarithmic scales to show the comparative speeds of a selection of living and nonliving things—from the scarcely discernible growth rate of some lichens, through various forms of locomotion, and up to the speed of light. On these two pages we assist comparisons between very different forms of motion by expressing all speeds in terms of the same unit— kilometers per hour (km/h). Elsewhere in the chapter we express speeds in whatever units are most appropriate for the various items of information.

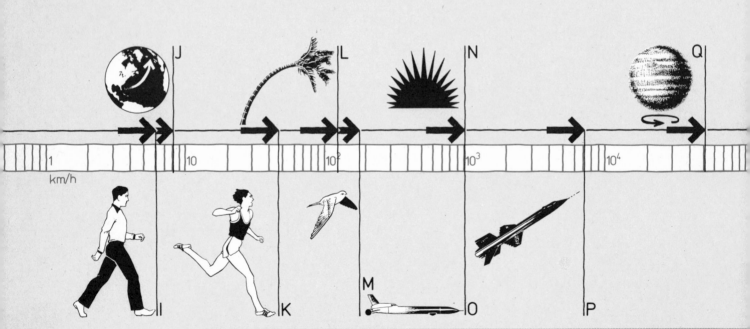

J          L            N              Q

1          10        $10^2$        $10^3$          $10^4$

km/h

I          K      M   O            P

**Earth has a rotational velocity at the Equator of 1040mph (1674km/h). This means that anyone standing on the Equator is traveling some 1.7 times faster than the official world land-speed record.**

**The orbital speed of an electron in a uranium atom (8,700,000km/h) is fifty times faster than the mean orbital velocity of Mercury around the Sun (172,404km/h).**

**The Gulf Stream current's average flow of 5.2mph (8.4km/h) is more than 18,000 times faster than an Antarctic glacier's average flow of 84.6yd (77.4m) a week.**

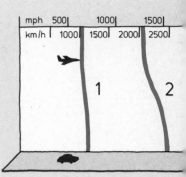

**Conversion of units** *left*
Listed are abbreviations and conversion factors for common units of speed. In addition to metric equivalents for US/imperial measurements and vice versa, we give the commonly needed conversions of mph into ft/s, and km/h into m/s.

**Knots for sailors**
Nautical speeds are given in knots (nautical miles per hour). There are two units: international knots (kn) and British (UKkn).
1kn = 1.1508mph
1kn = 1.8520km/h
1UKkn = 1.1515mph
1UKkn = 1.8531km/h

**Super Mach speeds** *right*
The Mach scale is used to express speeds faster than sound, with Mach 1 equal to the speed of sound, Mach 2 to twice the speed of sound, and so on. But the speed of sound is not a constant, since it depends on the substance through which the sound waves are passing, and on temperature. For land speeds (sea level, 15°C) Mach 1 is 760.98mph (1224.65km/h). Sound travels more slowly in the cooler stratosphere, and for air speeds Mach 1 is taken as 659.78mph (1061.78km/h).

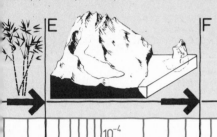

**Slow movers** *above*
Speeds slower than 1km/h are plotted on this scale.
**A** Growth rate of some lichens $10^{-10}$km/h
**B** Growth rate of a child, birth to 18yr, $8 \times 10^{-9}$km/h

**C** Speed at which some parts of the ocean floor split apart $10^{-8}$km/h
**D** Growth rate of *Eucalyptus regnans* $5 \times 10^{-7}$km/h
**E** Growth rate of bamboo $4 \times 10^{-5}$km/h

**F** Flow rate of Antarctic glaciers $5 \times 10^{-4}$km/h
**G** Speed at which a snail moves $5 \times 10^{-3}$km/h
**H** Walking speed of a giant tortoise $2 \times 10^{-1}$km/h

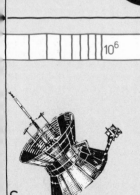

**Fast movers** *above*
On this scale we show speeds that exceed 1km/h.
**I** Brisk walking speed for a man 6km/h
**J** Average speed of Gulf Stream current 8km/h
**K** Fastest running speed for a man $4.3 \times 10$km/h

**L** Minimum speed for a hurricane $1.2 \times 10^2$km/h
**M** Fastest-moving creature, the spine-tailed swift, $1.7 \times 10^2$km/h
**N** Speed of sound, in air at sea level at 15°C, $10^3$km/h
**O** Official land-speed record $10^3$km/h

**P** Fastest speed for an air-launched, rocket-powered plane $7 \times 10^3$km/h
**Q** Rotational velocity of Jupiter, the fastest-rotating planet, $5 \times 10^4$km/h
**R** Mean orbital velocity of Mercury, the fastest-moving of Sun's planets, $2 \times 10^5$km/h

**S** Speed of the space probe *Helios B* $2 \times 10^5$km/h
**T** Red shift (velocity) of cluster in Virgo $4 \times 10^6$km/h
**U** Red shift of cluster in Corona Borealis $2 \times 10^7$km/h
**V** Speed of light $10^9$km/h

It is not surprising that we see lightning before we hear thunder, for light travels at 186,282 miles per second (roughly $10^9$ km/h)—more than 880,000 times faster than the 760.98 miles per hour (roughly $10^3$ km/h) that sound travels through air at sea level at 15°C.

©DIAGRAM

# SPEEDS IN NATURE

All things in nature—nonliving as well as living—are constantly on the move. Even the rock rafts that make up Earth's crust shift up and down and to and fro—but generally only by a fraction of an inch per year. Among living things change is more obvious. Plant growth, for example, can be accurately timed and measured.

**Plant growth** *left*
Shown here to scale are daily growth rates for some fast- and slow-growing plants. A bamboo can grow as many inches in one day as an average child grows in the first 10 years after birth. At the slow end of the plant growth spectrum are some types of lichen that take a century to grow just one inch.
**a** Bamboo 35.4in
**b** Certain seaweeds 17.7in
**c** Bermuda grass 5.9in
**d** *Albizzia falcatoria* 1.1in
**e** *Eucalyptus regnans* 0.5in
**f** Sitka spruce growing on polar tree line 0.0003in
**g** Some lichens 0.0001in

**Beaufort scale**
The diagram *below* and the table *right* give Beaufort scale wind force numbers together with the range of wind speeds to which each number is applied. (Note that speeds in mph and km/h are not exact equivalents.) Also included in the table are official descriptive titles for the Beaufort scale forces, and examples of physical manifestations that characterize them. The latter are indicated on the diagram by symbols.

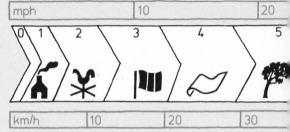

**Rivers of ice** *right*
A glacier is a frozen river that flows slowly down a valley. A body frozen into a glacier high up in its valley may eventually emerge perfectly preserved lower in the valley where the glacier is melting. Glaciers in different places flow at different rates. Shown here beneath a 66yd-long ice-hockey pitch are the distances traveled in one week by the ice in three types of glacier from three parts of the world.
**A** Alpine glacier 304.6yd
**B** Greenland glacier 236.9yd
**C** Antarctic glacier 84.6yd

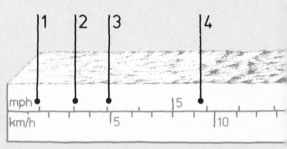

**1** Antarctic Circumpolar Current 0.9mph
**2** Mississippi River 2mph
**3** Amazon River 1.5–3mph
**4** Gulf Stream 4.6–5.8mph
**5** Pentland Firth 12.4mph
**6** Severn Bore 13mph
**7** Ch'ient'ang'kian Bore 15mph
**8** Ganges Bore 16.9mph
**9** Saltstraumen Current 18mph
**10** Lava Falls, Colorado River 30mph

Parts of the ocean floor split apart at the rate of about four inches a year. So two mermaids seated side by side on either side of a split could be at arm's length after fifteen years!

*A wind as fast as the fastest speed run by a man (27 mph) is classed as a "strong breeze" on the Beaufort scale. A wind as fast as a running cheetah (70 mph) is classed as a "storm."*

| Number | Description | Speed | | Characteristics |
|--------|-------------|-------|------|-----------------|
| 0 | Calm | <1mph | <1km/h | Smoke rises vertically |
| 1 | Light air | 1–3mph | 1–5km/h | Direction shown by smoke |
| 2 | Light breeze | 4–7mph | 6–12km/h | Direction shown by wind vane |
| 3 | Gentle breeze | 8–12mph | 13–20km/h | Wind extends a light flag |
| 4 | Moderate breeze | 13–18mph | 21–29km/h | Raises dust and loose paper |
| 5 | Fresh breeze | 19–24mph | 30–39km/h | Small trees in leaf start to sway |
| 6 | Strong breeze | 25–31mph | 40–50km/h | Umbrellas used with difficulty |
| 7 | Moderate gale | 32–38mph | 51–61km/h | Inconvenient to walk against wind |
| 8 | Fresh gale | 39–46mph | 62–74km/h | Twigs broken off trees |
| 9 | Strong gale | 47–54mph | 75–87km/h | Chimney pots and slates removed |
| 10 | Whole gale | 55–63mph | 88–102km/h | Trees uprooted; considerable damage |
| 11 | Storm | 64–75mph | 103–120km/h | Widespread damage |
| 12–17 | Hurricane | >75mph | >120km/h | Extremely violent |

**Windy mountain**
Mount Washington in the USA has experienced winds of up to 231mph (371km/h)— some 95mph (153km/h) beyond Beaufort scale force 17.

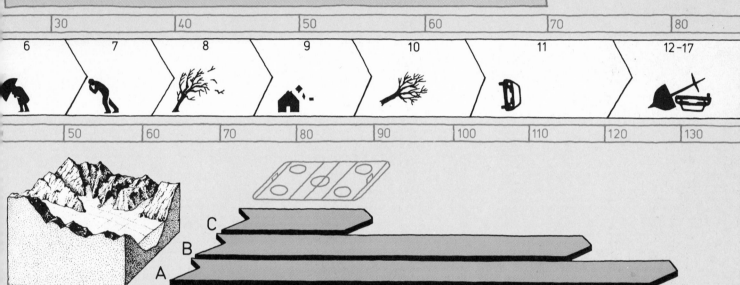

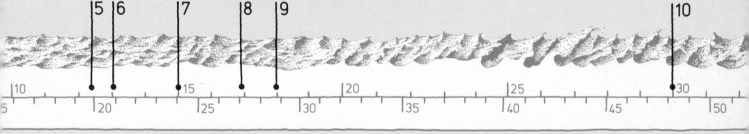

**Water speeds**
Listed *left* and shown *above* are the speeds that water moves in selected ocean currents, rivers, and bores (tidal waves that surge up rivers from narrow estuaries). Ocean-current speeds vary enormously. Thus Norway's Saltstraumen

Current is 20 times faster than part of the Antarctic Circumpolar Current. River flow varies with the slope of the bed. The speed of normal ocean waves depends largely on the winds that generate them. Many waves move through the sea at speeds of 18–56mph.

**Tsunamis**
Often misnamed tidal waves, tsunamis are giant, high-speed waves unleashed by sub-oceanic earthquakes. A tsunami can cross an ocean at up to 490mph. This is 8mph faster than the official speed record for a piston-engined plane.

**The tidal bore of England's River Severn has reached a top speed of 13mph, very slightly slower than the top speed recorded for a rowing eight over a 2000-meter still-water course (13.46mph).**

©DIAGRAM

# ANIMALS AND MAN

When it comes to natural movement many animals are faster than man, although man is by no means one of nature's slowcoaches. Just as man's inventions enable him to travel faster in the air than on land or in water, it is in the air that the highest of all animal speeds are recorded. The spine-tailed swift is at least half as fast again as the cheetah. The speeds given here have been standardized as far as possible, but when dealing with wild animals there is an almost inevitable lack of standard methods for timing and for measuring distances and wind speeds. Another complication is that exceptional individuals are sometimes taken to be representative of an entire species.

## Speeds in the air

*right* The racing pigeon would come a poor second in a race with the fastest of all birds, the spine-tailed swift. Selected insects are also included for comparison; small size makes their performances particularly impressive.

Spine-tailed swift 106.25mph
Pigeon 60mph
Hawk moth 33mph
Monarch butterfly 20mph
Honeybee 11mph

## Speeds on land

*right* The cheetah is the fastest animal on land, but only for distances up to about 350yd, after which the prong-horned antelope is faster. Man's fastest known speed was calculated from the top speed touched during a 100yd race.

Cheetah 70mph
Prong-horned antelope 60mph
Jackrabbit 45mph
Ostrich 30+mph
Man 27mph

## Speeds in water

*right* The sailfish is thought to be the fastest creature in water, but data on aquatic creatures is extremely difficult to verify. The speed of 5.19mph for man is calculated from the top speed touched in a sprint.

Sailfish 60+mph
Flying fish 40+mph
Dolphin 37mph
Trout 15mph
Man 5.19mph

## Slow and not so slow

*right* Here we compare the time taken by some of nature's slower creatures to travel 100m, which the world record holder J.R. Hines covered in 9.95sec and a typical young adult walks in about 1min.
**a** Mole 7hr 50min—3hr faster than a mechanical mole can burrow the same distance!
**b** Snail 2hr 4min
**c** Giant tortoise 22min
**d** Three-toed sloth 22min
**e** Spider 8min 50sec
**f** Centipede 3min 25sec—quite an achievement in view of its small size!

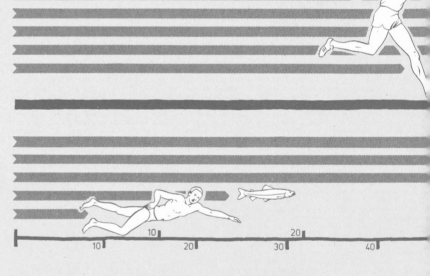

hours

*From a stationary start, man could hold
the lead over a modern sports car for
approximately 10 yd.*

**A close bet—over 110yd,
the fastest timed
greyhound (41.72mph
for 410yd) would have
lost by 3-4yd to the
fastest horse (43.26mph
for a 440yd race).**

**Fastest creature**
*right* The spine-tailed
swift from Asia is the
fastest creature alive.
Its highest reliably
measured speed is 106.25
mph, but claims have been
made for anything up to
219.5mph.

©DIAGRAM

**The English hare can
run over 250 times
faster than the giant
tortoise, but in Aesop's
fable, the tortoise won
the race.**

189

# HUMAN ACHIEVEMENTS

Man's muscular machinery has probably remained essentially the same for many thousands of years. Yet each year athletes continue to improve on existing world speed records. Most of the speeds given here would have seemed impossible in 1900, but few if any of them are now expected to be records in the year 2000.

**Sporting speeds**
*below* The diagram shows top speeds achieved by athletes in different speed events. Muscles or gravity provided the motive force for all these achievements, although the cyclist was aided by the slipstream of the vehicle ahead of him.

**1** Roller skating, 25.8mph over 440yd of road.
**2** Running, 27mph+ attained during 100yd dash.
**3** Speed skating, 30.22mph averaged over 500m.
**4** Skateboarding, 53.45mph in stand-up position.
**5** Luge tobogganing, 80mph+ recorded.

| Event | | Holder | Time | Speed |
|---|---|---|---|---|
| **A** 100m | Men | J. R. Hines (USA) | 9.95s | 10.05m/s |
| | Women | M. Göhr (GDR) | 10.88s | 9.19m/s |
| **B** 200m | Men | P. Mennea (Italy) | 19.72s | 10.14m/s |
| | Women | M. Koch (GDR) | 21.71s | 9.21m/s |
| **C** 400m | Men | L. E. Evans (USA) | 43.86s | 9.12m/s |
| | Women | M. Koch (GDR) | 48.60s | 8.23m/s |
| **D** 800m | Men | S. Coe (UK) | 1min 42.4s | 7.81m/s |
| | Women | T. Kazankina (USSR) | 1min 54.9s | 6.96m/s |
| **E** 1500m | Men | S. Coe (UK) | 3min 32.1s | 7.07m/s |
| | Women | T. Kazankina (USSR) | 3min 56.0s | 6.36m/s |
| **F** 5000m | Men | H. Rono (Kenya) | 13min 8.4s | 6.34m/s |
| **G** 10,000m | Men | H. Rono (Kenya) | 27min 22.4s | 6.09m/s |

**Track event records**
Listed *left* are details of world records for 12 track events, as at April 1, 1980. Each of the speeds given— also shown in the diagram *below*—is the number of meters run per second as averaged over the whole distance of the race.

*Olympic runners achieve faster average speeds over 200m than they do over 100m. This is because a comparatively slow speed for the first few meters of both these events is averaged out in the 200m by a longer distance run at full speed.*

*The fastest speed attained by a water skier (134.3mph) is almost exactly 10mph faster than the fastest speed touched by a skier on land (124.4mph).*

**6** Cresta run tobogganing, 90mph sometimes reached.
**7** Skibob, top speed of 103.4mph attained.
**8** Skiing, 124.4mph reached on a downhill course.
**9** Cycling, average speed of of 140.5mph over ¾mi, attained behind a windshield mounted on an automobile.

**Feats of leg power** *right*
The fastest speed touched by a runner, probably in excess of 27mph (**a**), is here compared with the top speed of 49.38mph attained by a cyclist without the help of a windshield (**b**).

©DIAGRAM

| 70 | 80 | 90 | 100 | 110 | 120 | 130 mph | 140 |
|---|---|---|---|---|---|---|---|

| 120 | 130 | 140 | 150 | 160 | 170 | 180 | 190 | 200 | 210 km/h | 220 |
|---|---|---|---|---|---|---|---|---|---|---|

**Master milers** *right*
Here we use clock faces, each representing one minute, to show the world record for one mile at different points in this event's history. In 1954 Roger Bannister became the first man to break the four-minute barrier. In 1979, twenty-five years later, Sebastian Coe achieved a time 10.4 seconds faster than Bannister's.
**a** W. Chinnery (UK) 4m 29.8s
**b** J.P. Jones (USA) 4m 14.4s
**c** G. Cunningham (USA) 4m 6.8s
**d** R. Bannister (UK) 3m 59.4s
**e** P. Snell (NZ) 3m 54.1s
**f** S. Coe (UK) 3m 49.0s

a **1868**
b **1913**
c **1934**
d **1954**
e **1964**
f **1979**

**Mary Decker (USA) has run an indoor mile in 4m 17.6s — an average speed of 14.4mph, compared with Sebastian Coe's world record average of 15.7mph.**

An American parachutist traveled marginally faster than the speed of sound during a record-breaking delayed-drop jump from a balloon in the stratosphere: he reached a maximum speed of 625.2mph at a height of 90,000ft above the ground.

# SPEEDS ON LAND

Land-speed records fell repeatedly as man exploited more effective kinds of motive force. In 1907 the steam-powered *Stanley Steamer* reached 150mph (241km/h), the then highest speed for a manned vehicle in any element. Since 1959 the fastest land vehicle has been a rail-mounted, unmanned rocket sled four times as fast as sound.

**High-speed cars**
The table *right* lists a selection of official land-speed record holders. (From 1911 only the average speed of two runs, in opposite directions, has qualified for official recognition.) The diagram *below* plots selected record-holders on a graph showing how record speeds increased as the years passed and as direct thrust replaced propulsion via the wheels. A wheel-driven vehicle reached 409.27mph in 1965. That year a jet car reached 600.60mph. Since 1970 rocket cars have led the field.

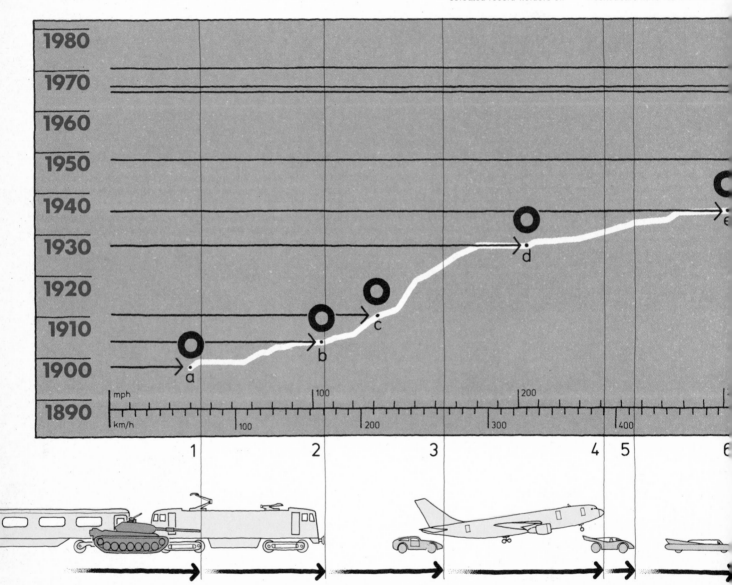

Fastest speeds (not official records) attained in different types of vehicle are:
418.504mph for a piston-engined car (R. S. Summers, *Goldenrod*, 1965)
429.311mph for a wheel-driven car (D. Campbell, *Proteus Bluebird*, 1964)
613.995mph for a jet-engined car (N. C. Breedlove, *Spirit of America — Sonic 1*, 1965)
739.67mph for a rocket-engined car (S. Barret, *Budweiser Rocket*, 1979)

To match the distance covered in one hour
by the US Air Force rocket sled (3090 miles),
the fastest-ever runner would have to
maintain his top speed of 27mph from
midday on Monday until 6am Saturday.

| Holder (year of record) | Vehicle | Speed | |
|---|---|---|---|
| **a** G. de Chasseloup-Laubat (1898) | Jeantaud | 39.24mph | 63.15km/h |
| **b** P. Baras (1904) | Darracq | 104.52mph | 168.20km/h |
| **c** B. Oldfield (1910) | Blitzen Benz | 131.72mph | 211.98km/h |
| **d** H. O. D. Segrave (1927) | Sunbeam | 203.79mph | 327.96km/h |
| **e** M. Campbell (1935) | Campbell Special | 301.13mph | 484.61km/h |
| **f** J. R. Cobb (1947) | Railton | 394.20mph | 634.39km/h |
| **g** A. Arfons (1964) | *Green Monster* | 536.71mph | 863.73km/h |
| **h** N. C. Breedlove (1965) | *Spirit of America—Sonic I* | 600.60mph | 966.55km/h |
| **i** G. Gabelich (1970) | *The Blue Flame* | 622.29mph | 1001.45km/h |

**First and last** *below*
In 1898 G. de Chasseloup-
Laubat in a Jeantaud (**a**) set
a land-speed record of
39.24mph. The present
record of 622.29mph, set in
1970 by G. Gabelich in *The
Blue Flame* (**i**) is 15.9 times
faster.

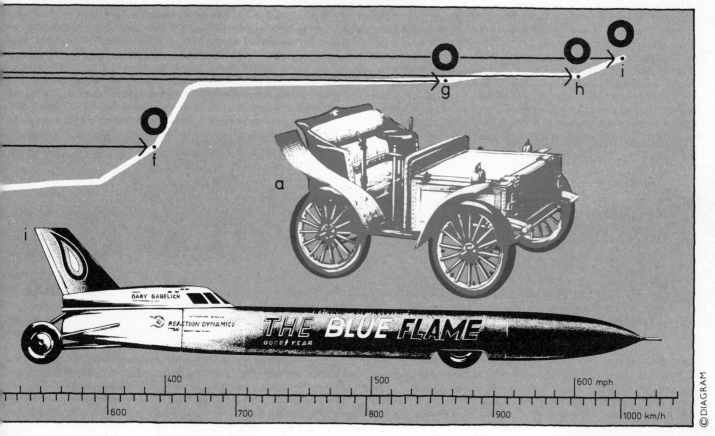

©DIAGRAM

**Hares and tortoises** *left*
Plotted against the same
scale as the graph of official
land-speed records are the
top land speeds of six
vehicles, most far slower
than recent land-speed
record holders. (Only in the
air do travelers routinely
approach the record speed

on land.) Listed in order of
their speeds these vehicles
are:
**1** Tank 45mph
**2** Regular electric
passenger train 106.25mph
**3** Production car 163mph
**4** Aircraft (landing) 242mph
**5** Racing car 257mph
**6** Motorcycle 307.69mph

**Rocket on rails** *below*
The highest speed so far
attained on land is 3090mph,
by an unmanned US Air
Force rocket-powered sled
on a railed track at
Holloman, New Mexico in
1959. This speed is almost
five times faster than the
regular land speed record.

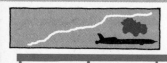

# SPEEDS ON WATER

The official world water-speed record is only just over half as fast as its land equivalent, and approximately one-seventh as fast as that in air. It is, however, the most dangerous event of the three—for a boat easily goes out of control at high speeds. Also included here for comparison are various other speed records on water.

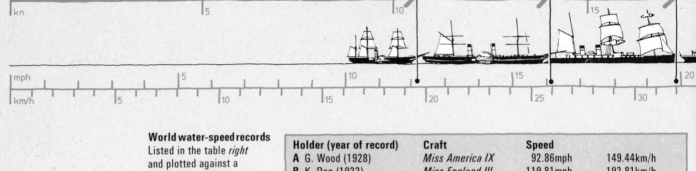

**World water-speed records**
Listed in the table *right* and plotted against a scale in the diagram *below* are selected holders of the official world water-speed record, first recognized in 1928. The last three—Campbell, Taylor and Warby—used jet-powered craft.

| Holder (year of record) | Craft | Speed | |
|---|---|---|---|
| A G. Wood (1928) | *Miss America IX* | 92.86mph | 149.44km/h |
| B K. Don (1932) | *Miss England III* | 119.81mph | 192.81km/h |
| C M. Campbell (1937) | *Bluebird* | 129.56mph | 208.50km/h |
| D M. Campbell (1939) | *Bluebird* | 141.74mph | 228.10km/h |
| E S. Sayres (1952) | *Slo-Mo-Shun IV* | 178.50mph | 287.26km/h |
| F D. Campbell (1964) | *Bluebird* | 276.33mph | 444.70km/h |
| G L. Taylor (1967) | *Hustler* | 285.21mph | 458.99km/h |
| H K. Warby (1978) | *Spirit of Australia* | 319.64mph | 514.39km/h |

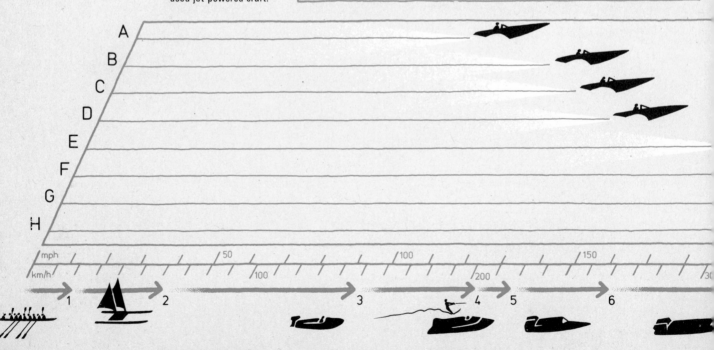

Since 1928 there has been a 3.4 times increase in the official water-speed record. Over the same period there has been a 3 times increase in the official land-speed record, and a 6.9 times increase in the official air-speed record.

**In 1952 the liner** *United States* **took the Blue Riband award for the fastest Atlantic crossing. Her average speed of 35.6 knots for an eastward crossing was only 3.4 times faster than the average speed for a similar crossing by** *Britannia,* **which won the award 112 years earlier.**

**A sailfish can swim half as fast again as the average speed maintained on the** *United States'* **Blue Riband run.**

# Speed

| Liner (year of record) | Average speed | | |
|---|---|---|---|
| a *Britannia* (1840) | 10.6kn | 12.2mph | 19.6km/h |
| b *Scotia* (1863) | 14.0kn | 16.1mph | 25.9km/h |
| c *Alaska* (1882) | 17.2kn | 19.8mph | 31.9km/h |
| d *Kaiser Wilhelm der Grosse* (1897) | 22.4kn | 25.8mph | 41.5km/h |
| e *Mauretania* (1909) | 25.9kn | 29.8mph | 48.0km/h |
| f *Bremen* (1929) | 27.9kn | 32.1mph | 51.7km/h |
| g *Queen Mary* (1938) | 31.7kn | 36.5mph | 58.7km/h |
| h *United States* (1952) | 35.6kn | 41.0mph | 66.0km/h |

**Blue Riband speeds**
Listed *left* and illustrated and plotted against the scale *below* is a selection of liners that made record transatlantic crossings from the United States to Europe to win the coveted Blue Riband award. Average speeds are given in international knots (see p. 185) and in miles and kilometers per hour. Two ships have held the record continuously for periods of 14 years: *Mauretania* from 1909–23, and *Queen Mary* from 1938–52. *United States* has now held the record for 28 years.

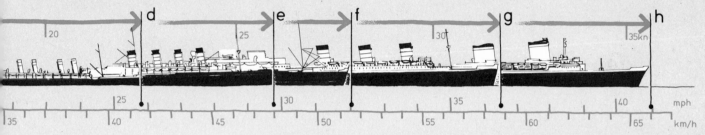

| Holder (year of record) | Craft | Record | Speed | |
|---|---|---|---|---|
| 1 East German team (1976) | | Rowing eight (2000m, still-water) | 13.46mph | 21.66km/h |
| 2 T. Colman (1977) | *Crossbow II* | Sailing speed | 38.46mph | 61.89km/h |
| 3 M. Frode (1977) | Class IIID Frode | Off-shore powerboat | 92.99mph | 149.65km/h |
| 4 D. Churchill (1971) | | Water-skiing speed | 125.69mph | 202.27km/h |
| 5 J. F. Merton (1973) | *Quicksilver* | Class ON powerboat | 136.38mph | 219.48km/h |
| 6 S. Williams (1977) | U-96 KYYX | Women's water-speed | 163.04mph | 262.38km/h |
| 7 L. Hill (1971) | *Mr Ed* | Propellor-driven | 202.42mph | 325.75km/h |

**Other records on water**
Described *left* and plotted *bottom* are official world records (April 1980) for selected water events. Conditions of recognition obviously vary from event to event, but each record listed is approved by its own international federation.

**Fastest speed on water**
The fastest speed ever attained on water is an estimated 345mph (556km/h) by K. Warby in 1978 in his *Spirit of Australia* (**H**). This is approximately 8% faster than his official water-speed record.

©DIAGRAM

# SPEEDS IN THE AIR

In the 73 years since Orville Wright's first controlled powered flight in 1903 official air-speed records have risen by an annual average equal to the speed of Wright's flight (30mph), for in 1976 an orthodox jet plane flew 73 times faster than Wright. Air-launched planes propelled by rockets are dramatically faster still.

**Air speed records**
The table *right* and the diagram *below* show details of official air-speed records spanning more than six decades. The speeds shown were all ratified by the Fédération Aéronautique Internationale. They exclude records set by air-launched aircraft. Vertical lines indicate Mach speeds: multiples of the speed of sound, taken as 659.78mph (1061.78km/h) in the stratosphere (see p. 185). From 1909 official record speeds doubled or more than doubled at intervals of 1, 10, 8, 24 and 6 years.

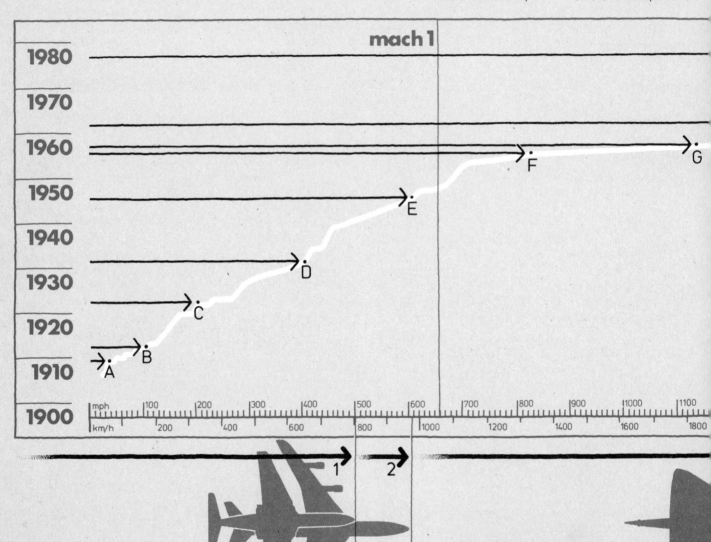

The official air-speed record (2193.17mph) is 3.6 times faster than the cruising speed of a Boeing 707 (604mph) and 1.5 times faster than that of *Concorde* (1450mph).

*The first man-powered air crossing of the English Channel was made in 1979 by Bryan Allen in* Gossamer Albatross. *His average speed of 8.2mph was less than one-fifth that of Louis Blériot, who in 1909 made the first air crossing of the Channel in his* Blériot XI *monoplane at an average speed of 42.7mph.*

The holder of the official air-speed record flew at a speed of 2193.17mph, or 3216.72 feet per second. The speed of a bullet from the US Army's current M16 rifle is even faster—3300ft per second.

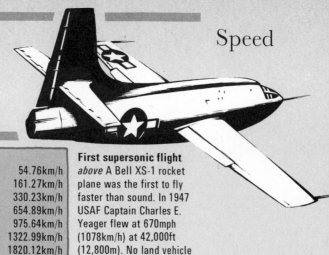

# Speed

**First supersonic flight**
*above* A Bell XS-1 rocket plane was the first to fly faster than sound. In 1947 USAF Captain Charles E. Yeager flew at 670mph (1078km/h) at 42,000ft (12,800m). No land vehicle matched his speed for the next 32 years.

| Holder (year of record) | Aircraft | Speed | |
|---|---|---|---|
| P. Tissandier (1909) | Wright biplane | 34.03mph | 54.76km/h |
| J. Védrines (1912) | Deperdussin monoplane | 100.21mph | 161.27km/h |
| S. Lecointe (1922) | Nieuport-Delage 29 | 205.20mph | 330.23km/h |
| G.H. Stainforth (1931) | Supermarine S6B | 406.94mph | 654.89km/h |
| H.J. Wilson (1945) | Gloster Meteor F4 | 606.25mph | 975.64km/h |
| H.A. Hanes (1955) | F-100C Super Sabre | 822.09mph | 1322.99km/h |
| P. Twiss (1956) | Fairey Delta 2 | 1131.76mph | 1820.12km/h |
| R.B. Robinson (1961) | McDonnell F4H-1F Phantom II | 1606.51mph | 2585.36km/h |
| E.W. Joersz & G.T. Morgan (1976) | Lockheed SR-71A | 2193.17mph | 3529.47km/h |

2  3  i  H  A  I

17952  US AIR FORCE  952

| | 1400 | 1500 | 1600 | 1700 | 1800 | 1900 | 2000 | 2100 | 2200 | 2300 | 2400 | mph |
| 2000 | 2200 | 2400 | 2600 | 2800 | 3000 | 3200 | 3400 | 3600 | 3800 | km/h |

©DIAGRAM

3

**Commercial speeds** *left*
For the traveling public air speeds lagged very far behind world air-speed records. By the late 1930s US passenger aircraft averaged 158mph (254km/h). By the early 1950s speeds reached 370mph (595km/h). Then the turbojet-powered

Comet and its successors pushed commercial cruising speeds higher. The three planes *left* span the range of cruising speeds for airliners, *Concorde* almost trebling the Comet's speed.
**1** Comet 4, 500mph
**2** Boeing 707, 604mph
**3** *Concorde*, 1450mph

**Fastest rocket plane** *below*
North American Aviation's air-launched, rocket-driven X-15A-2 attained a speed of 4534mph (7297km/h) in 1967. This was more than twice as fast as the official air-speed record of 2193.17mph (3529.47km/h) set some 9 years later.

# VEHICLE SPEEDS

In the early 1800s steam locomotives amazed spectators by moving as quickly as a horse could gallop. Today, vehicles on land and water and in air and space attain speeds undreamed of a lifetime ago. The speeds given here are chiefly top speeds touched, not official records set in specified conditions.

**Subsonic records**
Plotted on the scale *below* and listed in the table *right* are the fastest speeds achieved by certain types of vehicle on land, water, ice, snow and in air. The list excludes vehicles capable of producing supersonic performances.

Limitations of certain propulsive methods mean some of these speeds may be never more than marginally bettered. Thus the steam locomotive record set in 1938 still stood in 1980. But by then rail speeds were being doubled by the linear induction motor.

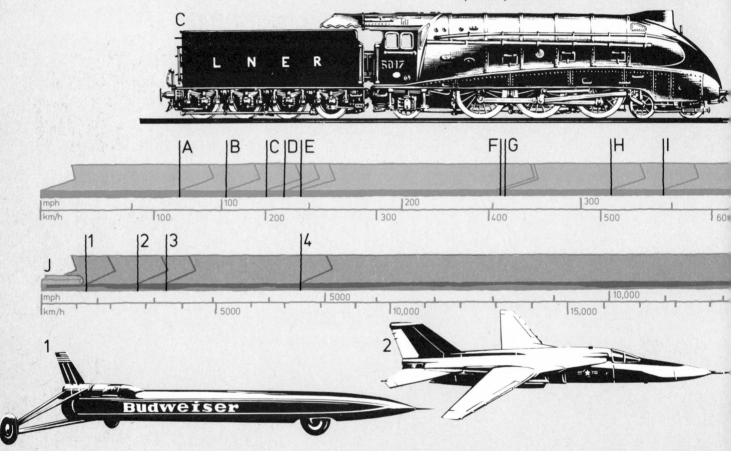

**Supersonic speeds**
Listed in the table *right* are the supersonic speeds reached by the vehicles *above* on land or in the air, or—for the command module—on reentering the atmosphere from space. All of these supersonic vehicles were manned.

| | | | |
|---|---|---|---|
| **1** | Rocket car *Budweiser Rocket* (1979) | 739.67mph | 1190.35km/h |
| **2** | Bomber American General Dynamics FB-IIIA | 1650mph | 2655.35km/h |
| **3** | Reconnaissance plane Lockheed SR-71A (1976) | 2193.17mph | 3529.47km/h |
| **4** | Rocket plane N American Aviation X-15A-2 (1967) | 4534mph | 7296.57km/h |
| **5** | *Apollo 10* command module (1969) | 24,791mph | 39,896.16km/h |

**In 1979 S. Barret in the rocket-powered car *Budweiser Rocket* touched a speed of 739.67mph. This is approximately 55 times faster than the 13.5mph reached in 1830 by George Stephenson's famous *Rocket* steam locomotive.**

*The jet-powered tracked hovercraft* L'Aérotrain 02 *has touched a speed of 255.3mph. This is three times faster than the average speed of 85mph for the fastest daily run of a British Rail train from London to Edinburgh.*

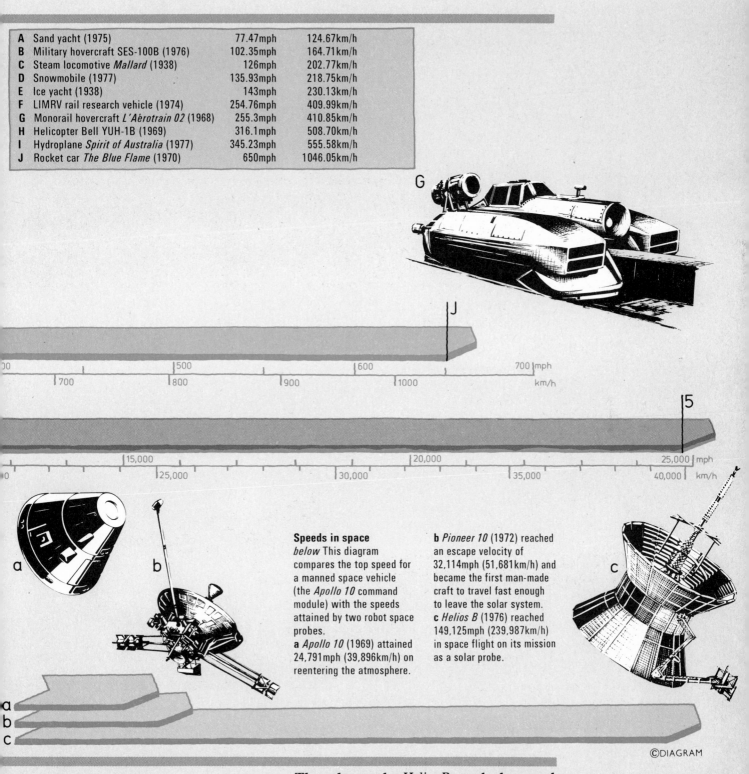

| | | | |
|---|---|---|---|
| **A** | Sand yacht (1975) | 77.47mph | 124.67km/h |
| **B** | Military hovercraft SES-100B (1976) | 102.35mph | 164.71km/h |
| **C** | Steam locomotive *Mallard* (1938) | 126mph | 202.77km/h |
| **D** | Snowmobile (1977) | 135.93mph | 218.75km/h |
| **E** | Ice yacht (1938) | 143mph | 230.13km/h |
| **F** | LIMRV rail research vehicle (1974) | 254.76mph | 409.99km/h |
| **G** | Monorail hovercraft *L'Aérotrain 02* (1968) | 255.3mph | 410.85km/h |
| **H** | Helicopter Bell YUH-1B (1969) | 316.1mph | 508.70km/h |
| **I** | Hydroplane *Spirit of Australia* (1977) | 345.23mph | 555.58km/h |
| **J** | Rocket car *The Blue Flame* (1970) | 650mph | 1046.05km/h |

**Speeds in space**
*below* This diagram compares the top speed for a manned space vehicle (the *Apollo 10* command module) with the speeds attained by two robot space probes.
**a** *Apollo 10* (1969) attained 24,791mph (39,896km/h) on reentering the atmosphere.

**b** *Pioneer 10* (1972) reached an escape velocity of 32,114mph (51,681km/h) and became the first man-made craft to travel fast enough to leave the solar system.
**c** *Helios B* (1976) reached 149,125mph (239,987km/h) in space flight on its mission as a solar probe.

©DIAGRAM

**The solar probe** *Helios B* **reached a speed of 149,125mph. Traveling at this speed for its entire journey it would have crossed the orbit of the Moon after about 1½ hours and reached the Sun in 26 days.**

# THE PLANETS

Although we cannot feel it, Earth is moving rapidly through space. Our planet's mean orbital velocity—the average speed at which it orbits the Sun—is some 66,641mph. Its rotational velocity at the Equator—the speed it turns on its axis—is 1040mph. Here we compare Earth's speeds with those of other planets.

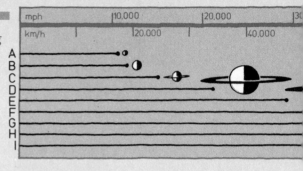

| Mean orbital velocity | | |
|---|---|---|
| A Pluto | 10,604mph | 17,064km/h |
| B Neptune | 12,147mph | 19,548km/h |
| C Uranus | 15,234mph | 24,516km/h |
| D Saturn | 21,565mph | 34,704km/h |
| E Jupiter | 29,216mph | 47,016km/h |
| F Mars | 53,980mph | 86,868km/h |
| G Earth | 66,641mph | 107,244km/h |
| H Venus | 78,364mph | 126,108km/h |
| I Mercury | 107,132mph | 172,404km/h |

**Orbital velocities** *left*
Listed are the planets' mean orbital velocities, from slowest to fastest. The nearer a planet is to the Sun the faster it has to travel to counteract the Sun's gravitational force that would otherwise pull the planet toward it.

**Orbital velocity scale**
*above* In this diagram the mean orbital velocities of the planets are shown against an mph and km/h scale. The speed for Mercury, with the highest orbital velocity, is about 10 times faster than that for Pluto, with the lowest.

**Race to the Moon**
*right* Here the orbital velocities of the planets are compared by marking the distance traveled by each planet in one hour on a line representing the center-to-center distance between Earth and Moon, 238,840mi (384,365km).

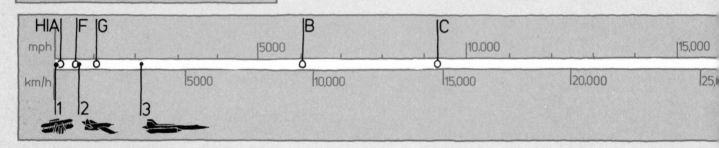

| Rotational velocity at equator | | |
|---|---|---|
| H Venus | 4.05mph | 6.52km/h |
| I Mercury | 6.73mph | 10.83km/h |
| A Pluto | 76.56mph | 123.21km/h |
| F Mars | 538mph | 866km/h |
| G Earth | 1040mph | 1674km/h |
| B Neptune | 6039mph | 9719km/h |
| C Uranus | 9193mph | 14,794km/h |
| D Saturn | 22,892mph | 36,840km/h |
| E Jupiter | 28,325mph | 45,583km/h |

**Rotational velocities**
Listed *left* and plotted on the scale *above* are the planets' equatorial rotational velocities. The diagram also shows the speeds of representative air and space vehicles.
**1** *Flyer 1*, first controlled flight, 30mph (48km/h)
**2** Bell XS-1, first aircraft

to break the sound barrier, 670mph (1078km/h)
**3** Lockheed SR-71A, fastest aircraft, 2193mph (3529km/h)
**4** *Sputnik 1*, first satellite, 17,750mph (28,565km/h)
**5** *Pioneer 10*, planetary research craft, 32,114mph (51,681km/h)

**Size and speed** *below*
The planets (shown to scale) are here drawn in order of their rotational velocities (from slowest to fastest). In general, the larger the planet the greater is its equatorial rotational velocity. Venus (**H**) is the exception—its heavy atmosphere causing it to rotate most slowly of all.

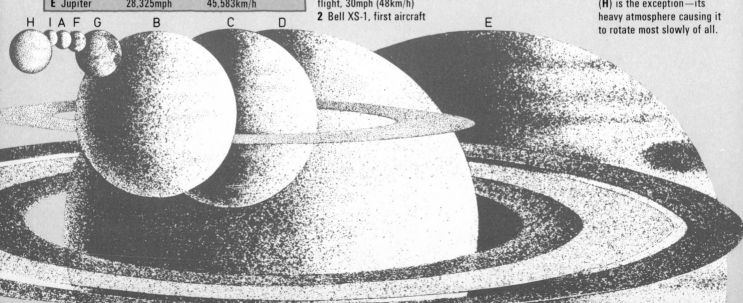

**Mercury has the fastest mean orbital velocity but the second slowest equatorial rotational velocity. Jupiter has the fastest equatorial rotational velocity while ranking fifth for mean orbital velocity.**

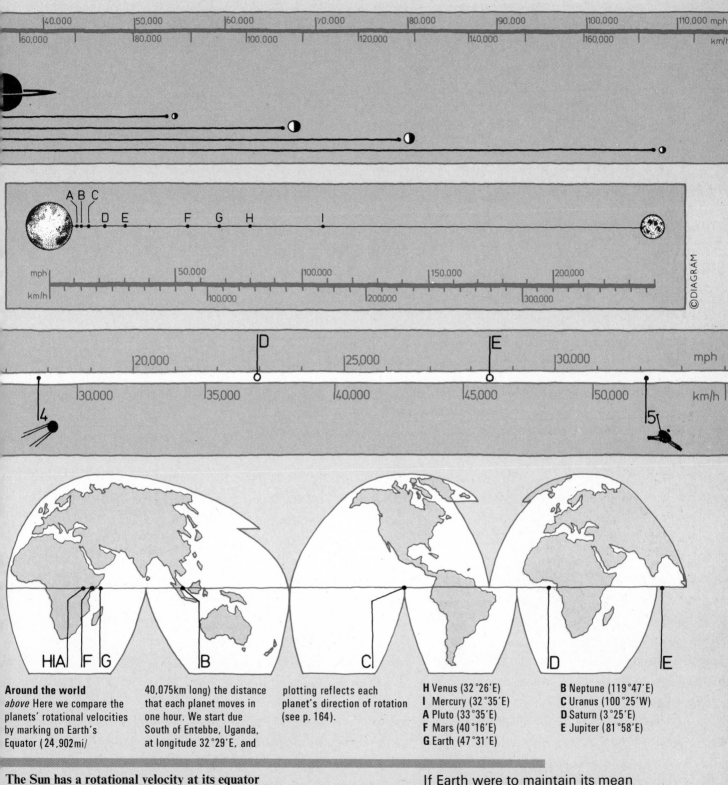

©DIAGRAM

**Around the world**
*above* Here we compare the planets' rotational velocities by marking on Earth's Equator (24,902mi/ 40,075km long) the distance that each planet moves in one hour. We start due South of Entebbe, Uganda, at longitude 32°29′E, and plotting reflects each planet's direction of rotation (see p. 164).

**H** Venus (32°26′E)
**I** Mercury (32°35′E)
**A** Pluto (33°35′E)
**F** Mars (40°16′E)
**G** Earth (47°31′E)

**B** Neptune (119°47′E)
**C** Uranus (100°25′W)
**D** Saturn (3°25′E)
**E** Jupiter (81°58′E)

**The Sun has a rotational velocity at its equator of 4461mph. This is 1101 times faster than that of Venus, 4.3 times faster than that of Earth, and 6.3 times slower than that of Jupiter.**

If Earth were to maintain its mean orbital velocity of 66,641mph but were to head toward the Sun, we would have only 58 days to make our escape!

# CHAPTER 10

Woodcut illustrations from two books on arithmetic published in Augsburg in 1514. The first, from a work by Köbel, shows a simple line abacus, with ruled lines to show the different decimal orders and counters placed on or between the lines. The second, from a book by Böschensteyn, shows the working out of a problem with blackboard and chalk.

# NUMBER

Vast numbers of people from all over the world are shown flocking to London's Great Exhibition of 1851 in George Cruikshank's frontispiece to *The World's Show* by Christopher Mayhew.

Lottery tickets from different countries make an interesting collage. The odds of winning a fortune are determined by the number of tickets sold.

# NUMBERS

Here we look at the different number systems and number names that are basic to our perception of the world. Natural numbers, the first to have been used, are all the whole numbers from one to infinity. Integers consist of the natural numbers, zero, and also the minus numbers (−1, −2 etc.). Rational and real numbers include all the fractions and decimals between the whole numbers, while imaginary numbers are those that do not exist, such as the square root of a minus number. Numbers are the "tools" used for making and explaining all the other types of measurement devised by man and described in other chapters of this book.

| International | US | Size | Indices |
|---|---|---|---|
| Ten | Ten | 10 | $10^1$ |
| Hundred | Hundred | 100 | $10^2$ |
| Thousand | Thousand | 1000 | $10^3$ |
| Million | Million | 1,000,000 | $10^6$ |
| Milliard | Billion | 1,000,000,000 | $10^9$ |
| Billion | Trillion | 1,000,000,000,000 | $10^{12}$ |
| | Quadrillion | 1,000,000,000,000,000 | $10^{15}$ |
| Trillion | Quintillion | 1,000,000,000,000,000,000 | $10^{18}$ |

| | |
|---|---|
| Couple | = 2 |
| Pair | = 2 |
| Half dozen | = 6 |
| Dozen | = 12 |
| Score | = 20 |
| Quarter century | = 25 |
| Half century | = 50 |
| Century | = 100 |
| Gross | = 144 |

**Names and numbers** *left*
The table lists special names applied to some common amounts. Particular number systems are also used in specialized areas such as music (duet, trio, quartet etc.) and multiple births (twins, triplets, quadruplets etc.).

**Counting in tens** *above*
In our numerical system we separate our numbers into groups by multiplying or dividing them by ten. This table gives the special names applied to some of these groups; there are two systems in current use—international and US.

**Indicative indices** *above*
Indices are small numbers that indicate how many times one number must be multiplied by itself to give a second number. 100 (10 x 10) can be written as $10^2$; 1000 (10 x 10 x 10) as $10^3$; 1,000,000 as $10^6$, and so on. Similarly 0.001 (which is $1 \div 10 \div 10 \div 10$) can be written as $10^{-3}$, the minus sign indicating how many times the unit must be divided by ten.

$10^4$
$10^3$
$10^2$

K

A B C D E F G H I J

**Scale of natural numbers** *above* Natural numbers are the whole numbers from one to infinity. This logarithmic scale represents the natural numbers that man uses to quantify the phenomena of his universe, some of which are listed by the scale (**K-R**) on the facing page.

*The approximate number of molecules in one cubic centimeter of water is 33,000,000,000,000,000,000,000 (3.3 x $10^{22}$).*

**An international billion is one thousand times bigger than a US billion. An international trillion is one million times bigger than a US trillion.**

There are an estimated $10^{80}$ atoms in the universe.

**Fixed quantities** *right*
Although many quantities, such as the population of the world or the number of cars manufactured annually, are always changing, others remain constant. Here we list a few of these, which appear at the beginning of the scale *below*.

| | |
|---|---|
| **A** | 1 Empire State Building |
| **B** | 2 sexes |
| **C** | 3 sides to a triangle |
| **D** | 4 playing card suits |
| **E** | 5 fingers on a hand |
| **F** | 6 legs on an insect |
| **G** | 7 wonders of the world |
| **H** | 8 legs on a spider |
| **I** | 9 solar planets |
| **J** | 10 Commandments |

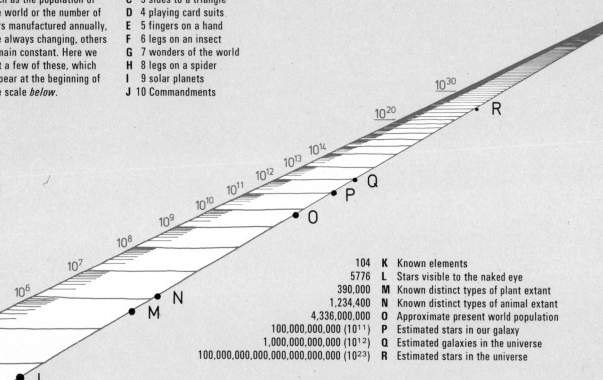

| | | |
|---|---|---|
| 104 | **K** | Known elements |
| 5776 | **L** | Stars visible to the naked eye |
| 390,000 | **M** | Known distinct types of plant extant |
| 1,234,400 | **N** | Known distinct types of animal extant |
| 4,336,000,000 | **O** | Approximate present world population |
| 100,000,000,000 ($10^{11}$) | **P** | Estimated stars in our galaxy |
| 1,000,000,000,000 ($10^{12}$) | **Q** | Estimated galaxies in the universe |
| 100,000,000,000,000,000,000,000 ($10^{23}$) | **R** | Estimated stars in the universe |

**Rational numbers** *right*
Rational numbers are a means of expressing numbers as parts of a whole. The number below, or after, the dividing line is called the denominator, and tells us how many parts the whole has been divided into. The number above, or before, the line is called the numerator, and tells us how many of these parts we have. The principle is shown in the fractions listed in the first column of the table.

| | |
|---|---|
| 1/1 | = 1 |
| 1/2 | = 0.5 |
| 1/3 | = 0.3333333333333333 |
| 1/4 | = 0.25 |
| 1/5 | = 0.2 |
| 1/6 | = 0.1666666666666666 |
| 1/7 | = 0.1428571428571428571 |
| 1/8 | = 0.125 |
| 1/9 | = 0.1111111111111111111 |
| 1/10 | = 0.1 |
| 1/11 | = 0.0909090909090909090 |
| 1/12 | = 0.0833333333333333333 |
| 1/13 | = 0.0769230769230769230 |
| 1/14 | = 0.0714285714285714285 |
| 1/15 | = 0.0666666666666666666 |
| 1/16 | = 0.0625 |
| 1/17 | = 0.0588235294110764705 |
| 1/18 | = 0.0555555555555555555 |
| 1/19 | = 0.0526315789473684210 |
| 1/20 | = 0.05 |

**Decimal numbers** *left*
Decimals are alternative methods of expressing fractions that are not whole numbers. Each column to the right of the decimal point has one-tenth of the value of the previous column, so the number is divided into tenths, hundredths, thousandths etc. For example: 0.2 = 2/10; 0.03 = 3/100; 0.234 = 234/1000. The decimal equivalents of some fractions are shown in the table *left*. For some fractions, the decimal numbers stretch to infinity in a variety of repeating patterns.

**Irrational numbers** *below*
Irrational numbers cannot be expressed as fractions, and as decimals they reach to infinity without repeating the same series of numbers. Examples are π (the circumference of a circle ÷ twice the radius) and the square root of two.

$\Pi = 3.1415926\ldots$

$\sqrt{2} = 1.4142135\ldots$

For one hundred thousand, the Indians have a quantity known as a *lakh*, written 1,00,000. Ten *lakhs* (equal to one million) is written 10,00,000. One hundred *lakhs* (equal to ten million) is termed a *crore*, and written 1,00,00,000.

© DIAGRAM

# NUMBER SYSTEMS

As civilizations developed, the exact quantification of items became necessary for purposes such as barter, tax, and calendar predictions of times and seasons. Many number systems were developed; the degree of sophistication varied, but each system had a base number that divided the units into manageable groups.

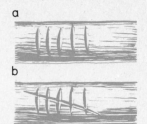

**Making a mark** *left*
The first method of making a record of an exact number of objects involved notching a stick or scratching a rock with one mark for each object (**a**). Sometimes groups of marks were indicated as shown (**b**).

**A** The Babylonians used a unit system, with only a few different symbols. Most numbers were made by building up series of these basic symbols in bases of ten and six, and by varying their placing.

**B** The Egyptians also used a unit system on a base of ten. Placing was variable; examples have been found written from left to right, right to left, and top to bottom.

**C** The Mayans used many systems, of which one is described here. It is a complex unit system based on five and twenty, in which placing is critical.

**D** The Hebrew system took letters of the alphabet and used these as symbols for their numbers. Although the system is on base ten, there are individual symbols for many of the higher numbers, such as 30 and 300.

**E** The Ionic system is also based on an alphabet. Like the Hebrew system, the Ionic is on base ten yet has symbols for many of the higher numbers.

**F** The Roman system is basically a unit system on bases of five and ten, but some of its symbols are the first letters of the names of of the numbers, for instance C for 100 (centum in Latin).

|   | 0 | 1 | 2 | 3 | 4 | 5 | 6 | 7 | 8 | 9 | 10 | 50 | 100 | 500 | 1000 |
|---|---|---|---|---|---|---|---|---|---|---|----|----|-----|-----|------|
| A | | | | | | | | | | | | | | | |
| B | | I | II | III | IIII | | | | | | ∩ | | | | |
| C | | • | •• | ••• | •••• | — | | | | | | | | | |

|   | 0 | 1 | 2 | 3 | 4 | 5 | 6 | 7 | 8 | 9 | 10 | 50 | 100 | 500 | 1000 |
|---|---|---|---|---|---|---|---|---|---|---|----|----|-----|-----|------|
| D | | א | ב | ג | ד | ה | ו | ז | ח | ט | י | כ | ק | ר | א |
| E | | A | B | Γ | Δ | E | F | Z | H | Θ | I | N | P | Φ | /A |
| F | | I | II | III | IV | V | VI | VII | VIII | IX | X | L | C | D | M |

**1980**

**Making a date!**
Shown *left* is the date 1980 in modern Western numerals. The same date is depicted *right* in each of the number systems described *above*, keyed in by their identifying letters.

Here we represent 1980 with the dots and dashes of the International Morse Code used by telegraphists.

**Zeroes** *left*
Early number systems with a fixed value for every symbol had no need for zeroes. Zero symbols such as the Mayan (**1**), Hindu (**2**) and Arabic (**3**) permitted more compact number systems in which placing gives each numeral its value.

**Use of the zero** *right*
Zero allowed the indication of an empty column or line in a number, so keeping the other symbols in an exact value ratio. The examples show an addition with the use of zeroes (**a**), and the false result obtained when they are omitted (**b**).

```
a  10613+        b  1613+
    3200              32
     109              19
      80               8
   ─────            ─────
   14002             1672
```

**G** The Hindu system of numbering gives each number from zero to nine a symbol of its own with no other meaning—the symbols are not pictures or letters. Numbers above nine are built up on a base ten system using the basic symbols.
**H** The Arabic system, like the Hindu system, gives a symbol to every number from zero to nine, and builds up its higher numbers in the same way. This is the system on which Western numerals are based.
**I** Chinese numbering is a mixture of units (for the first three numbers) and individual symbols.

| | 0 | 1 | 2 | 3 | 4 | 5 | 6 | 7 | 8 | 9 | 10 | 50 | 100 | 500 | 1000 |
|---|---|---|---|---|---|---|---|---|---|---|---|---|---|---|---|
| G | ० | १ | २ | ३ | ४ | ५ | ६ | ७ | ८ | ९ | २० | ५० | २०० | ५०० | २००० |
| H | ٠ | ١ | ٢ | ٣ | ٤ | ٥ | ٦ | ٧ | ٨ | ٩ | ١٠ | ٥٠ | ١٠٠ | ٥٠٠ | ١٠٠٠ |
| I | | 一 | 二 | 三 | 四 | 五 | 六 | 七 | 八 | 九 | 十 | 五十 | 百 | 五百 | 千 |

$1 \times 1000 \, (10^3)$   $9 \times 100 \, (10^2)$   $8 \times 10$   $0 \times 1$

## 1980

$1 \times 1728 \, (12^3)$   $1 \times 144 \, (12^2)$   $9 \times 12$   $0 \times 1$

## 1190

$1 \times 1024 \, (2^{10})$   $1 \times 512 \, (2^9)$   $1 \times 256 \, (2^8)$   $1 \times 128 \, (2^7)$   $0 \times 64 \, (2^6)$   $1 \times 32 \, (2^5)$   $1 \times 16 \, (2^4)$   $1 \times 8 \, (2^3)$   $1 \times 4 \, (2^2)$   $0 \times 2$   $0 \times 1$

## 1110111100

**Base ten** *above*
The base of a number system sets the points at which notation changes significantly in symbol or in placing. Our numbers are to base ten; a number in one column has ten times the value of the same number in the column to the right.

**Base twelve** *above*
If a number system is based on a factor of twelve, the units move into the left hand column at every twelfth unit instead of every tenth, and each column has the value of a power of twelve. The number 1980 is shown here to base twelve.

**Binary** *above*
The binary system uses a base of two. Each column has a value of a power of two, and the only numerals used are 0 and 1, since every two units require a move into the next column. Shown here is the number 1980 in binary notation.

MCMLXXX

一千九百八十

F

I

१९८०

١٩٨٠

G

H

©DIAGRAM

# LINES AND SHAPES

Numbers can help us to define and reproduce specific shapes. All shapes are based on the concepts of points and the lines that join them. By counting the points and lines in a given shape and then reproducing exactly their lengths, contours and relationships to one another, duplicate shapes can be constructed.

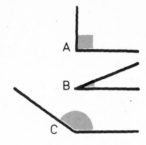

**Angles** *left*
An angle is the inclination one to another of two lines that meet at a point.
**A** Right angle, an angle of exactly 90° (see p. 210).
**B** Acute angle, less than a right angle.
**C** Obtuse angle, greater than a right angle.

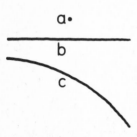

**Lines and points** *left*
Lines and points are in most people's minds inseparable from the marks used to represent them.
**a** Point, marked by a dot.
**b** Straight line, the shortest distance between two points.
**c** Curved line, a line that is nowhere straight.

**Types of line** *right*
Straight lines can be described in precise terms.
**1** Horizontal, a level line.
**2** Vertical, an upright line.
**3** Oblique, a line inclining to the right or the left.
**4** Parallel, two or more lines in the same direction that cannot meet.

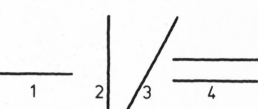

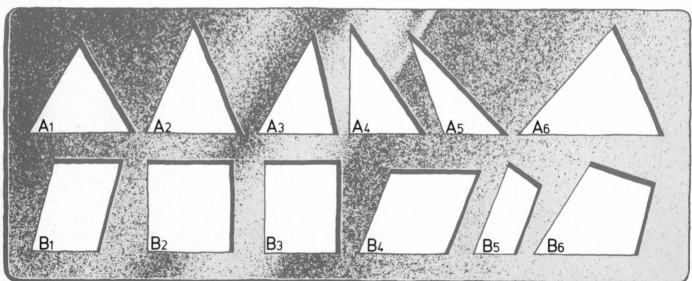

**Triangles**
A triangle is a figure contained by three straight sides. Some specific forms of triangle are illustrated *above* (**A**), and described in the list *far right*. The internal angles of any plane triangle always total exactly 180°.

**Quadrilaterals**
A quadrilateral is a figure contained by four straight sides; various types are shown *above* (**B**). If criteria listed in the table *right* are fulfilled, the shape will have have a particular name. Shapes outside these criteria are irregular.

**A1** Equilateral triangle: all sides equal
**A2** Isosceles triangle: two equal sides
**A3** Scalene triangle: no two sides equal
**A4** Right-angled triangle: contains one right angle
**A5** Obtuse-angled triangle: contains one obtuse angle
**A6** Acute-angled triangle: contains three acute angles
**B1** Parallelogram: opposite sides are parallel
**B2** Square: equal sides and four right angles
**B3** Rectangle: equal opposite sides and four right angles
**B4** Rhombus: equal sides but no right angles
**B5** Trapezium: two parallel sides
**B6** Irregular: no parallel sides

**A triangle drawn on a sphere breaks the Euclidian law that the internal angles of a triangle equal 180°. Our example has three right angles (270°).**

The ancient Egyptians obtained a right angle with a piece of rope divided into 12 equal sections by 12 knots. One man (**a**) held the first knot and the other end of the rope. A second man (**b**) held the knot three sections from the first one. A third man (**c**) held the knot five spaces after the second man's knot and four from the end.

**Circle** *left*
A circle is a plane figure contained by one curved line, every point of which is equally distant from the point at the circle's center. The line bounding the circle is called the lcircumference.

**Features of a circle** *right*
**a** Radius, a straight line joining the center and any point on the circumference.
**b** Diameter, a straight line joining opposite points on the circumference.
**c** Sector, the area between any two radii.
**d** Arc, the line along the circumference joining any two points.
**e** Chord, the straight line joining any two points on the circumference.
**f** Segment, the area bounded by an arc and a chord.
**g** Tangent, a straight line touching the circumference at right angles to a radius.

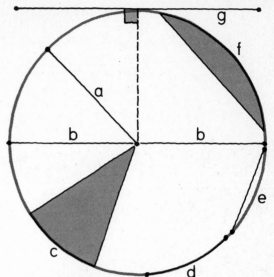

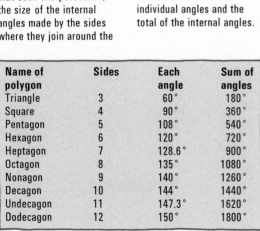

**A**   **B**

**Polygons** *above*
A polygon is a plane figure bounded by straight lines. If its sides or angles are unequal, the polygon is irregular (**A**); if they are equal, it is regular (**B**) and will fit into a circle with all its vertices touching the circumference (*right*).

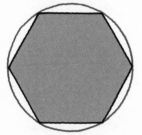

**Regular polygons**
Listed in the table *below* are regular polygons, from three-sided to twelve-sided. The table gives their correct names, the number of sides that each one possesses, the size of the internal angles made by the sides where they join around the perimeter, and the sum of these angles. The diagram *right* shows the same polygons with sides of equal length throughout. As the number of sides increases, so do the size of the individual angles and the total of the internal angles.

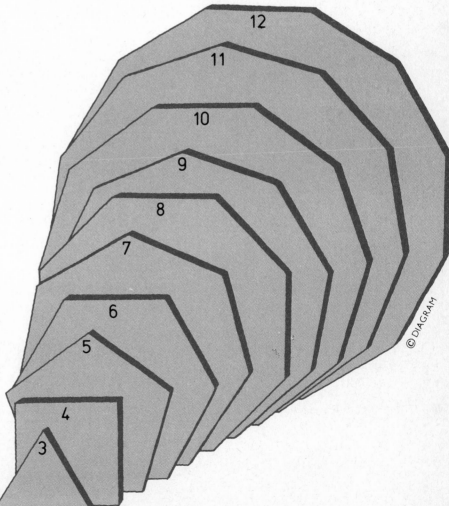

| Name of polygon | Sides | Each angle | Sum of angles |
|---|---|---|---|
| Triangle | 3 | 60° | 180° |
| Square | 4 | 90° | 360° |
| Pentagon | 5 | 108° | 540° |
| Hexagon | 6 | 120° | 720° |
| Heptagon | 7 | 128.6° | 900° |
| Octagon | 8 | 135° | 1080° |
| Nonagon | 9 | 140° | 1260° |
| Decagon | 10 | 144° | 1440° |
| Undecagon | 11 | 147.3° | 1620° |
| Dodecagon | 12 | 150° | 1800° |

© DIAGRAM

# ANGLES

On this page we compare three systems of measuring angles, all based on divisions of a circle. The original system of degrees was devised by the ancient Mesopotamians, and is still the most widely used system today. The radian is favored by modern mathematics; the grade, or gon, developed in 1792, is a metric measurement of angle.

**Degrees in a circle** *right*
Here we give the names of some regular divisions of the circle, based on the degree system. The degree is subdivided into the minute, and the minute into the second, in the ratios indicated.

| | |
|---:|:---|
| 360° | = 1 circle |
| 90° | = 1 right angle |
| 60° | = 1 sextant |
| 45° | = 1 octant |
| 30° | = 1 sign |
| 1° | = 60 minutes (60′) |
| 1′ | = 60 seconds (60″) |
| 21,600′ | = 1 circle |
| 1,296,000″ | = 1 circle |

**Degrees** *right, below*
The degree system divides the circle into 360 degrees (360°). If XY is a quarter of a circle, its angle XZY in degrees is 360 divided by four, which equals 90° (known as a right angle). A semicircle has an angle of 180°.

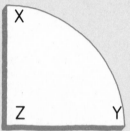

**Radians** *right, below*
A radian is the angle at the center of a circle that cuts off an arc on the circumference equal in length to the radius. If the arc XY equals the radii ZX and ZY, the angle XZY equals one radian (1 rad), and 1 rad equals 57.2958°.

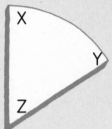

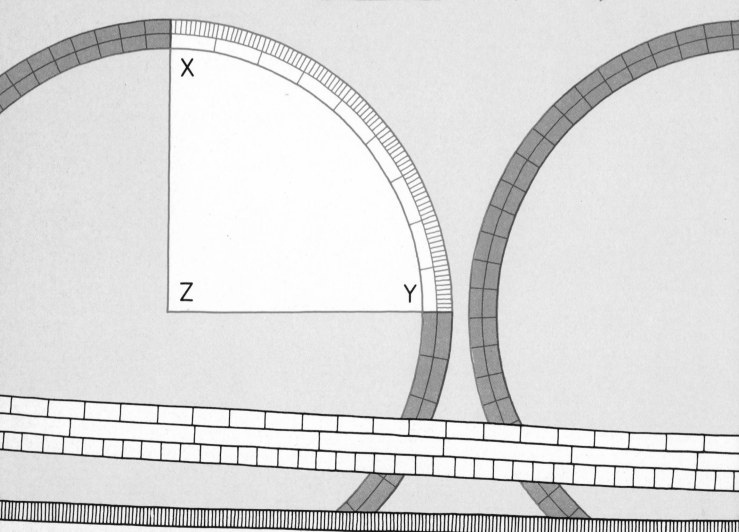

A good target rifle can place all its shots to within one minute of angle. This means that at 1000 yards it is able to hit a 10-inch diameter bullseye with every shot.

360° = 6.283183 rads
1 rad = 100 centirads
1 rad = 1000 millirads
1 rad = 1000 angular mils
360° = 400 grades
grade = 100 centigrades
grade = 100 new minutes
grade = 1000 milligrades
grade = 10,000 new seconds

**Radians and grades** *left*
The list gives the number of radians and grades in a circle, and also the names and values of some of their most common subdivisions.

**Grades** *right, below right*
A grade, or gon, is one-hundredth of a right angle. When XY is a quarter of the circumference, then the angle XZY is equal to 100 grades. Each circle contains 400 grades, and one grade is equal to 0.9°.

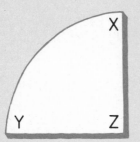

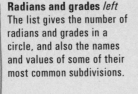

**Conversion tables** *left*
These tables are for converting degrees to centirads and grades, and vice versa. To use them, first find the figure to be converted in the central column of the relevant table; its equivalent can then be found in the appropriate column to the right or the left as indicated by the headings above.

| Degrees | | Centirads | Degrees | | Grades |
|---|---|---|---|---|---|
| 0.5730 | 1 | 1.7453 | 0.9 | 1 | 1.1111 |
| 1.1459 | 2 | 3.4907 | 1.8 | 2 | 2.2222 |
| 1.7189 | 3 | 5.2360 | 2.7 | 3 | 3.3333 |
| 2.2918 | 4 | 6.9813 | 3.6 | 4 | 4.4444 |
| 2.8648 | 5 | 8.7266 | 4.5 | 5 | 5.5555 |
| 3.4378 | 6 | 10.472 | 5.4 | 6 | 6.6667 |
| 4.0107 | 7 | 12.217 | 6.3 | 7 | 7.7778 |
| 4.5837 | 8 | 13.963 | 7.2 | 8 | 8.8889 |
| 5.1566 | 9 | 15.708 | 8.1 | 9 | 10.000 |
| 5.7296 | 10 | 17.453 | 9.0 | 10 | 11.111 |
| 57.296 | 100 | 174.53 | 90.0 | 100 | 111.11 |
| 114.59 | 200 | 349.07 | 180.0 | 200 | 222.22 |
| 171.89 | 300 | 523.60 | 270.0 | 300 | 333.33 |
| | | | 360.0 | 400 | 444.44 |

**Angles as length** *bottom left* These two sets of three lines represent parts of the circumference of two circles; the first (**ABC**) of radius 112.9ft (34.4m) and the second (**DEF**) of radius 676.8ft (206.3m). On these circles are marked the lengths of:
**A** Minutes (1′ = 10mm)
**B** Centirads (1c = 34.4mm)
**C** Centigrades (1cg = 5.4mm)
**D** Seconds (1″ = 1mm)
**E** Millirads (1m = 206.24mm)
**F** Milligrades (1mg = 3.24mm)

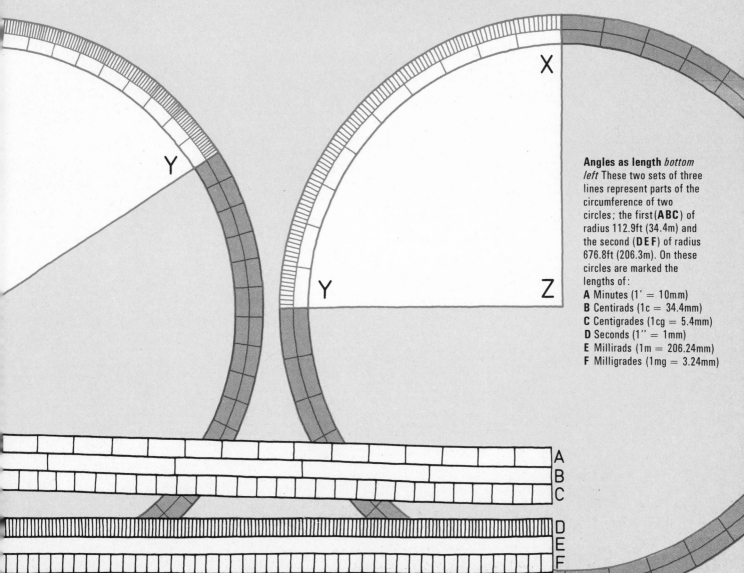

© DIAGRAM

# SOLID FORMS

Three-dimensional solid forms have area, volume and depth. It is the addition of depth that distinguishes them from two-dimensional geometric shapes. Any solid form made up of plane faces is given the general name of "polyhedron." Solids that include curved surfaces are named according to the shape of the curve.

**A**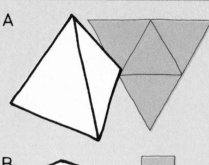

**Non-regular solids**
*left* Some of the most common are shown here.
**1** Sphere
**2** Spheroid
**3** Torus
**4** Cone
**5** Cylinder
**6** Prism
**7** Pyramid (if its base has four or more sides)

**Regular solids** *right*
If the surfaces of a solid are regular polygons of equal size, it is called a regular solid. There are only five possible regular solids and of these, three have surfaces that are equilateral triangles. Here we illustrate the regular solids and also show you how they can be made by cutting and folding a piece of card. Names of the regular solids are given here with the number of sides in brackets.
**A** Tetrahedron (4)
**B** Hexahedron or cube (6)
**C** Octahedron (8)
**D** Dodecahedron (12)
**E** Icosahedron (20)

**Containing a regular solid**
*below* One property of a regular solid is that when it is placed in a sphere, all its corners will touch the sphere.

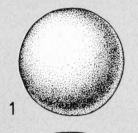

1

2

3

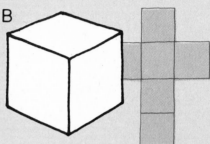

**B**

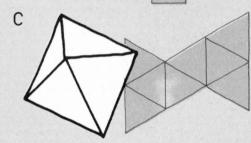

**C**

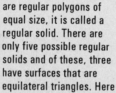

**D**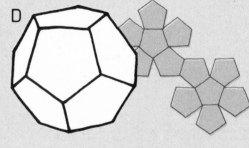

4

5

**E**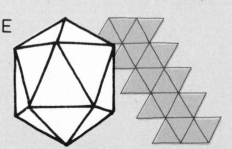

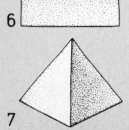

6

7

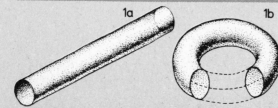
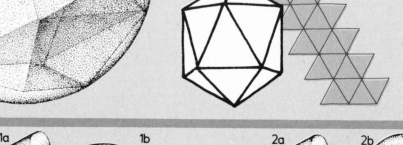

1a          1b          2a          2b

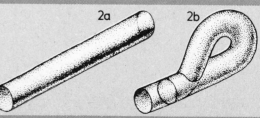

Followers of Pythagoras in Ancient Greece believed that earth is made of cubes, air of octahedrons, fire of tetrahedrons and water of icosahedrons. The dodecahedron was the symbol of the universe as a whole.

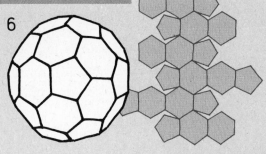

## Semi-regular solids

*right* Semi-regular solids have surfaces or faces composed of more than one type of polygon. For example, the cuboctahedron (**2**) has faces that are squares and equilateral triangles. The truncated icosidodecahedron (**8**) has squares, hexagons and decagons. Like regular solids, all semi-regular solids fit into a sphere.

For any solid form with flat faces, the number of edges equals the number of faces plus the number of corners minus two. For example the cuboctahedron has 12 corners and 14 faces; it therefore has 24 edges.

A selection of semi-regular solids is included here.

**1** Truncated octahedron or mecon
24 corners, 14 faces
**2** Cuboctahedron or dymaxion
12 corners, 14 faces
**3** Truncated cuboctahedron
48 corners, 26 faces
**4** Snub cube
24 corners, 38 faces
**5** Rhombicuboctahedron or square spin
24 corners, 26 faces
**6** Truncated icosahedron
60 corners, 32 faces
**7** Icosidodecahedron
30 corners, 32 faces
**8** Truncated icosidodecahedron
120 corners, 62 faces
**9** Snub dodecahedron
60 corners, 92 faces
**10** Rhombicosidodecahedron
60 corners, 62 faces

1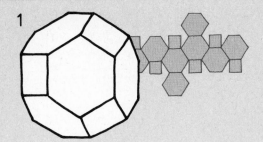

2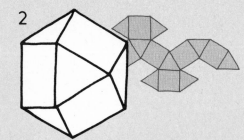

3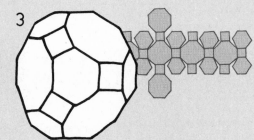

4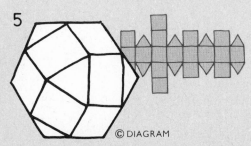

5

6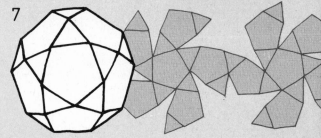

7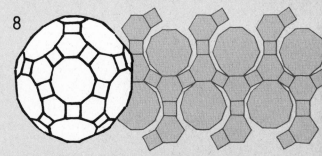

8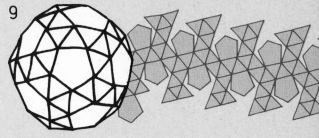

9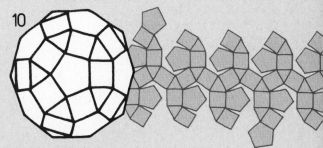

10

© DIAGRAM

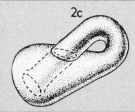

## When inside is outside

*left* Compared are two forms made by joining the ends of a cylinder.
**1** If we join the ends of a cylinder (**a**) in the usual way, we form a torus (**b**), because the ends point in opposite directions when they meet.
**2** For a Klein bottle both ends of the cylinder (**a**) must be pointing in the same direction when they meet. It is made by putting one end through the wall of the cylinder (**b**), and then joining it to the other end from the outside (**c**). This extraordinary solid has only a single surface, and thus no "inside" or "outside."

# NUMBER SHAPES

If every whole number is represented by the equivalent number of dots, the numbers fall into groups or "series" in which each number can be formed into a certain geometric shape, such as a square or a pyramid. The general term for these series is "polygonal numbers." Some of the simple series are shown on these two pages.

**Comparing the series** *right*
The table shows the series to which each number from one to twenty belongs. One belongs to five different series, four and ten to four series, and the other numbers to either three or two series.

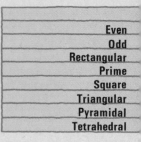

| | |
|---|---|
| **Even** | |
| **Odd** | |
| **Rectangular** | |
| **Prime** | |
| **Square** | |
| **Triangular** | |
| **Pyramidal** | |
| **Tetrahedral** | |

**Even numbers** *left*
All numbers that can be divided by two are called "even" numbers. We can show this series of numbers geometrically by beginning with a block of two, and adding a similar block of two for every successive even number.

2    4    6    8    10    12
**Even**

**Odd numbers** *left*
All those numbers that cannot be divided by two without a single unit remaining are called "odd" numbers. This series is built by beginning with a single dot and then adding a block of two for every successive odd number.

1    3    5    7    9    11    13
**Odd**

**Rectangular numbers** *left*
Some numbers can be divided into two or more equal parts that can be arranged to form a rectangle. Rectangular numbers are always the product of (the result of multiplying) two smaller numbers, for instance 8 = 4 x 2.

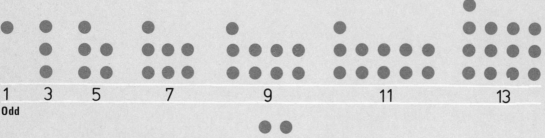

4    6    8    9    10    12    14
**Rectangular**

**Prime numbers** *left*
A prime number is a number greater than one that cannot be divided by any number other than one and itself. This means that prime numbers cannot be fitted into square or rectangular shapes.

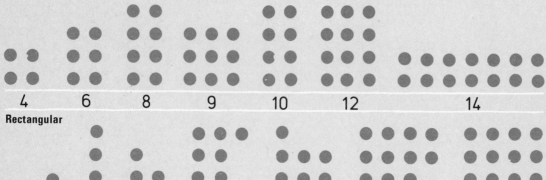

2    3    5    7    11    13    17    19
**Prime**

A "perfect" number is a number of which the sum of all its divisors exactly equals itself. An example is 6 (of which the divisors are 1, 2 and 3). There are only seven perfect numbers between 1 and 40,000,000 (6; 28; 496; 8128; 130,816; 2,096,128; 33,550,336).

*From 1 to 20 there are 11 rectangular numbers, 10 odd numbers, 10 even numbers, 8 prime numbers, 5 triangular numbers, 4 square numbers, 4 tetrahedral numbers, and 3 pyramidal numbers.*

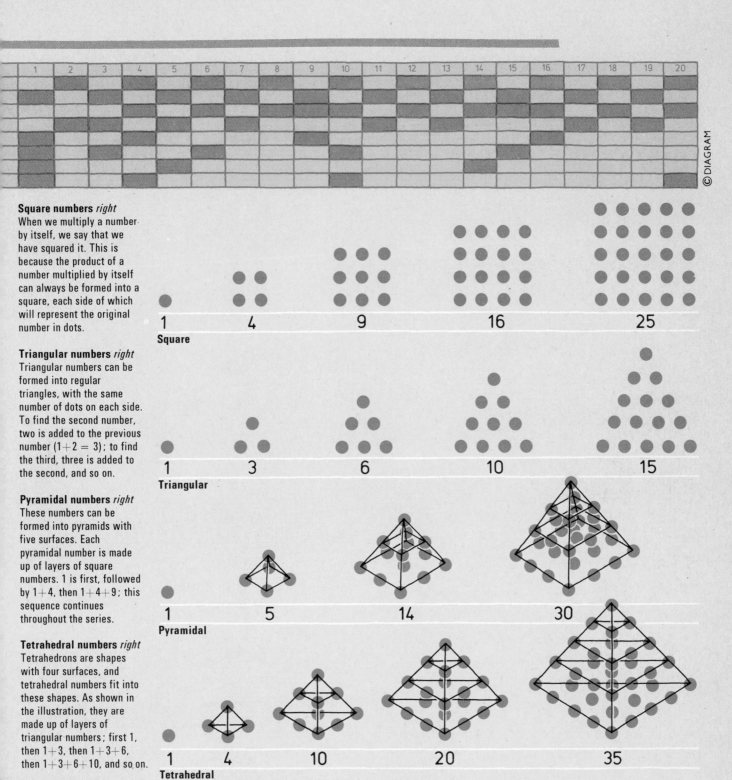

© DIAGRAM

**Square numbers** *right*
When we multiply a number by itself, we say that we have squared it. This is because the product of a number multiplied by itself can always be formed into a square, each side of which will represent the original number in dots.

**Square**

**Triangular numbers** *right*
Triangular numbers can be formed into regular triangles, with the same number of dots on each side. To find the second number, two is added to the previous number $(1+2 = 3)$; to find the third, three is added to the second, and so on.

**Triangular**

**Pyramidal numbers** *right*
These numbers can be formed into pyramids with five surfaces. Each pyramidal number is made up of layers of square numbers. 1 is first, followed by $1+4$, then $1+4+9$; this sequence continues throughout the series.

**Pyramidal**

**Tetrahedral numbers** *right*
Tetrahedrons are shapes with four surfaces, and tetrahedral numbers fit into these shapes. As shown in the illustration, they are made up of layers of triangular numbers; first 1, then $1+3$, then $1+3+6$, then $1+3+6+10$, and so on.

**Tetrahedral**

**Cannonballs were commonly stacked in pyramids. A stack 10 high would contain a total of 385.**

# ANIMAL LIMBS

Many creatures have legs that serve as props and as levers aiding locomotion. Nature produces such limbs in an astonishing variety of numbers and designs. Some limbs that support or move a body are not technically speaking legs, but rather arms or feet. But we include some here because of their locomotive function.

**Legs roll call**
The beasts *right* and *below* are ranged in order of number of legs (indicated for each animal). Most of those with six or more legs are small members of that great backboneless group, arthropods, creatures whose name means jointed legged.

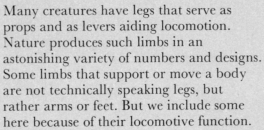

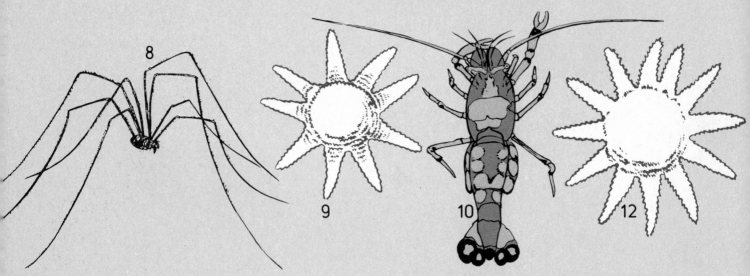

1 Edible snail, a mollusk that crawls on one muscular foot. Its muscles thrust back on the ground to push the snail forward.
2 Flamingo, a biped (two-legged like all other birds and man). Long, stilt-like legs help it to wade in shallow lagoons.

3 Tripod fish. Two long rays from the pectoral fins and one from the tail stop this deep-sea fish sinking when it rests on soft mud.
4 Giraffes and most other mammals, reptiles, and amphibians are tetrapods: animals stably supported on four legs and feet.

5 Most starfish have five limbs called arms. Starfish haul themselves along on many tiny tube feet poking out beneath each arm.
6 The human louse is an insect. This huge group of six-legged arthropods includes ants, beetles, bees, flies and moths.

7 Springtails are insects, and so have six true legs. But a forked springing organ at the hind end acts as a kind of seventh leg.
8 Harvestmen are arachnids, eight-legged arthropods related to the scorpions and spiders. (The 8-armed octopus is a mollusk.)

9 A 9-armed sunstar. This type of starfish can have up to 50 arms.
10 Shrimp. A decapod (10-footed) crustacean, as are crabs and lobsters.
12 Sunstar with 12 arms. Individuals of the species *Solaster papposus* can have 8–13 arms.

200

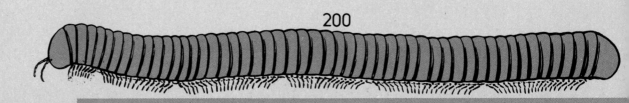

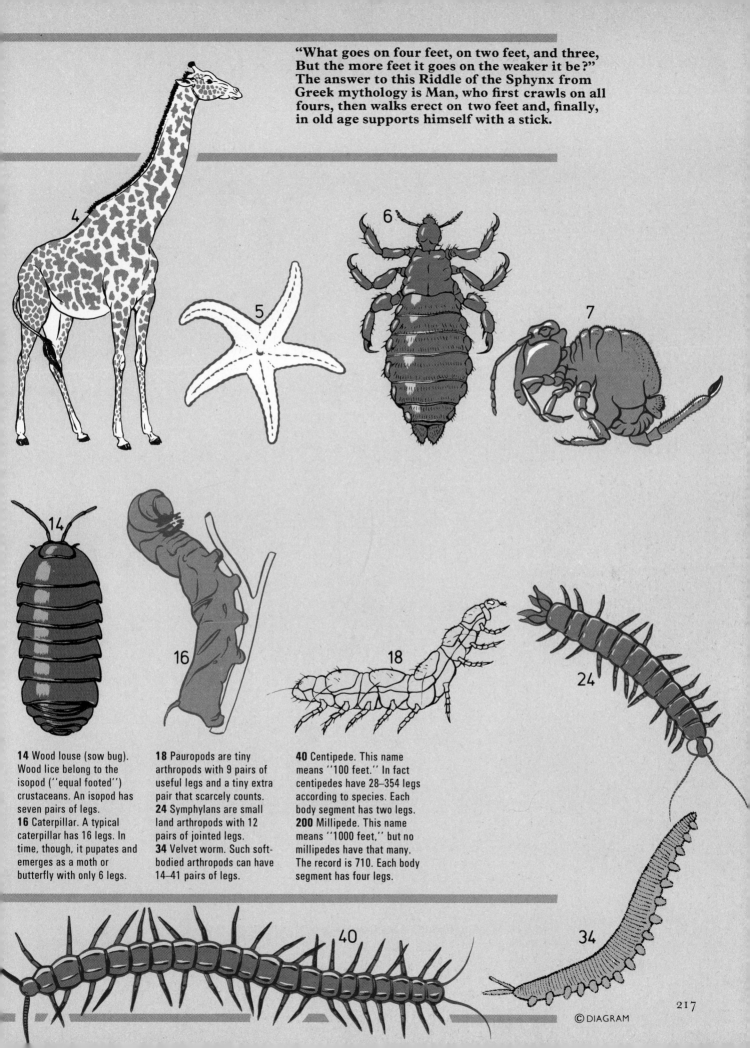

"What goes on four feet, on two feet, and three,
But the more feet it goes on the weaker it be?"
The answer to this Riddle of the Sphynx from
Greek mythology is Man, who first crawls on all
fours, then walks erect on two feet and, finally,
in old age supports himself with a stick.

**14** Wood louse (sow bug). Wood lice belong to the isopod ("equal footed") crustaceans. An isopod has seven pairs of legs.
**16** Caterpillar. A typical caterpillar has 16 legs. In time, though, it pupates and emerges as a moth or butterfly with only 6 legs.

**18** Pauropods are tiny arthropods with 9 pairs of useful legs and a tiny extra pair that scarcely counts.
**24** Symphylans are small land arthropods with 12 pairs of jointed legs.
**34** Velvet worm. Such soft-bodied arthropods can have 14–41 pairs of legs.

**40** Centipede. This name means "100 feet." In fact centipedes have 28–354 legs according to species. Each body segment has two legs.
**200** Millipede. This name means "1000 feet," but no millipedes have that many. The record is 710. Each body segment has four legs.

217

© DIAGRAM

# ANIMAL OFFSPRING

Each kind of creature tends to produce enough eggs or young to keep up the numbers of its species. The elephant— a long-lived mammal with few enemies— bears only one calf in about two years. At the opposite extreme is the evidently vulnerable ocean sunfish, which lays 300 million eggs in a single spawning.

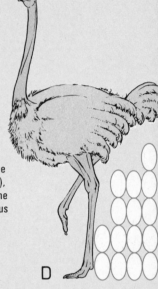

### Mammals
Births per mother commonly range from one in elephants (**A**) to 13 in opossums (**B**). Tenrecs, pigs and mice have all produced record litters of over 30. The human record for multiple births is 10—but no babies survived.

### Birds
Clutch size ranges from one in the emperor penguin (**C**), to 15 in the ostrich (**D**). One limiting factor is the surplus food needed by each egg-layer. In two weeks a blue tit eats enough to lay a 10-egg clutch that weighs more than she does.

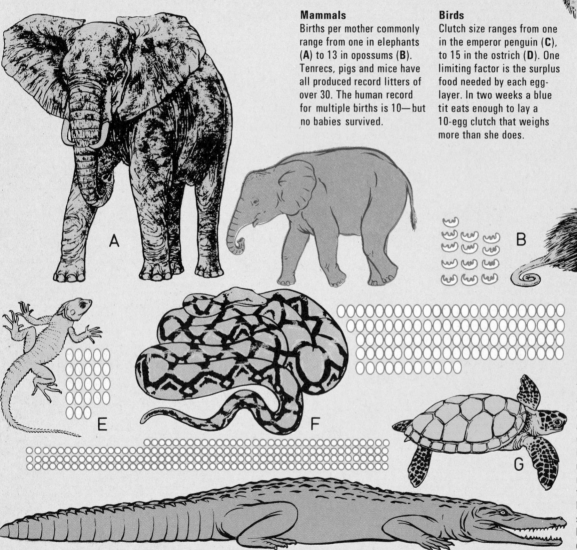

### Reptiles
Most reptiles lay eggs but some give birth to living young. Eggs or babies number from one to several dozen. Few lizards can rival the common agama (**E**), laying an average of 16.6 and up to 23 eggs. Even more prolific are some snakes. Pythons (**F**) average a clutch of 29 but may exceed 100. The reptiles' record is held by marine turtles. When a female green turtle (**G**) hauls ashore, on average she lays 104 eggs; the listed peak is 184. Nile crocodiles (**H**) lay some 60 eggs and a Mississippi alligator has laid 88.

**In her life a green turtle lays an average of 1800 eggs. Of these, some 1395 don't hatch, 374 hatchlings quickly die, and only 3 live long enough to breed.**

The highest officially recorded number of children born to one mother is 69, to a Russian peasant woman in the 18th century. They comprised four sets of quadruplets, seven sets of triplets, and 16 pairs of twins.

In favorable conditions *Escherichia coli*, a bacterium of the human gut, splits in two every 15 minutes to reproduce. In 24 hours one bacterium can become $4 \times 10^{28}$.

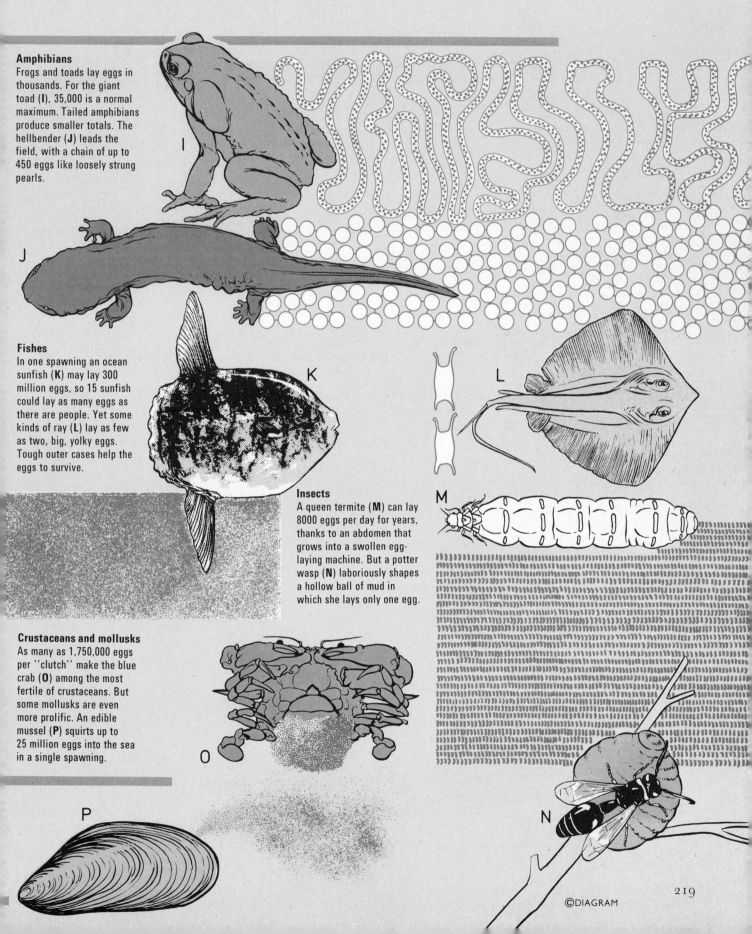

## Amphibians

Frogs and toads lay eggs in thousands. For the giant toad (**I**), 35,000 is a normal maximum. Tailed amphibians produce smaller totals. The hellbender (**J**) leads the field, with a chain of up to 450 eggs like loosely strung pearls.

## Fishes

In one spawning an ocean sunfish (**K**) may lay 300 million eggs, so 15 sunfish could lay as many eggs as there are people. Yet some kinds of ray (**L**) lay as few as two, big, yolky eggs. Tough outer cases help the eggs to survive.

## Insects

A queen termite (**M**) can lay 8000 eggs per day for years, thanks to an abdomen that grows into a swollen egg-laying machine. But a potter wasp (**N**) laboriously shapes a hollow ball of mud in which she lays only one egg.

## Crustaceans and mollusks

As many as 1,750,000 eggs per "clutch" make the blue crab (**O**) among the most fertile of crustaceans. But some mollusks are even more prolific. An edible mussel (**P**) squirts up to 25 million eggs into the sea in a single spawning.

219

©DIAGRAM

# POPULATION 1

Of the people alive today approximately 64% live in Asia, 11.1% in Europe, 10.5% in Africa, 8.4% in North America, 5.5% in South America and 0.5% in Oceania. On these two pages we look at the historical growth of population, at population by continent, and at the largest national populations in the world and in Europe.

**World population today**
Listed *right* and used for the diagram *below* are the most recent UN world and continental population figures available (mid-1979 provisional estimates). Asia including the USSR has 64% of the world total, without the USSR it has 58%.

| World | 4,336,000,000 |
|---|---|
| a Asia* | 2,773,000,000 |
| b Europe | 482,000,000 |
| c Africa | 456,000,000 |
| d N America | 364,000,000 |
| e S America | 239,000,000 |
| f Oceania | 22,000,000 |

*Includes USSR

If the entire population of China were acrobats standing one on another's shoulders (each adding 4ft to the height of the column) they would extend out into space more than three times farther than the distance from Earth to Moon.

The estimated population of the world increased by 2.7 times in the 250 years from 1650 to 1900. In less than one-third of this time, from 1900 to the present day, it has increased by a further 2.9 times.

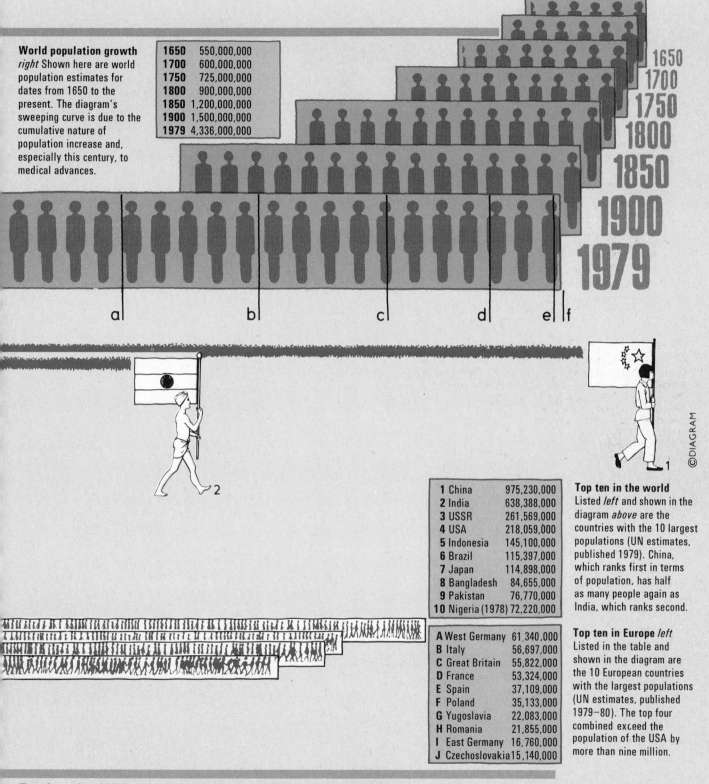

**World population growth**
*right* Shown here are world population estimates for dates from 1650 to the present. The diagram's sweeping curve is due to the cumulative nature of population increase and, especially this century, to medical advances.

| 1650 | 550,000,000 |
|------|-------------|
| 1700 | 600,000,000 |
| 1750 | 725,000,000 |
| 1800 | 900,000,000 |
| 1850 | 1,200,000,000 |
| 1900 | 1,500,000,000 |
| 1979 | 4,336,000,000 |

©DIAGRAM

| 1 China | 975,230,000 |
|---------|-------------|
| 2 India | 638,388,000 |
| 3 USSR | 261,569,000 |
| 4 USA | 218,059,000 |
| 5 Indonesia | 145,100,000 |
| 6 Brazil | 115,397,000 |
| 7 Japan | 114,898,000 |
| 8 Bangladesh | 84,655,000 |
| 9 Pakistan | 76,770,000 |
| 10 Nigeria (1978) | 72,220,000 |

**Top ten in the world**
Listed *left* and shown in the diagram *above* are the countries with the 10 largest populations (UN estimates, published 1979). China, which ranks first in terms of population, has half as many people again as India, which ranks second.

| A West Germany | 61,340,000 |
|---------------|------------|
| B Italy | 56,697,000 |
| C Great Britain | 55,822,000 |
| D France | 53,324,000 |
| E Spain | 37,109,000 |
| F Poland | 35,133,000 |
| G Yugoslavia | 22,083,000 |
| H Romania | 21,855,000 |
| I East Germany | 16,760,000 |
| J Czechoslovakia | 15,140,000 |

**Top ten in Europe** *left*
Listed in the table and shown in the diagram are the 10 European countries with the largest populations (UN estimates, published 1979–80). The top four combined exceed the population of the USA by more than nine million.

During the 1970s world population increased annually at a rate of 1.9%. If this same rate is maintained until the end of the century, world population in the year 2000 will be approximately 6400 million, an increase of 48% compared to the present day.

# POPULATION 2

On these two pages we look at population figures for some of the world's largest cities. Different sources publish widely differing figures for city populations—a consequence of the problems involved in differentiating the population of a city itself from that of its suburbs. We use the most recent UN figures (mostly for the mid-1970s).

| | | |
|---|---|---|
| **1** | Mexico City | 8,628,000 |
| **2** | Tokyo | 8,592,000 |
| **3** | New York | 7,482,000 |
| **4** | Sao Paulo | 7,199,000 |
| **5** | London | 7,028,000 |
| **6** | Moscow | 6,942,000 |
| **7** | Seoul | 6,879,000 |
| **8** | Bombay | 5,971,000 |
| **9** | Cairo | 5,921,000 |
| **10** | Rio de Janeiro | 4,858,000 |

**World's largest cities**
*right* Listed in the table and located on the map are the world's 10 most populous cities. Symbols of people (1 = 200,000) show their comparative populations. The largest, Mexico City, has twice as many people as Norway.

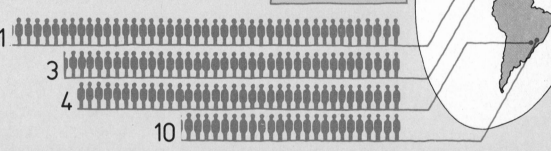

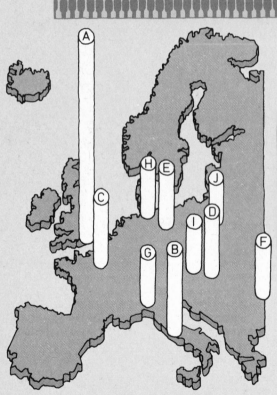

$\mathbf{\dot{Y}}$ = 100,000

| | | |
|---|---|---|
| **A** | London | 7,028,000 |
| **B** | Rome | 2,884,000 |
| **C** | Paris | 2,290,000 |
| **D** | Budapest | 2,076,000 |
| **E** | West Berlin | 1,951,000 |
| **F** | Bucharest | 1,807,000 |
| **G** | Milan | 1,705,000 |
| **H** | Hamburg | 1,699,000 |
| **I** | Vienna | 1,593,000 |
| **J** | Warsaw | 1,449,000 |

**Largest European cities**
Listed *above* and shown in these two diagrams are the 10 European cities with the largest numbers of people. London's population has declined recently, but it is still nearly 2½ times as big as that of Rome, the second city in the list.

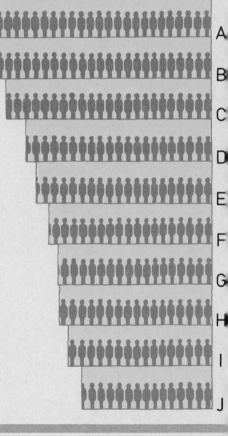

Of London's estimated 7,028,000 inhabitants, only about 5600 (0.08%) live in the municipal area officially known as the "City of London."

If all the inhabitants of Mexico City were to stand side by side (allowing 18 inches per person) they would cover a distance of 2451 miles, only 3 miles short of the Great Circle distance from Mexico City to Quebec.

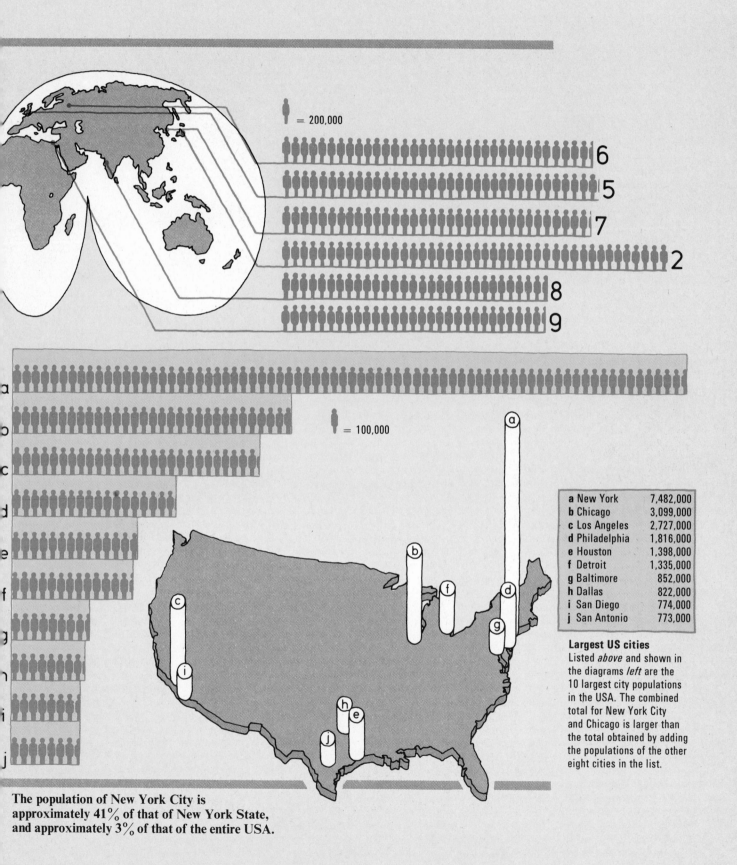

$†$ = 200,000

6
5
7
2
8
9

a
b
c

$†$ = 100,000

d
e
f
g
h
i
j

| a | New York | 7,482,000 |
| b | Chicago | 3,099,000 |
| c | Los Angeles | 2,727,000 |
| d | Philadelphia | 1,816,000 |
| e | Houston | 1,398,000 |
| f | Detroit | 1,335,000 |
| g | Baltimore | 852,000 |
| h | Dallas | 822,000 |
| i | San Diego | 774,000 |
| j | San Antonio | 773,000 |

**Largest US cities**
Listed *above* and shown in the diagrams *left* are the 10 largest city populations in the USA. The combined total for New York City and Chicago is larger than the total obtained by adding the populations of the other eight cities in the list.

**The population of New York City is approximately 41% of that of New York State, and approximately 3% of that of the entire USA.**

223

© DIAGRAM

# SPORTS TEAMS

Man has devised a great variety of sporting activities for different numbers of participants. Here we concentrate on the numbers of players involved in different team sports—from the maximum of 43 named players for a professional game of American football to the four riders, excluding substitutes, required for polo.

**Playing with numbers** *right*
A professional American football team (**1**) can have up to 43 players in uniform, but only 11 of them are allowed on the field at any time. An ice hockey team (**2**) consists of 17 players, of whom only six may be on the ice at the same time.

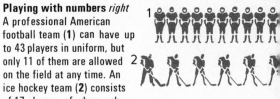

| Sport | | A | B | C |
|---|---|---|---|---|
| a | Australian rules football | 18 | 2 | |
| b | Gaelic football | 15 | | 3 |
| c | Hurling | 15 | | 3 |
| d | Rugby union | 15 | | 2 |
| e | Rugby league | 13 | 2 | |
| f | Canadian football | 12 | * | |
| g | Lacrosse (women's) | 12 | | * |
| h | Korfball | 12 | * | |
| i | American football | 11 | 32 | |
| j | Speedball | 11 | 5 | |
| k | Bandy | 11 | 3 | |
| l | Soccer | 11 | 2 | |
| m | Cricket | 11 | | * |
| n | Field hockey | 11 | 2 | |
| o | Lacrosse (men's) | 10 | 9 | |
| p | Baseball | 9 | * | |
| q | Softball | 9 | 6 | |
| r | Rounders | 9 | | * |
| s | Team handball | 7 | 5 | |
| t | Water polo | 7 | 4 | |
| u | Netball | 7 | | * |
| v | Ice hockey | 6 | 11 | |
| w | Volleyball | 6 | 6 | |
| x | Basketball | 5 | 7 | |
| y | Roller hockey | 5 | 5 | |
| z | Polo | 4 | | * |
| **A** | Maximum number per team allowed on the field | | | |
| **B** | Substitutes permitted for any reason | | | |
| **C** | Substitutes to replace sick or injured players | | | |
| * | Actual number unspecified in official rules | | | |

a       c       e       f,i

**18 15 13 12**

a       c       e       f

**Players and substitutes**
The first column of figures in the table *above* and the large numbers beneath the illustrations *right* indicate the maximum numbers of players in different types of team who are allowed on the field, or other playing area, at any one time in a game. The other two columns in the table show maximum numbers of permitted substitutes, differentiating between their use for tactical purposes and their more limited use merely to replace players who are incapacitated during play.

If a team of men wanting to play lacrosse to international rules had mistakenly bought the rule book for the women's game, they would find themselves with two too many players on the field, but an insufficient number of substitutes.

**The 43 named players for a professional American football game could be divided instead into teams (without substitutes) for all of the following: soccer, cricket, baseball, volleyball and ice hockey.**

The largest number of spectators ever to crowd into a stadium to watch any game was 199,854, for the Brazil versus Uruguay soccer international in Rio de Janeiro on July 16, 1950. This total works out at some 9084 spectators for every player on the field.

# VEHICLE CAPACITIES

In developing the best vehicle to meet a particular transportation requirement, designers must strike a balance between the numbers of people likely to make use of the service, and other factors such as safety, comfort and speed. Here we compare the numbers of people carried by various types of land, air and water vehicle.

**Land transport** *right*
Here we show a selection of land vehicles together with the number of passengers they are authorized to carry.
**a** London taxi, 4
**b** Greyhound bus, 43
**c** London bus (RML), 72
**d** World's longest bus, US-built for Middle East, 187

**Air transport** *right*
Combined passenger and crew capacities are here shown for a range of civil aircraft, from executive jet to jumbo.
**1** Beechcraft H18, 11
**2** *Concorde*, 148
**3** Boeing 707, 221
**4** Boeing 747, 500

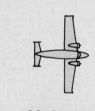

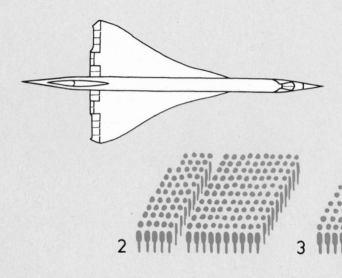

1   2   3

**Water transport** *right*
Drawn here is a selection of vessels, with their combined complements of passengers and crew.
**A** Venetian gondola, 5
**B** *Mayflower*, about 130
**C** Commercial hovercraft, SR-N4/Mk 3, 428
**D** *Queen Elizabeth 2*, 2931

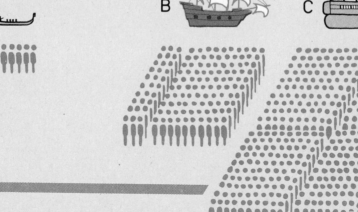

A   B   C

A Venetian with a gondola able to take four passengers at a time would have to make 733 journeys to ferry out the crew and passengers of the QE2.

The 500 passengers and crew from a Boeing 747 jumbo jet would require seven London double-decker buses or 125 London taxi cabs to take them from the airport into town.

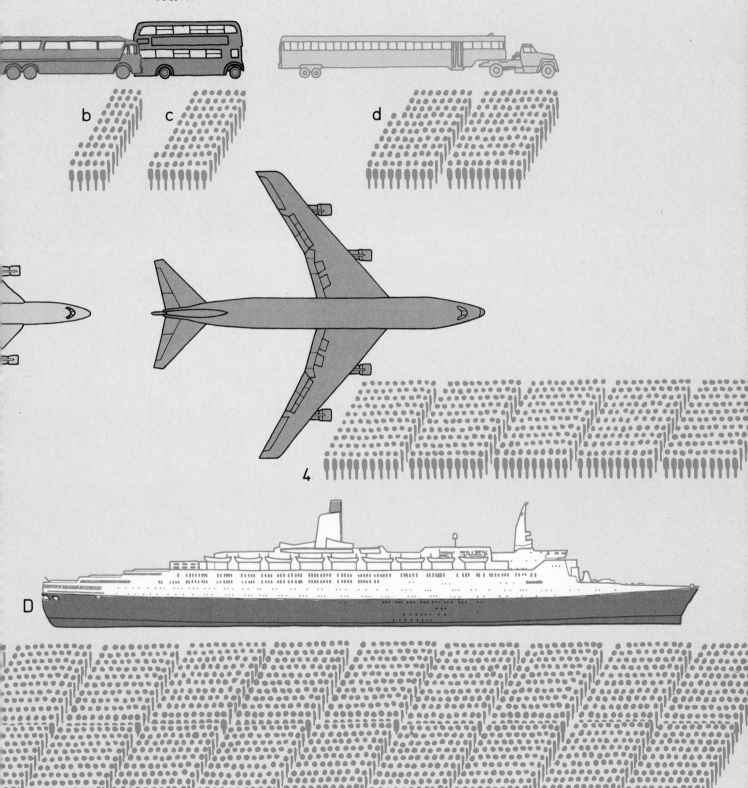

b

c

d

4

D

© DIAGRAM

# ODDS

The laws of probability are fundamental to any game of chance. Here we use three activities—tossing a coin, throwing dice, and poker—to demonstrate some basic principles. Odds can be expressed in two ways: for example, when a six-sided die is thrown, the chances of getting a specified number are 1 in 6, or 5 to 1.

**Heads to win** *right*
The diagram illustrates all the possible combinations of heads (**a**) and tails (**b**) for a coin tossed once, twice and three times in a row (with the situation after three throws summarized by the small circles below line 3). For example: the chance of heads in any one toss is 1 in 2; two heads in two tosses has the odds of 1 in 4 (1 in $2^2$); three heads in three tosses has the odds of 1 in 8 (1 in $2^3$). Following the same principle, ten heads in ten tosses has the odds of 1 in 1024 (1 in $2^{10}$).

**Dicing with fate**
A six-sided die has an equal probability of landing on any of its six faces, therefore the probability of any specified number appearing at the top after a throw is 1 in 6. If two dice are thrown, the probability of a particular total appearing on the two faces varies with the number of combinations of the numerals 1 to 6 that will form that total. The table *right* shows all the possible totals from tossing two dice, and the ways in which they are formed. The chart *left* presents the same information classified by the total produced (**a**). From this information, odds against each total can be reckoned (**b**)—for instance, the chances of throwing a total of seven are 1 in 6 (1/6).

|  | a | b |
|---|---|---|
|  | 12 | 1/36 |
|  | 11 | 1/18 |
|  | 10 | 1/12 |
|  | 9 | 1/9 |
|  | 8 | 5/36 |
|  | 7 | 1/6 |
|  | 6 | 5/36 |
|  | 5 | 1/9 |
|  | 4 | 1/12 |
|  | 3 | 1/18 |
|  | 2 | 1/36 |

|   | 1 | 2 | 3 | 4 | 5 | 6 |
|---|---|---|---|---|---|---|
| **1** | 2 | 3 | 4 | 5 | 6 | 7 |
| **2** | 3 | 4 | 5 | 6 | 7 | 8 |
| **3** | 4 | 5 | 6 | 7 | 8 | 9 |
| **4** | 5 | 6 | 7 | 8 | 9 | 10 |
| **5** | 6 | 7 | 8 | 9 | 10 | 11 |
| **6** | 7 | 8 | 9 | 10 | 11 | 12 |

**Odds for combinations in a four-child family are:**
three of one sex and one of the other, 1 in 2;
two girls and two boys, 3 in 8;
three girls and one boy, 1 in 4;
three boys and one girl, 1 in 4;
four children of the same sex, 1 in 8;
four girls, 1 in 16; four boys, 1 in 16.

If we were to draw all the possible combinations of five cards to the size of those below, we would need 393,782 more pages. If we were to lay out all the cards of the possible hands, side by side, actual size, they would stretch over 484 miles (779km).

**Five in the hand** *right*
A person dealt five playing cards from a regular deck of 52 cards receives one combination out of a possible total of 2,598,960 (ignoring, as for poker, the order in which the different cards are dealt).

| A | | B | C |
|---|---|---|---|
| **1** Royal flush (ace, king, queen, jack, 10 of one suit) | | 4 | 1 in 649,740 |
| **2** Straight flush (five consecutive cards of one suit) | | 36 | 1 in 72,193 |
| **3** Four of a kind (four cards of one denomination) | | 624 | 1 in 4165 |
| **4** Full house (three of one denomination, two of another) | | 3744 | 1 in 694 |
| **5** Flush (five cards of one suit) | | 5108 | 1 in 509 |
| **6** Straight (five consecutive cards of different suits) | | 10,200 | 1 in 255 |
| **7** Three of a kind (three cards of one denomination) | | 54,912 | 1 in 47 |
| **8** Two pairs (two of one denomination, two of another) | | 123,552 | 1 in 21 |
| **9** One pair (two of one denomination) | | 1,098,240 | 1 in 2.4 |

**Poker combinations**
Listed in the table *left* and illustrated by examples *below* are the nine most commonly accepted scoring combinations of cards—or "hands"—at 52-card poker. Column **A** in the table names and describes these scoring hands, column **B** lists the number of ways in which each of them can be made up, and column **C** lists the probability of their being dealt. The chances of being dealt a hand other than one of these nine is roughly 1 in 2 (1 in 1.9953014).

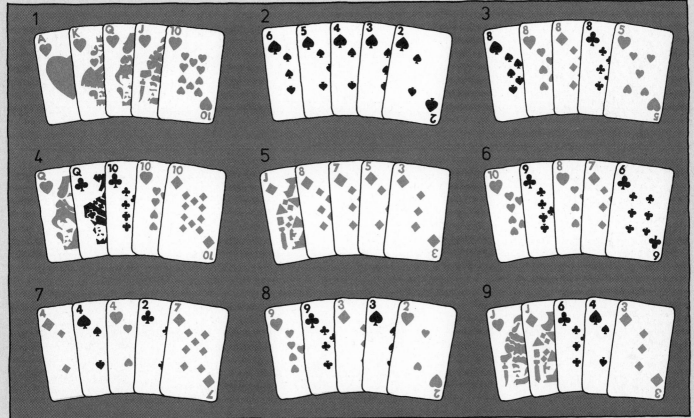

© DIAGRAM

If 26 tiles, each bearing one letter of the alphabet, are placed face-down, the odds of the first three tiles to be picked up spelling, in the correct order, the word "end" are 1 in 15,600.

# INDEX

European countries are shown fitted within the vast area of the Indian subcontinent in this illustration from an educational book published in Calcutta in 1940.

This illustration from an early 20th century edition of Cassell's *Encyclopaedia* gives a visual comparison of the relative heights of some famous buildings.

The comparative heights
of mountain peaks in
different ranges are shown
in this scale diagram from
*Systematische Bilder-
Gallerie* first published in
Germany in 1825–27.

# INDEX

234

# UNITS INDEX

*Savvy*

WRITER'S NOTEBOOK

# INKBLOT

## Ideas, Advice, and Examples to Inspire Young Writers

by Rebecca Langston-George

Nadia Higgins

Laura Purdie Salas

Heather E. Schwartz

**CAPSTONE PRESS**

a capstone imprint

APR 2018

# TABLE OF CONTENTS

# Introduction

You already know how to write. Everyone knows how to write, right? But everyone can learn to write even better. By picking up a pen or opening your laptop, you can create new worlds, construct the future, interpret or even reinvent the past. Whether it's a short story, a poem, a play, or nonfiction, you can invent phrases and use language in new ways. You can cause people to gasp with disbelief at your plot twists or make them laugh out loud. When you are the writer, you are in charge of whatever universe you choose to create.

Are you ready to get started? Beginning your writing journey is easy. You'll discover how to tap your inspiration and plot like a pro. You'll breathe life into your characters or real-life scenarios to create memorable works of poetry and prose.

Not sure whether you want to focus on short stories, poems, drama, or creative nonfiction forms such as essay or memoir? This book will help you hone your craft with examples of great work from, and profiles of, masters of the art of writing. Best of all, this book is chock-a-block with writing exercises to help you on your way to mastering the arts of creative fiction and nonfiction.

# Chapter 1

# Writing Captivating Short Stories

Like its cousin the novel, a short story is a work of fiction. It also has a plot, a theme, and a conflict. Short stories usually have one easy-to-follow plot rather than the complex, multi-layered plots found in novels. With a smaller cast of characters and a shorter length, a short story can be read in one sitting. While there is no set rule on a short story's length, typically short stories have fewer than 20 pages. Sometimes short stories are compiled into a collection. These collections might feature stories with a similar theme or stories using the same characters.

Reading short stories will help you become a better writer. Great writers are also great readers because they learn from example. Some of today's great short-story writers found inspiration from their peers, and you can too. Why not check out their work? You can read a short story in one sitting, so if you're serious about being a short story writer, make it your goal to read several a week.

# GET INSPIRED

## What If?

Can you guess the number-one question authors are asked? It's "Where do you get your ideas?" The answer is easy—inspiration is everywhere! New ideas are just waiting to be discovered. The trick is to train yourself to look for inspiration around you. Asking questions often gets your creative juices flowing.

One way to get inspired is to ask "What if?" Washington Irving asks this question in his classic short story "Rip Van Winkle." Irving takes an everyday event, napping, and asks what would happen if a person didn't wake up from his nap for 20 years?

"On awakening he found himself on the green knoll from whence he had first seen the old man of the glen. He rubbed his eyes—it was a bright, sunny morning . . . 'Surely,' thought Rip, 'I have not slept here all night.' Upon returning to his home everything had changed. "It was with some difficulty that he found the way to his own house, which he approached with silent awe, expecting every moment to hear the shrill voice of Dame Van Winkle. He found the house gone to decay—the roof fallen in, the windows shattered, and the doors off the hinges. A half starved dog that looked like Wolf was sulking about it. Rip called him by name but the cur snarled, showed his teeth and passed on. This was an unkind cut indeed— 'My very own dog,' sighed poor Rip, 'has forgotten me.'"

Choose an everyday activity and ask yourself, "What if?" What if this task took a strange turn? Make a list of activities you do every day, such as brushing your teeth, eating breakfast, tying your shoes, or opening your school locker. Choose one action, and let your imagination run wild! What if your bowl of corn flakes made ears of corn sprout from your head? What if you reached into your locker for a book and a hand pulled you into a new world? Take 5–10 minutes and jot down as many ideas as possible. When you are finished, tuck away your list for a while. Come back to it later for story inspiration.

PLAN

crea

# Set Up a Great Story with Setting

Another great way to get inspired is to look at pictures of different places. The place and time where a story occurs is its setting, and looking at unique settings can spark story ideas. To get started, all you need are a few pictures and your curiosity. Try doing an Internet search for images or thumbing through old magazines for setting pictures. Pick pictures that appeal to you, such as places you'd like to travel to or places you've visited and loved. Look for settings that convey the tone or feel you want your story to have. For example, if you want to write a spooky story, choose images that have an eerie feel.

Choose the picture on this page that you find the most interesting, or find another picture of a place that intrigues you. Make a list of everything that could happen there. Don't be fooled by your preconceived ideas about the setting. Dig deep and consider what unexpected things might take place. What problem might have occurred here? Who or what might be lurking outside the picture frame? How has the scene changed from 100 years ago? What historical event might have happened here? What could happen in the future? Craft one to three paragraphs describing the picture's setting for use in a short story.

# News Flash

Real-life stories happen around you every day. Your friends, family, and neighbors are all living out real-life dramas. The TV, movies, Internet, and newspapers are chock-full of reports of daily events. One way to create a great short story is to find inspiration in real life. Many authors use nonfiction events and flesh out the details to create interesting pieces of fiction. Start carrying a journal, and write down bits and pieces of real-life events. Weave in some imagination, and you've got a story.

Watch the nightly news. Jot down notes on a story that interests you. Let the nonfictional news inspire a fictional story of your own. For example, let's say one of the news shows features a story about a dog that was lost for six months and suddenly showed up back at his house. His paws were worn and bloody, indicating he had walked a long distance. How did he become lost? How did he make his way home? What adventures did he have along the way? Invent the dog's story.

Create your own pourquoi tale to explain why something is the way it is. Animal pictures can help inspire your next amazing tale. Glue lots of animal pictures on a piece of poster board. Write down questions next to the pictures. Next to a lobster picture you could write, "How a lobster got his pincers." After you've put several animals and questions on your inspiration board, choose one and develop a story.

Write your idea here

Write your idea here

Write your idea here

Write your idea here

Write your idea here

How a lobster got his pincers.

Write your idea here

Write your idea here

Write your idea here

Write your idea here

13

## AUTHOR PROFILE:

### Ray Bradbury

Ray Bradbury made science fiction writing popular. His short story collection, *The Martian Chronicles*, is among his best-known works. In 1932 when Ray was 12 years old, he met a carnival magician named Mr. Electrico. Mr. Electrico touched Ray with his sword and proclaimed "Live forever!" This left a great impression on young Ray. Pehaps he thought he could live forever by leaving behind his stories. Right then and there, he started writing every day. He would later make it his goal to write at least 1,000 words a day. The author of more than 500 publications, Ray wrote, "The need to write, to create, coursed like blood through my body."

Science fiction is a popular genre—or specific type—of fiction. These highly creative tales are set in a believable but fictitious future. A science fiction story might take place on Earth, on a space ship, or even on a distant planet! They may features aliens, lifelike robots, or any other creature that the author can dream up.

It takes plenty of practice and talent to weave in futuristic elements without breaking the flow of a story. Remember, despite the fantastic marvels of science and technology, science fiction still must feel real and relatable on some level or readers lose interest. Every good writer knows that a story rooted in genuine human emotions and well-thought-out details can win readers' hearts. Sound fun? Want to give it a shot?

To try writing a science fiction story, why not take a classic fairy tale, like "Cinderella," for example, and rewrite the story in a future setting of your creation.

Maybe in your sci-fi story, Cinderella is a robotic technician who can't attend an intergalactic dance because she has to work. Even if she were able to attend, poor Cinderella certainly has no proper ballroom attire. Use your imagination to dream up her futuristic fairy godmother. What amazing transportation will shuttle her to the dance? Are her fantastic shoes heels or sneakers? Are they made of titanium or lunar crystals? Let your imagination play!

# PLOT YOUR COURSE

## Plotted Plans

Life is a chain or series of events and interactions—and so is a short story. Just as in real life, if you don't plan ahead, your story is going nowhere!

Story plots flow from the beginning to the middle and conclude with endings. In a short story, we call that the "progression of the plot." The progression of the plot is the thread that connects all elements of a story and keeps readers engaged.

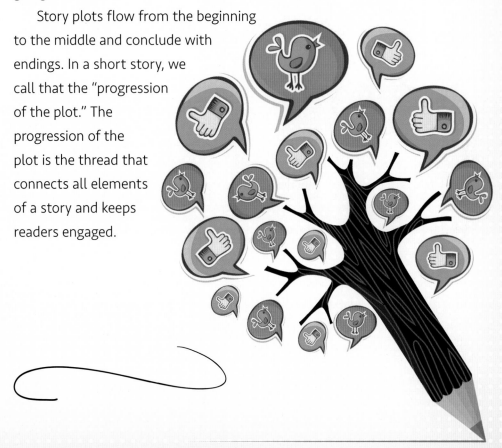

If you break it down a little further, a plot has five basic parts. Exposition introduces the story's characters and setting. When a conflict, or problem, takes root and grows, it's called rising action. Climax is the point at which the conflict is at its height, and the scales tip toward change. The conflict drops off and things begin to return to normal during falling action. The last part is resolution, in which the conflict is solved. Although plotting takes a little time, in the end you'll find you saved time! A good plan will save you from staring off into space and wondering what happens next.

# Visualize!

One way to plan your plot is to think of your story like a movie. First visualize the events that may play out in your story. Then sketch them out, storyboard style. To create a filmstrip, divide a long strip of paper into six boxes. The first box is your beginning, or exposition. The next two boxes are part of your middle, also known as rising action. The fourth box is your climax. Box number five is your falling action and box six shows the resolution, or ending. Use a pencil to sketch pictures of what will happen in each scene. Write down some words as well, if you like. Remember, you're creating a writing plan, not an art project, so try not to get distracted with colored pencils or markers. Once you've visualized your story and planned it out, the real fun begins!

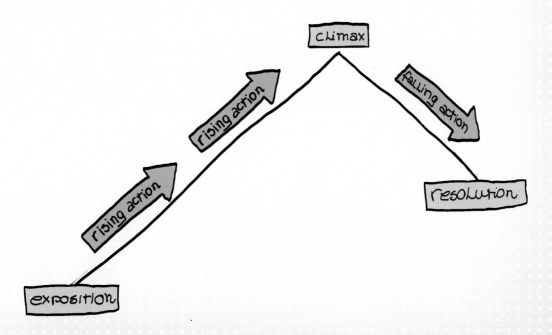

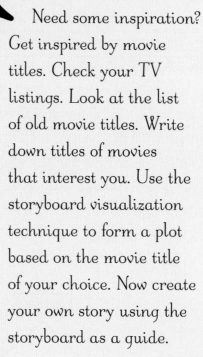

YOUR TURN

Need some inspiration? Get inspired by movie titles. Check your TV listings. Look at the list of old movie titles. Write down titles of movies that interest you. Use the storyboard visualization technique to form a plot based on the movie title of your choice. Now create your own story using the storyboard as a guide.

# Conflict Drives the Story Forward

Conflict is a problem in the story that must be realized or overcome. WIthout conflict, a story is nothing more than a long description. When conflict is introduced, a story's gears start turning. Conflict can be a physical battle, a battle of wills, a fight for justice, or an emotional battle. Readers love to root for a character to win. Writers provide characters with conflicts to overcome so readers can sympathize and cheer them on. Conflict is the key to a great tale. All the world's problems boil down to four basic types of conflict:

CHARACTER

VS.

CHARACTER

two characters struggle with one another

CHARACTER

VS.

NATURE

nature is the enemy that a character must overcome

CHARACTER

VS.

SELF

a character struggles against his or her own feelings

CHARACTER

VS.

SOCIETY

a character fights against an unjust society, government, or rule

# Getting to Know: Jack London

Jack London is famous for his stories involving characters struggling against nature. In his short story "How to Build a Fire," a man builds a fire outdoors when it is 50 degrees below zero (-46 degrees Celsius). He has only minutes to light it before he freezes, but nature conspires against him.

"He should not have built the fire under the spruce tree. He should have built in the open. . . . High up in the tree one bough capsized its load of snow. This fell on the boughs beneath, capsizing them. . . . It grew like an avalanche, and it descended without warning upon the man and the fire, and the fire was blotted out! The man was shocked. It was as though he had just heard his own sentence of death."

## YOUR TURN

Write a story in which nature is the enemy. Think of a situation in which someone would have to struggle to survive. An earthquake, flood, tornado, or avalanche might play a role in your story. Or a character could suffer hardships as a result of extreme heat, cold, or thirst. Make nature the villain that tests the limits of your character. Add some complications and pour on the drama. Your character's life is at stake. Will he or she survive? It's up to you.

# Conflict Causes Characters to Change

Every story needs a conflict, but remember—not just any old conflict will do! A story's conflict has to serve a purpose and seem natural and believable within the story. It has to make a difference in the characters' lives and force them to face their problems. Have you ever heard the saying "What doesn't kill you makes you stronger?" Conflict pushes characters to the edge emotionally or physically.

The conflict serves as a trial. Faced with difficult problems, characters are challenged and tested. They come out of the ordeal changed in some way, usually for the better. Conflict might cause characters to mature, be more compassionate, shift viewpoints, or understand things in a new light.

You've probably experienced conflict with other people in your life. Have you ever argued with a brother or sister? Do you always see eye to eye with your parents? Has a good friend ever disappointed you? These are all examples of character vs. character conflict. Any two people who spend time together on a regular basis are bound to have some conflict. Make a bubble map like the one shown. List all the relationships you have. Choose two characters from the bubble map and create a story about them in which a conflict arises. Think about how the conflict will make at least one of the characters change and grow by the end. Write your story.

# Bubble Map:

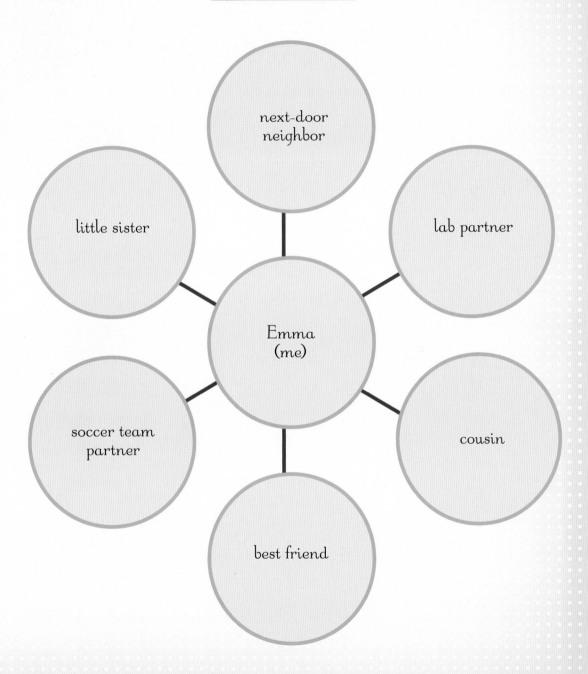

next-door
neighbor

little sister

lab partner

Emma
(me)

soccer team
partner

cousin

best friend

# Make It Believable

Even with a great plot and an interesting conflict, a story can fall flat if it isn't believable. You want your reader to feel as though she has tumbled into your story world and is experiencing the action, not just reading about it. To create a world readers can get lost in, you need to infuse your story with vivid descriptions. Use specific, authentic details so your readers experience events along with the characters.

**Let's take a look at two ways to describe eating a peach.**

1. Maya ate a peach. It tasted very good.

2. Maya bit into the soft, golden peach. Velvety peach skin tickled the tip of her nose. Sweet, sticky juice trickled down the corner of her mouth, and she licked it up, not wanting to waste a single glorious drop.

Which is more interesting? The first one tells you what Maya does. The second one shows you what Maya does and uses lots of sensory detail. Think of your five senses—sight, hearing, smell, taste, and touch. In the second description the writer appeals to the readers' sense of sight, taste, and touch. Including sensory details will help your reader experience your story.

**YOUR TURN**

Describe something happening in one of these pictures. Include some sensory details such as how things look, feel, smell, sound, and taste. As you write, try to make your reader experience what is happening right along with the characters you create.

## AUTHOR PROFILE:

### Sandra Cisneros

Sandra Cisneros incorporates both Spanish and English words into her stories. Her writing shifts between the two languages so she can select just the right word. She feels the two languages give her twice as many words and meanings to select from and help her express herself. She is best known for her collection of coming-of-age stories in "The House on Mango Street." In it, Cisneros captures the everyday life of young Hispanic Americans. A former teacher, Cisneros has also created workshops for would-be writers. Her writing is characterized by unusual formats such as notes, overheard snippets of gossip, and poems.

# BREATHE LIFE INTO YOUR CHARACTERS

## Characters Have History

Imagine meeting someone new for the first time. Naturally you want to learn all about him or her—what kind of activities he or she enjoys, what you have in common, whether he or she is kind or brave or wacky. You're curious about your new friend's background and personality. When meeting a character in a great story, readers have a similar reaction. They want to know more. As a writer it's your job to deliver interesting characters that seem like genuine people. This is called characterization. The key to creating great characters is to treat them like real people with real-life histories. Think of it this way—if you're writing about a character who is 15 years old, that character has experienced 15 years of living before stepping in to your story. He or she has hopes, dreams, secrets, and fears. Writers call that a character's backstory. Use your character's backstory to create a seemingly real person who readers will relate to.

Imagine that your character keeps a special memory box. It is filled with things such as movie ticket stubs, photos, school play programs, notes from friends, certificates from school activities, and cards from holiday and birthday gifts. Write a diary entry in which your character describes the events surrounding one of these special items. Assume that your character has a vivid memory of the source of the item, so describe the experience thoroughly. What can you reveal about your character through physical description? Use your character's thoughts and actions to create a believable memory and history before the present.

# Unique Qualities

In addition to thinking about your character's history, think about what makes your character unlike anyone else. What makes him or her stand out in a crowd? What qualities does he or she possess? Make a list of your character's personality traits. Is he or she brave? Untrustworthy? Kind? Generous? Now list some of your character's quirks, or peculiar habits. Maybe she's always late and out of breath. Perhaps he rides a unicycle everywhere. Does she insist on wearing high-top sneakers even to the prom? Generating character qualities and quirky traits will help you develop a believable, interesting character. Writers who skip these character development exercises sometimes find their characters are like cardboard cut-outs. They lack dimension and depth.

# Get Inside Your Character's Head

Now try getting even further inside your character's head. Think about the saying "Actions speak louder than words." Ask yourself how your character would act in different situations. This will help you dig even deeper into your character's true self and reveal some of your character's secrets.

If she had $1,000, what would she spend it on?

If your character could change one thing about his or her appearance, what would it be?

If your character could save just one item from a fire, what would it be? Why?

What silly thing does he or she do when no one is watching?

What does your character fear most?

What secret does your character have that he or she doesn't want anyone to know?

If your character could meet anyone living or dead who would it be and why?

What does your character wish people would understand about him or her?

YOUR TURN

Choose a picture of a person from an Internet image search and create a fictional character using the photo. First, list everything you can imagine about this person. What pictures are on his or her phone? What food will this person absolutely not eat and why? What's the person's happiest memory? Use your answers to write a story featuring your new character.

## AUTHOR PROFILE:

# Walter Dean Myers

Walter Dean Myers wrote more than 100 books for young people. He was awarded two Newbery honor medals for his work and served as the National Ambassador for Young People's Literature. *145th Street: Short Stories* is a collection of 10 connected short stories about inner city life in Harlem. Having grown up playing basketball and reading books at the library in Harlem, Myers often set his stories there.

Myers struggled in school, but a teacher saw promise in his writing. Even though he dropped out of school, Myers remembered his teacher's advice and wrote at night after work. In addition to fiction, Walter Dean Myers also wrote picture books and nonfiction. He died in 2014.

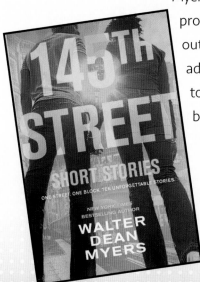

# GETTING TO THE POINT

## Point of View

Have you ever argued with a friend? Perhaps you wondered why your friend couldn't see your side of things. People interpret events differently based on what they know and how it affects them. That's called point of view. In a story two characters can experience and view the same situation in different ways because their different backgrounds color how they interpret the same events. That's why your best friend may not always see things your way. When writing a story you have to choose which point of view you'll use to tell the story.

# First Person

If you write as if the main character is narrating, or telling the story, you're using first person point of view. One clue to identifying first person point of view is the use of first person pronouns such as I, me, and my. Writing in first person gives readers a close, intimate view of a character's true nature.

Edgar Allan Poe uses first person point of view in his short story "The Tell-Tale Heart." In it a madman tells the story of a crime he commits. Notice the use of first-person pronouns and how the character speaks like a madman.

"True!—nervous—very, very dreadfully nervous I had been and am; but why will you say that I am mad? The disease had sharpened my senses—not destroyed—not dulled them. Above all was the sense of hearing acute. I heard all things in the heaven and in the earth. I heard many things in hell. How, then, am I mad? Hearken! And observe how healthily—how calmly I can tell you the whole story."

# Third Person

When a narrator tells the story, you are using third person point of view. If your narrator only knows the actions being played out, it's called third person limited. If your narrator sees all and knows all, it's called third person omniscient point of view. Writing in third person gives readers a broad overview of things.

Jack London narrates his short story "In a Far Country" using a third person point of view. Notice how third person point of view is like a sports announcer telling what is happening.

"When the world rang with the tale of Arctic gold, and the lure of the North gripped the heartstrings of men, Carter Weatherbee threw up his snug clerkship, turned the half of his savings over to his wife, and with the remainder bought an outfit. . . . Like many another fool, disdaining the old trails used by the Northland pioneers for a score of years, he hurried to Edmonton in the spring of the year; and there, unluckily for his soul's welfare, he allied himself with a party of men."

Take a few paragraphs from a story and rewrite them from a different point of view. Start with the excerpts from "In a Far Country" and "The Tell-Tale Heart." As you rewrite "In a Far Country" in first person, get inside Carter Weatherbee's head. Tell his thoughts and hopes as he prepares for his trip to the Arctic. You'll likely find that changing the story to first person makes the reader feel closer to the main character. When you change "The Tell-Tale Heart" into third person point of view, you'll want to step outside of the madman's head a bit and narrate as an observer rather than the madman himself. Ask yourself whether the story is more interesting from the madman's point of view or the third person narrator's. Next, try experimenting with different points of view in the stories you write.

# Theme

Most stories have a theme, or life lesson. The theme is often the point of the story, or the big idea the author wants the reader to understand. To figure out the theme, look at the root of the conflict and the ending. A story's title might hint at its theme as well. Stories rarely state the theme explicitly. Usually you have to put on your thinking cap to figure it out. Ask yourself what the main character has learned.

# Getting to Know: Charles Dickens

In Charles Dickens' "A Christmas Carol," Ebenezer Scrooge is stingy and unkind to his workers, family, and friends until he is visited by three spirits who show him the fault of his stingy ways. The story's end shows us its theme, which might be expressed as—giving is good for the soul.

"He became as good a friend, as good a master, and as good a man, as the good old city knew. . . . Some people laughed to see the alteration in him, but he let them laugh. . . . His own heart laughed: and that was quite enough for him. . . . And it was always said of him, that he knew how to keep Christmas well, if any man alive possessed the knowledge. May that be truly said of us, and all of us! And so, as Tiny Tim observed, God bless us, every one!"

Sometimes authors discover the meaning of their stories as they write them. But why not try building a story around a theme? The first step is to choose a proverb, or wise saying, about how to live life. Choose a proverb you truly believe in and this exercise will be much easier. After you've chosen a proverb, spend some time brainstorming different conflicts that might illustrate the proverb. Be sure to consider the setting, characters, and plot. What is the best way to show rather than tell your message? Use your best idea to write a contemporary story based on the proverb. Here are some examples:

Two wrongs don't make a right.

When the going gets tough the tough get going.

There's no place like home.

One man's trash is another man's treasure.

The early bird catches the worm.

Honesty is the best policy.

## Agatha Christie

Best known for creating the amateur sleuth Miss Marple and the retired detective Hercule Poirot, Agatha Christie didn't set out to become one of the most famous female writers. Following World War I (1914–1918) young Agatha began working in a pharmacy giving out medication. Though she was good at her job, she found the work boring. Boredom and a dare from her sister led Christie to take up her pen. She wrote her first detective story "The Mysterious Affair at Styles" starring Belgian detective Hercule Poirot. But her pharmaceutical background came in very handy when killing off characters with poison. In fact, her descriptions of poisonings were so convincing that her stories even got reviews in pharmacy magazines! Agatha Christie often found inspiration in children's nursery rhymes, which is evident in some of her stories' titles, such as "How Does your Garden Grow?" and "Four and Twenty Blackbirds."

# SPECIAL TECHNIQUES

A great plot, conflict, and well-developed characters will take you far in writing a short story. But seasoned writers have a few more tricks up their sleeves.

# Foreshadowing

Remember the story of Hansel and Gretel? Hansel left a trail of bread crumbs so he and his sister could find their way home. Believe it or not, authors often leave a trail of clues or hints to help the reader find her way to the story's solution. This is called foreshadowing. Foreshadowing often calls the reader's attention to an object or action that will later be important in the story. You've probably experienced foreshadowing if you've ever been able to solve a book's mystery or problem before the ending.

# Getting to Know: Edgar Allan Poe

Edgar Allan Poe hints at the twisted ending of "The Cask of Amantillado" with foreshadowing. The narrator wants revenge, so he lures Fortunato to a deep underground crypt with plans to seal him inside. In order to lead Fortunato to his doom, the narrator must first gain his trust. Notice how Poe points out that trust at the beginning of the story to foreshadow Fortunato's death, or "immolation," at the narrator's hands.

> "It must be understood, that neither by word nor deed had I given Fortunato cause to doubt my good will. I continued, as was my wont, to smile in his face, and he did not perceive that my smile now was at the thought of his immolation."

Later in the story, Fortunato breaks into a coughing spell. The narrator fakes concern for Fortunato, but Fortunato insists, "The cough is a mere nothing; it will not kill me. I shall not die of a cough." The narrator replies, "True — true." This is strong foreshadowing. It is beginning to become clear that Fortunato won't die of his cough, but he will die of something!

Think about the ending of a story you want to write. Hint at the ending of your story by planting relevant objects or actions earlier in your story. For example, a story that climaxes in a dangerous mountain climb might foreshadow this event by sprinkling mentions of rope, hiking shoes, dangerous conditions, or falling rocks throughout the story.

# Plot Twists

Sometimes you want to let the reader in on the action early in the story by foreshadowing. Other times you want to keep your reader guessing right to the end. When you lead your reader down one road, and then take a sudden, surprising turn in another direction, that's called a plot twist. If you've ever read a book or seen a movie and thought "I didn't see that coming!" then you've experienced a plot twist. O. Henry was the master of the plot twist. He always had something up his sleeve that the reader didn't expect.

# Figurative Language

If you want to borrow the car, I want your bedroom clean as a whistle first.

You've been quite the couch potato lately.

I told you a million times—clean your room!

Sometimes language is not intended to be taken literally, or word for word. Instead it expresses an imaginative description or comparison, or figurative language.

Think of figurative language as the seasoning you add to your writing. Shake a little figurative language into your writing, but don't dump in too much. Treat figurative language in a story like you'd treat salt in a recipe. A pinch of salt adds flavor, but a cup of salt ruins the soup. Two kinds of figurative language you can add into your writing are similes and metaphors.

# Simile

A simile compares two things using the word "like" or the word "as." Similes show how one thing is similar to another. Here are two examples from Sir Arthur Conan Doyle's first Sherlock Holmes story, "A Study in Scarlet."

Watson describes a man who considers himself a detective:

"This amateur bloodhound caroled away like a lark while I meditated upon the many-sidedness of the human mind."

The amateur detective tells Sherlock Holmes he has solved the mystery:

"I have made the whole thing as clear as day."

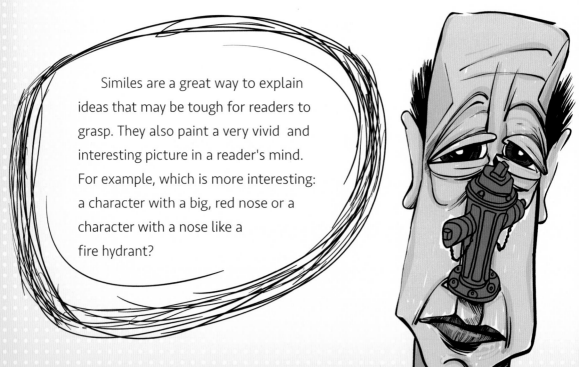

Similes are a great way to explain ideas that may be tough for readers to grasp. They also paint a very vivid and interesting picture in a reader's mind. For example, which is more interesting: a character with a big, red nose or a character with a nose like a fire hydrant?

# Metaphor

A metaphor compares two things by stating one thing is something else. Unlike its cousin the simile, a metaphor doesn't use any signal words such as "like." Take a look at these metaphors.

A character describing Sherlock Holmes says,

"You'll find him a knotty problem, though."

Sherlock Holmes quotes his own writing to Watson:

"So all life is a great chain, the nature of which is known whenever we are shown a single link of it."

Watson responds without knowing Holmes was the author:

"I never read such rubbish in my life."

Holmes descibes his crime-solving work with Watson:

"There's the scarlet thread of murder running through the colorless skein of life, and our duty is to unravel it, and isolate it, and expose every inch of it."

Both metaphors and similes can make powerful comparisons and visual images. They are both great tools for your writing. So how do you chose which one to use?

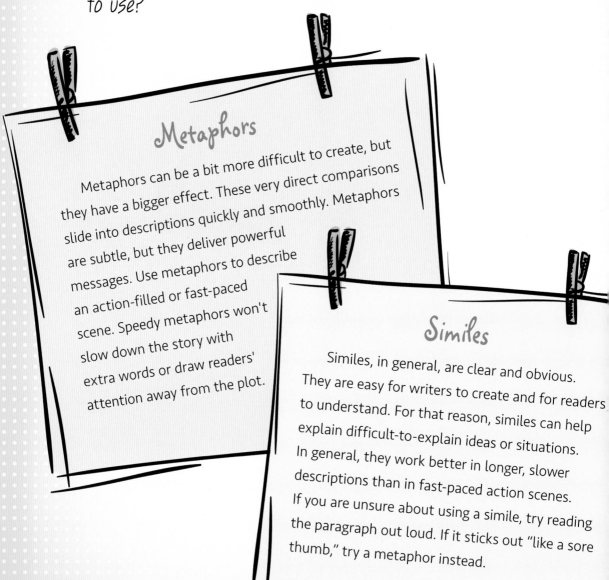

## Metaphors

Metaphors can be a bit more difficult to create, but they have a bigger effect. These very direct comparisons slide into descriptions quickly and smoothly. Metaphors are subtle, but they deliver powerful messages. Use metaphors to describe an action-filled or fast-paced scene. Speedy metaphors won't slow down the story with extra words or draw readers' attention away from the plot.

## Similes

Similes, in general, are clear and obvious. They are easy for writers to create and for readers to understand. For that reason, similes can help explain difficult-to-explain ideas or situations. In general, they work better in longer, slower descriptions than in fast-paced action scenes. If you are unsure about using a simile, try reading the paragraph out loud. If it sticks out "like a sore thumb," try a metaphor instead.

Write a scene using at least one simile and one metaphor. One way to incorporate a simile is to use it to describe a character. For example, you could write she's as _____ as a _____. An easy way to create a metaphor is to start with a simile, then take away the "like" or "as." For example, if you write the simile "she's as delicate as a daisy" just rewrite it and omit "as" and you get "She's a delicate daisy," which is a metaphor. Easy peasy!

# Keep It Fresh

It's fun and inspirational to try out new writing techniques. But wait—have you ever heard the saying "Know thyself?" Another excellent way to improve your writing is to take a close look at what you already know and practice!

Grab a couple samples of your writing, or, if possible, completed stories that you have written. Now imagine you are reading your work for the very first time. Sometimes it helps to read it out loud—especially if you don't normally do so. As you read, keep your eyes and ears open for quirks, habits, and repetition. Do you use one particular word over and over? Use an online thesaurus to look up synonyms for those poor, repeated, overworked words! Do you end every other sentence with an exclamation point? Make sure only the sentences that are truly *exclaimed* get this exceptional punctuation.

On the other hand, if every sentence ends in a period, why not break it up with an occasional question? Remember to vary your sentence structure and length too. Work to create sentences and paragraphs that you can read with a natural rhythm and without stumbling. Like a great new haircut or outfit, change is good! By "knowing thyself," including thy writing habits, you will find even more ways to grow as a writer.

**YOUR TURN**

You might think that the shorter the story, the easier it will be to write. But that's not necessarily so! Want to test it out? For this writing exercise, try writing a ultra-short story. Limit your entire story to 200, 150, or even 100 words. Remember, even ultra-short stories need to have essential story elements. The characters and situations should feel real and full, and the plot must have a beginning, middle, and end.

Ultra-shorts force you to use crisp, precise language—no thoughtless repetition. When you have a word limit, each word becomes more important. But remember, no matter what you are writing, conciously choosing the best, freshest words possible is always a good practice!

"The difference between the right word and the almost right word is the difference between lightning and a lightning bug."

-Mark Twain, *The Wit and Wisdom of Mark Twain*

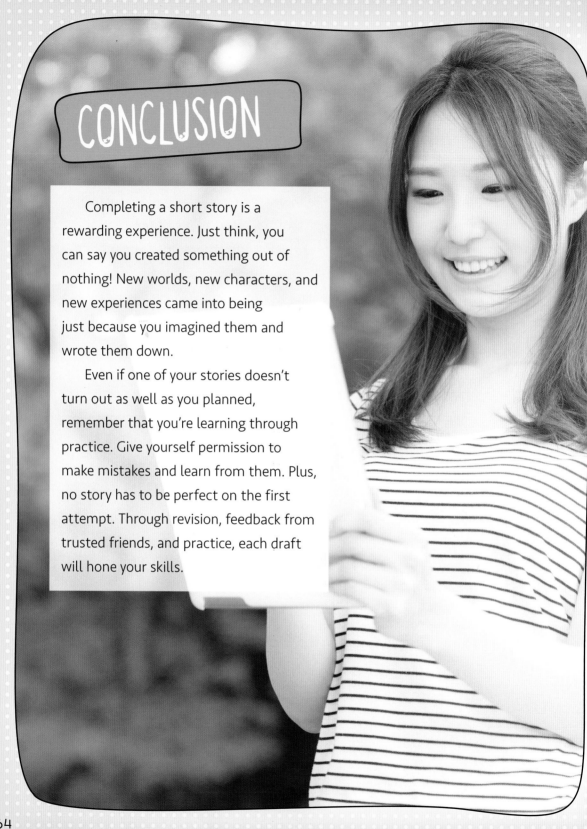

# CONCLUSION

Completing a short story is a rewarding experience. Just think, you can say you created something out of nothing! New worlds, new characters, and new experiences came into being just because you imagined them and wrote them down.

Even if one of your stories doesn't turn out as well as you planned, remember that you're learning through practice. Give yourself permission to make mistakes and learn from them. Plus, no story has to be perfect on the first attempt. Through revision, feedback from trusted friends, and practice, each draft will hone your skills.

# Chapter 2

# Writing Poignant Poetry

Poets have limitless imaginations. They're often quirky and love to observe things in their own unique way. When they look at a crow, for instance, they might think of a scoop of licorice ice cream or a splash of oil. Poets love to pinpoint just the right words to describe things. They often love music, and that includes the sounds of letters and words. They can be very particular about the way a poem looks on the page.

Does this sound like you? Congratulations, you're a poet!

Poets write poetry. No surprise there. But there are habits (besides just "sit down and write") that can make you an even better poet.

# Habit 1: Embrace

Poets tend to think a little differently and feel things really deeply. And that's a good thing. For instance, read how Kate Coombs describes her relationship with poetry—in a poem called "Poems."

i.

it's time to sleep
but the poems
lope up my spine howling
like I'm their moon.

ii.

it's time to sleep
but the poems
inventory my dreams
like pinball machines.

iii.

it's time to sleep
but the poems come
waving their eyestalks
like metaphors
swinging their spider legs,
pittering their lavender feet.

iv.

the poems come
flipping the world like a pancake
flipping the world
the way water flips light.

–Kate Coombs, "Poems," author of *Water Sings Blue*, *The Runaway Princess*, and more, all rights reserved

Coombs' phrases are unusual, right? That's exactly what makes them memorable! Her passion for language, image, and music comes through loud and clear. Poets embrace offbeat words and phrases, and they dig deeper into their emotions. You can bet no two poets will express an experience in the exact same way. Indeed, it is a poet's individual spin on the world that makes poems special and unique.

**YOUR TURN**

Coombs describes poetry as something that invades her life and turns her world upside down. What picture comes to your mind when you think of the word "poetry"? A silver stream that makes you calm and relaxed? A booming concert that makes you want to dance? A high-power microscope to study something in detail?

Write a poem that brings poetry to life. You might want to describe how a poem moves, what it eats or thinks, what it wears, and more.

# Habit 2: Read More to Write Better

Athletes watch other athletes perform. They study what works and what doesn't. They see what techniques have been tried and what techniques they want to use. This same approach works for writing poetry.

To become a better poet, you've got to start reading poetry. In fact, read lots of it—old poetry, new poetry, rhyming, and non-rhyming. Read library books, song lyrics, literary journals, and whatever else you can get your hands on. Make poetry part of your daily life.

When you find a poem you love, read it again. Do certain words or phrases surprise you? Is the poem fun to read aloud? Jot down your thoughts using sticky notes or a notebook. Save a copy of the poem

and highlight your favorite words and lines. You could even make a handmade book of your favorite poems.

Of course, you won't like every poem you read. However, even a poem you don't particularly like may have lessons for you. Why don't you like it? Is it too long? Is it boring? Is it confusing? Think about what you don't like in poems, and work to avoid those qualities in your own poetry.

Studying other poets' work will strengthen your own writing skills, so hit up your local library for some fresh poetry books. While you're there, create a book-spine poem. Browse the shelves and pull out books with interesting titles. Then try stacking books so the titles on the spines form a poem when read from top to bottom. Take a picture of your book-spine poem to share with friends.

# Thanhha Lai

Advice to young writers: "Read what you like, not because it's popular. Read it because you feel something. It's from feeling something that you're going to produce your own work."

–Thanhha Lai

Thanhha Lai was born in Vietnam in the 1960s. While her father was fighting in the Vietnam War (1959–1975), her mother worked to support the family. At the end of the war, in 1975, her family moved to Alabama. Lai wrote a novel in verse based on the culture shock of that move. *Inside Out & Back Again* won a National Book Award.

# from "American Address"

Mother's face crinkles
like paper on fire.
She tells Brother Quang
to clamp shut his mouth.

--Thanhha Lai, all rights reserved, from *Inside Out & Back Again*

**YOUR TURN**

In the excerpt from "American Address," Thanhha Lai doesn't use the words "angry" or "mad." By showing Mother's face crinkling and comparing it to burning paper, Lai portrays the emotion clearly. When was the last time your mom or another adult in your life got really mad or sad or surprised? Can you write a brief poem to show an emotion without ever naming it? In the first two lines, compare the adult's face to something that will suggest the emotion. Then add two lines and have your adult take action that also shows the emotion.

# Habit 3: Don't Lose Your Ideas

Every writer knows that the best ideas pop up at totally random times—in the shower, on the bus, or in the hallway at school. Like shooting stars, your brightest ideas can appear out of nowhere, and they disappear equally fast!

Don't lose your ideas—keep an idea notebook. Or, if you prefer, stash your ideas in a folder. You can use almost anything from a memo phone app to a fish bowl to an empty donut bucket. No matter where you keep them, gather and save those fleeting, glittering ideas before they're gone.

# SO MANY CHOICES!

Pop, hip-hop, dubstep, orchestral—there are lots of styles of music. Similarly, there are many types of poems. There are rhyming poems, of course. But poems don't have to rhyme. Some poems don't rhyme and don't seem to have any obvious rules at all. Those poems are called free verse. Coombs' poem "Poems" is an example of free verse. But other non-rhyming poems have specific forms, each with its own rules. Try a few. You'll probably find that the limitations of poetry forms push your creativity and add an extra goal or challenge to the writing process.

If you aren't feeling one form, try another! Just like music, you'll probably find that some forms can move you, while others might leave you shaking your head. Which form will you take to? There's only one way to find out.

# Found Poem

## (So Easy It Feels Like Cheating—But It's Not)

A found poem borrows words or short phrases from something already published, such as a newspaper article or speech, to make a poem. The result might be enchanting, funny, or dark—and it will probably sound different from the poems you usually write. If you feel like you're always writing in the same style, a found poem will help ease you out of your comfort zone.

To try writing a poem that makes use of someone else's words, a magazine or newspaper is a good place to start. Make a copy or print-out of something that grabs you. As you read, highlight the words and phrases that you like. Play with, narrow down,  and rearrange your chosen words to create a poem. As long as it's not exactly word for word, and you don't use more than 100 or so words, it is considered fair use.

Poet David L. Harrison read a travel article about a French food trend of adding seaweed (long used by Japanese chefs) to different foods. He chose words from that article to create a whimsical poem about food and culture.

# JUST ADD ALGAE

You'll find algae
in your bread near
Luxemburg Gardens.

Blame it on
the Japanese.

The hot French thing?
Developing a taste
for seaweed,
briny but delicate,
adding layers of flavors.

Sea bass slices,
raw oysters,
three kinds of algae . . .

Developing a taste
for seaweed,
that sushi staple?
Blame it on
the Japanese.

–David L. Harrison, author of *Pirates,
Cowboys*, and more, all rights reserved

Found poem source: "Just Add Algae,"
*Condé Nast Traveler*, June 2010

# Haiku

## (Short and Seasonal)

A haiku is a short poem that captures a moment in nature. Today's American haiku form is based on an old Japanese form. The American haiku usually has 3 lines. Many poets stick to a 5-7-5 syllable count. That means line 1 has 5 syllables, line 2 has 7, and line 3 has 5. The word "whispers" has two syllables: whis-pers. The word "together" has three: to-ge-ther. "New" is a one-syllable word. Saying a word out loud while you clap to each syllable can make it easier to hear the syllables.

Here's a modern haiku using the strict syllable count:

spring wind whispers by
birches gossip together
new leaves coming soon

–Kelly Ramsdell Fineman, all rights reserved

Some poets ignore the syllable count. They just focus on writing a brief poem that precisely shows one single moment in nature.

## Here's an example of that kind of haiku.

autumn wind
the cat in a frenzy
chasing leaves

–Diane Mayr, all rights reserved

## YOUR TURN

To begin, head outside and look around. Find some action, such as squirrels playing or a shadow moving. Then write four traditional 5-7-5 haiku, one for each season. Make sure a word in each haiku shows the season. And that the haiku relates to the action.

# Acrostic

## (Read Down, Then Across)

Lively
Acrobatic
Understanding
Respectful
Amazing

Did you ever have to write your name down your paper and then come up with words to describe yourself that started with each letter? That's an acrostic!

Acrostics can be entertaining—and challenging! The trick is to pick words that delight, surprise, feel natural, and start with the right letter. Check out the next acrostic by a poet who loves everything about Christmas—except one particular food.

# UNWANTED GUEST

Blessings
Upon
This

Wintery
Holiday!
Yuletide's

Twinkling
Hours--
Even

Flying
Reindeer!—
Utterly
Irresistible
Turkey

Cranberries
Apple pie
Knockout
Eggnog . . .

–J. Patrick Lewis, former U.S. Children's Poet Laureate, all rights reserved

**YOUR TURN**

What holiday do you love? Can you think of one tiny part of it that you don't love (like the fruitcake)? Write an acrostic about it. Do you notice that fruitcake is not mentioned in the poem "Unwanted Guest"? Only readers who realize it's an acrostic will get the reward of the answer being spelled out. Try not to use the word that you spell out in the body of your poem.

## AUTHOR PROFILE:

### Adelaide Crapsey

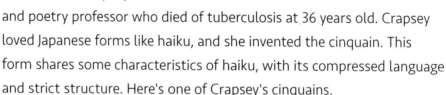

Adelaide Crapsey was a literature and poetry professor who died of tuberculosis at 36 years old. Crapsey loved Japanese forms like haiku, and she invented the cinquain. This form shares some characteristics of haiku, with its compressed language and strict structure. Here's one of Crapsey's cinquains.

## NIAGARA

(Seen on a Night in November )

How frail

Above the bulk

Of crashing water hangs,

Autumnal, evanescent, wan,

The moon.

–by Adelaide Crapsey, poem in the public domain

# Cinquain

## (2, 4, 6, 8, 2 Do We Appreciate?)

A cinquain is a non-rhyming form. It always has five lines of 2, 4, 6, 8, and 2 syllables. Generally cinquains rely on sensory description to paint a scene and make the reader feel a certain mood.

**YOUR TURN**

Take a shot at writing a cinquain inspired by the image on this page. Sometimes the first or last line names the topic of the poem. In Crapsey's cinquain, you don't know until the final line that the topic is the moon. In a longer poem, this might be irritating, but it works fine in a short form like this. It builds up suspense. If you like that effect, try revealing your topic in the last 2-syllable line, and use the first four lines to describe or hint at it.

# Fibonacci

## (Good, Honest Fun)

Here's an unusual poetic form: a Fibonacci. The Fibonacci sequence is a pattern that occurs in nature in nautilus shells, waves, pine cones, and more. The pattern is this: each row equals the sum of the two rows before.

A six-line Fibonacci poem has syllable counts of 1, 1, 2, 3, 5, and 8. To make powerful Fibs, leave out lazy words, such as "the" and "a," when possible. Fill your Fibs with strong verbs and specific nouns. Here's a slightly disgusting Fib!

Cat
heaves:
hair ball.
Hork hork hork.
What a squicky noise.
Cleanup needed in upstairs hall!

–Kelly Ramsdell Fineman, all rights reserved

Fibonaccis can be as long as you want. But be warned. If you write a 10-line Fib, that last line will have 55 syllables! The topic is open, so this is an opportunity to try something random. Here's an idea: Grab a paint chip (a sample) at the hardware store. Use the name of the paint color as the title and topic for your Fibonacci. In case you don't have access to a hardware store, here are three paint color names to choose from:

American Cheese

Plum Perfect

Potter's Wheel

# TO RHYME OR NOT TO RHYME

## Rhyming Is Harder Than It Looks

Some people's favorite poems are song lyrics. Lyrics usually rhyme, and a lot of young writers want to write rhyming poems too. Unfortunately, an idea for a rhyming poem that sounds great in your head might be disappointing when you get it down on paper. Creating meaningful, original rhymes is no easy task.

Why is excellent, natural-sounding, interesting verse so hard to write? Here are a few common pitfalls:

- Many poets read aloud well and auto-correct their own rhythm problems without realizing it. The word "going," for example, has the accent on the "go" syllable. But a poet who is rhyming "going" with "spring" might pronounce it as "goING."

- Rhyme takes over meaning, resulting in nonsense or overused words. If you write a rhyming poem about a girl who skis, and you mention that she has fleas, your reader will know that you put that in just for the rhyme. Try to make your rhymes sound natural—like it's a coincidence that the perfect words for your poem happen to rhyme!

- Focusing on rhyme and rhythm and ignoring other elements such as metaphor and imagery (using words related to  the senses to create a world for your reader). That results in a less interesting poem.

- Filler words like "oh," "so," and "and" water down many rhyming poems.

So now you know why rhyme is challenging. But if you're wild for rhyme, attack it and have fun with it.

# Three Kinds of Rhyme

All rhyme is not equal. There are three different kinds. Perfect rhyme is traditional rhyme. "Skis" and "fleas" are perfect rhymes. Then there's near rhyme, which is when you use words with similar sounds at the ends of lines. "Woods," "good," and "foot" are near rhymes. And, finally, there's internal rhyme. That's when perfect rhyme is used inside lines instead of at the end. You'll see that in the poem "Body Art," where "speckles" and "freckles" are internal rhymes.

All these types of rhyme are great. It's just a matter of consistency. If you use perfect rhyme in 90 percent of your poem, you can't use near rhyme in 10 percent. It's always obvious and jarring to the reader. In that case, it's best to choose a whole new pair of rhyming words.

# Find the Beat

Besides good rhyme, you need good meter, or rhythm. Your meter is the pattern of your accented syllables (the ones you emphasize or say a little louder) and your unaccented syllables (the ones you do not say louder). Mark your syllables to see the pattern—and where you've broken it.

Start with the last line on your poem, and read it aloud as if it's just a normal sentence. Highlight or make the accented syllables all capitals. Repeat, moving up, line by line, through your poem. Then look for the patterns.

In this example, the capitalized syllables show where one reader emphasized the sound. The number of accented beats is in parentheses after each line.

## MISSING HUE

| | |
|---|---|
| When GRASS is ALL done GROWing, | (3) |
| and it's NOT yet TIME for SNOWing, | (3) |
| there's a NEITHer/ALmost SEAson IN beTWEEN | (5) |
| when LEAVES turn BROWN and WRINKly, | (3) |
| and they TWIRL to EARTH all CRINKly. | (3) |
| Every FALL, i WONder WHAT beCAME of GREEN. | (5) |

–JoAnn Early Macken, author of *Waiting Out the Storm; Flip, Float, Fly*; and more, all rights reserved

Read the poem out loud, and clap on the capitalized syllables. Do you hear the rhythm? If this feels difficult to you, don't worry. Every poet who has ever written a good rhyming poem has written at least 100 bad ones! Keep working on rhyme, but spend time on free verse or non-rhyming forms, too. That way you'll challenge yourself but also produce poems you're really proud of!

YOUR TURN

Write a six-line poem about how you would spend your perfect day. Follow the rhyme and meter pattern of "Missing Hue," so you have two sets of three lines, with 3, 3, and 5 accented beats. You don't have to use the same rhyming words, just the pattern. So the end words of lines 1 and 2 would rhyme, 4 and 5 would rhyme, and 3 and 6 would rhyme. If you have another topic in mind, go for it!

# When the Little Words Are Very, Very Boring

Poetry's strength lies in its concentration of images and details in very few words. Filler words like "a," "very," and "so" tend to weaken poems. As you write, try to stuff every single line full of as much detail and content as possible. Don't waste your space with meaningless words like "and then" or "very, very."

## GARAGE SALE JEANS

Who was the kid
who wore you before
you became my favorite jeans?

You had a shell
in your back pocket.
I wonder what it means.

I wish I could
meet that old kid
who wore you long ago.

Garage sale jeans
keep secrets
new owners never know.

–Amy Ludwig VanDerwater, author of *Forest Has a Song*, all rights reserved

**YOUR TURN**

What's in your closet that used to be someone else's? Do you have a vintage skirt? Hand-me-downs from an older sister? A boyfriend's jacket? Choose a single item and write a rhyming poem with three-line stanzas. Remember to weed out those meaningless little words.

# When Out of Order Are the Words

When rhyming, try to make your phrasing sound natural. For instance, this does not sound natural:

No one answered when he knocked,
so to the store he slowly walked.

Nobody says, "to the store he slowly walked." They say, "He slowly walked to the store." When you move the verb to the end, it's a neon arrow pointing at the problem. You want your poem to seem effortless, but inverted word order lets your reader see you sweat.

Read aloud as you write. Your lines should feel fairly natural to say. Ask yourself, "Would my friends look at me like I had grown an extra head if I said this in a conversation?" If the answer's yes, check to see if inverted word order is the problem. If the verb comes before the subject, it's inverted. It's also inverted if a phrase that gives more detail about the verb comes before the verb. This is the case in the above example: "to the store" would come after "he slowly walked" in normal conversation.

## AUTHOR PROFILE:

# Emily Dickinson

Emily Dickinson was a 19th-century Massachusetts poet. Even though she lived a solitary life, she wrote often of love and loss. She wrote almost 1,800 poems, mostly rhyming. Dickinson's first poetry book wasn't published until after her death, but today she is considered one of the creators of uniquely American poetry.

## A BOOK.

He ate and drank the precious words,
His spirit grew robust;
He knew no more that he was poor,
Nor that his frame was dust.
He danced along the dingy days,
And this bequest of wings
Was but a book. What liberty
A loosened spirit brings!

–by Emily Dickinson, poem in the public domain

## YOUR TURN

Quick! Grab your cell phone or some other favorite tech device. Write a rhyming poem that tells about the wonderful things that everyday object does for you.

# POETRY BUILDING BLOCKS

# Ready to Cook Up a Poem

A good chef uses many basic ingredients all the time—salt, sugar, flour, etc. She turns them into everything from pancakes to pot pies. It's the same with poetry. There are some basic great poetry ingredients that you will use to cook up your best poems, whether they are rhyming, free verse, or specific forms.

## Can You Smell It?

Poems need sensory language—words related to your five senses. And don't settle for just sight words (shiny, burgundy, towering). Also work in textures (bumpy, feathery, soft), smells (bleach, cinnamon, wet dog), and sounds (crack!, meow, sob) and even tastes (salt, chlorine, tangy). Sensory words make the difference between:

Her backpack was stuffed with books and papers.

    and

Crumpled papers spilled from the musty green backpack in Lost and Found.

Sensory language makes poems unique and memorable. Here are a few lines from "Something Told the Wild Geese" by Rachel Field:

All the sagging orchards
Steamed with amber spice,
But each wild breast stiffened
At remembered ice.

In that excerpt, Field uses words that call to mind movement (sagging, stiffened), temperature (steamed, ice), color (amber), smell (spice), and texture (wild breast—goose feathers—and ice). Masterful!

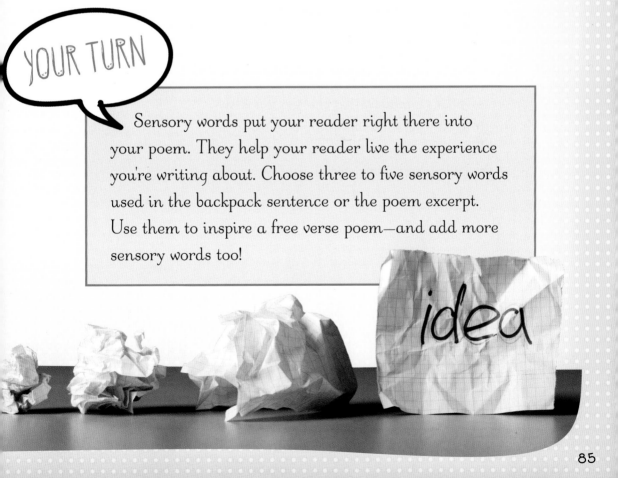

YOUR TURN

Sensory words put your reader right there into your poem. They help your reader live the experience you're writing about. Choose three to five sensory words used in the backpack sentence or the poem excerpt. Use them to inspire a free verse poem—and add more sensory words too!

idea

# Comparisons

## (But a Bus Is NOT Like a Puppy!)

Comparison is a key ingredient is many poems. Metaphors and similes both compare two unlike things. But they do it in different ways. Metaphors say that one thing is another thing.

## HOW IS A MEADOW AN OCEAN?

A meadow's an ocean with wild waves of wheat
Thunder's a drummer that's keeping storm's beat

A bus is a puppy that runs down the street
A desk is a robot with round, metal feet

A metaphor's a window that changes our view,
A gift to unwrap, something old made brand new

--Laura Purdie Salas, all rights reserved

Each line in that poem contains a metaphor. A bus is not really like a puppy! Still, the comparison can help you see a bus in a new way. By calling a bus "a puppy that runs down the street," the poem makes the bus seem eager and friendly. But if you were writing about the worst bus ride of your life, maybe you'd write, "A bus is a jail cell with seats of concrete." The comparison should tell your reader how to feel about the object.

Similes also compare two unlike things. They do that using the word "like" or "as."

The announcement sawed like a knife at my spine
Tulips were like yellow buckets, catching the rain

Kate Coombs' poem says that poems flip the world "like a pancake." That's a simile.

YOUR TURN

Write a rhyming list poem about your bedroom, using metaphors and/or similes. Try to avoid comparing your bedroom to other kinds of rooms. Compare it to things that are completely different.

# Repetition
# Repetition

We tend to repeat important things and things we like. Peek in your closet. Do you see lots of stripes? Or mostly red? That repetition shows something about you.

It's the same in a poem. Repetition emphasizes important words or phrases. It tells the reader, "Pay attention!" Repetition also enhances the musicality of a poem. That's the feeling of words sounding wonderful, with flows and pauses in all the right places. Look at "but the poems" in the Kate Coombs' poem. This repeated phrase does both of these jobs.

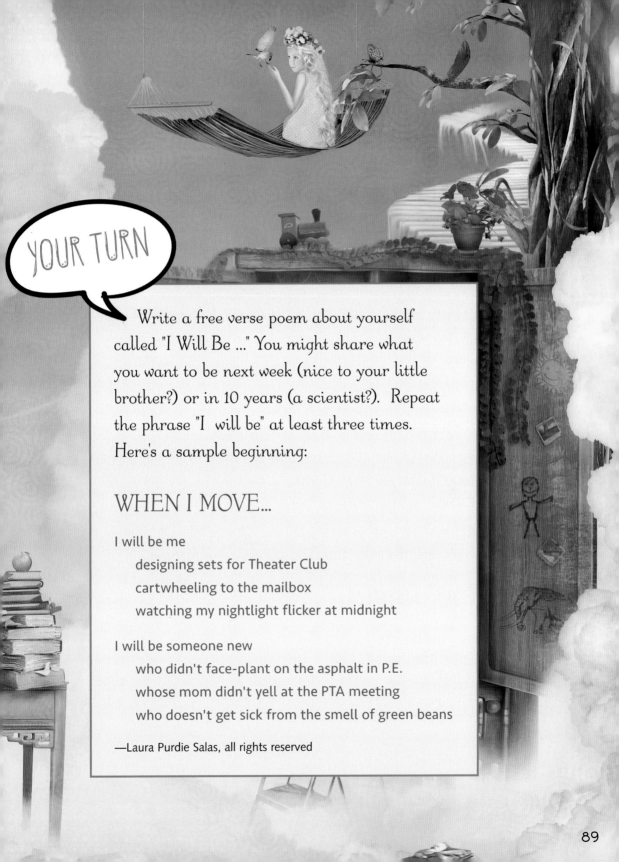

**YOUR TURN**

Write a free verse poem about yourself called "I Will Be ..." You might share what you want to be next week (nice to your little brother?) or in 10 years (a scientist?). Repeat the phrase "I will be" at least three times. Here's a sample beginning:

## WHEN I MOVE...

I will be me
    designing sets for Theater Club
    cartwheeling to the mailbox
    watching my nightlight flicker at midnight

I will be someone new
    who didn't face-plant on the asphalt in P.E.
    whose mom didn't yell at the PTA meeting
    who doesn't get sick from the smell of green beans

—Laura Purdie Salas, all rights reserved

# Alliteration, Assonance, and Consonance: Making Sounds Sound Fun

A begging beagle. A thick vanilla milkshake. A sweater of fur and feathers. The way words sound together is an important element of poetry. Playing with sounds will make your poem more pleasing to the ear.

Alliteration is when a sound is repeated at the start of several words (like the /b/ sounds in "begging beagle"). Assonance is a repeated vowel sound inside words—like the three /i/ sounds in "thick vanilla milkshake." And consonance is a repeated consonant sound inside words—like the /r/ sounds in "sweater of feathers and fur."

Can you find the alliteration and assonance in this haiku?

## ABANDONMENT

Sparrow sweetly sings
melancholy melody;
her mate, on the ground.

—Matt Forrest Esenwine, all rights reserved

Here's another poem that uses repeated sounds. This is a triolet—
an eight-line poem with a certain pattern of rhyme and meter. As
you read it, what consonant sound do you notice repeated in the first
three lines?

Hawks circle fields and furrows,
slicing spirals in the sky.
Field mice scurry into burrows.
Hawks circle fields and furrows,
keeping watch for shifting shadows
seeking spots where field mice hide.
Hawks circle fields and furrows
slicing spirals in the sky.

–Susan J. Blackaby, from *Nest, Nook & Cranny*, all rights reserved

Did you hear the /er/ sound in circle, furrows, scurry, and burrows?
And the /k/ sound in Hawks, circle, sky, and scurry?
Those are examples of consonance.

# WHAT SHOULD YOU WRITE ABOUT?

## When You're Short on Ideas

What if you're ready to write a poem but the words won't come? Take American writer Jack London's advice: "Don't loaf and invite inspiration; light out after it with a club . . ."

That's right—you need to jump down a poem's throat and drag those reluctant words onto the page. There are a ton of different things you can try to get the words flowing. One day, one thing will work, and the next time, something different might work. The important thing is to take action!

One thing that can really help is to change where you're writing. Go to a coffee shop or lie in a hammock. It's amazing how a new setting can loosen up words!

# Marilyn Singer

New York poet Marilyn Singer was a high school English teacher. One day she wrote a story at the Brooklyn Botanic Garden, and she followed that with lots of imaginative, award-winning books and poetry. She says, "I really love writing poetry and challenging myself, so who knows what wacky idea I'll have next?" When she's not writing, Marilyn is usually laughing or dancing.

## BODY ART

No season stamps me like summer—
with suntan and sand,
mosquito bites and streaks of sweat,
seaweedy speckles, scores of freckles.

As August ends, I muse
   on just how much I'll miss
these annoying or appealing
temporary tattoos.

–Marilyn Singer, author of *Mirror Mirror*, *Rutherford B.: Who Was He?*, and more, all rights reserved

# Look Around

## (It's Like I've Never Seen a Jelly Bean Before!)

Lots of poetry is descriptive. Look closely—at a chain link fence, your guinea pig, or a red jelly bean. Try taking a magnifying glass with you on a little poetry field trip. Study something small. What does it look like, sound like, feel like? How can you make your reader think, "I will never look at a jelly bean the same way again!"?

YOUR TURN

Pick a nearby object and write a poem from its point of view. Tell the object's secrets in the poem. For example, if you are a stapler, what could you confess? Maybe your stapler will say: *I have a bad habit of biting / My metal jaws snap at paper!*

## AUTHOR PROFILE:

### Nikki Grimes

"I wouldn't call myself lucky, because hard work and perseverance form the bedrock of my success."

–Nikki Grimes, author of Words with Wings,
Planet Middle School, and more

California poet Nikki Grimes gave her first public poetry reading at age 13. Her New York City childhood included foster homes, dangerous neighborhoods, and too many schools to remember. Writing helped her cope, and she began publishing her poems while still in school. She has since written many award-winning poetry books.

YOUR TURN

Nikki Grimes used writing to cope with hard situations as a teen. What's something hard you've faced? Write an "I Am From . . ." poem, sharing about the places, people, and events that have shaped you. Include at least a couple of challenges you've dealt with. For instance:

## I AM FROM . . .

I am from scorching Julys in my lungs
and seashells between my toes.
I am from lonely holidays and
cousins never known.
I am from a small, silent family
with many rules and few hugs.
I am from dreams of snow and song
and books for best friends.

–by Laura Purdie Salas, all rights reserved

# Excavate Your Idea Notebook

## (I Knew I Kept These for a Reason)

Don't forget to check in on your idea notebook (or file, or whatever) regularly. Those ideas won't do you any good if you never go back to them!

> "I do, however, keep a 'notebook' 'in the cloud.'... I always make time to jot down every poetical idea at the moment it pops into my head. Then when I find I have time to write, I rummage through this treasure trove of ideas for one that I would like to work on and develop."

> –Kenn Nesbitt, U.S. Children's Poet Laureate, 2013-2015, author of The Armpit of Doom, I'm Growing a Truck in the Garden, and more

# Try a Poetic Form

## (Are You in the Mood for a Cinquain?)

Do you have a topic in mind but you don't know how to start? Choose a poetic form! Suppose your topic is the last school dance. Here are some possible first steps:

### HAIKU

Think about arriving at the dance and getting out of the car. Show that scene in a haiku, using a word that tells the reader what season it is.

### ACROSTIC

Write DANCE down your page. Brainstorm words about the dance: who you hung out with; the music; dancing or standing and watching; your clothes; the best moment; the worst moment, etc. Start matching up words and phrases with the letters you wrote down the page.

### CINQUAIN

Choose your first two-syllable line. How can you introduce the dance? Epic? Funny? Flailing? Lonely? Perfect?

### RHYMING FORM

Brainstorm words about the dance and list rhyming words for those key words.

## MAKE IT BETTER

# What Do You Mean, I'm Not Finished?

Growing a poem is like growing a plant. You start with a seed, or an idea. You plant it by writing a first draft. Then you feed it what it needs to grow. For a poem, that's time and revision.

You might focus on a different element, like sound or meaning, in each revision. With each draft, your poem will get leaner, stronger, better. How many drafts will you need to do? Some writers do three or four drafts. Others do many more. Basically you revise until you feel like the poem says what you want it to say in the best way you can say it.

You can use these revision techniques for any kind of poem: rhyming, free verse, haiku, acrostic, etc. Revising a rhyming poem takes longer, because you still have to make sure the right words rhyme and that the rhythm is the way you want it. But that's okay. Give yourself time to revise. Your poems deserve it!

# Revising for Word Choice

## (Words are Easy. Great Words Take More Work.)

Nikki Grimes on poetry:

> "If it's done well, no words are wasted or minced. . . . I love that
> poetry can make a beeline for the heart."

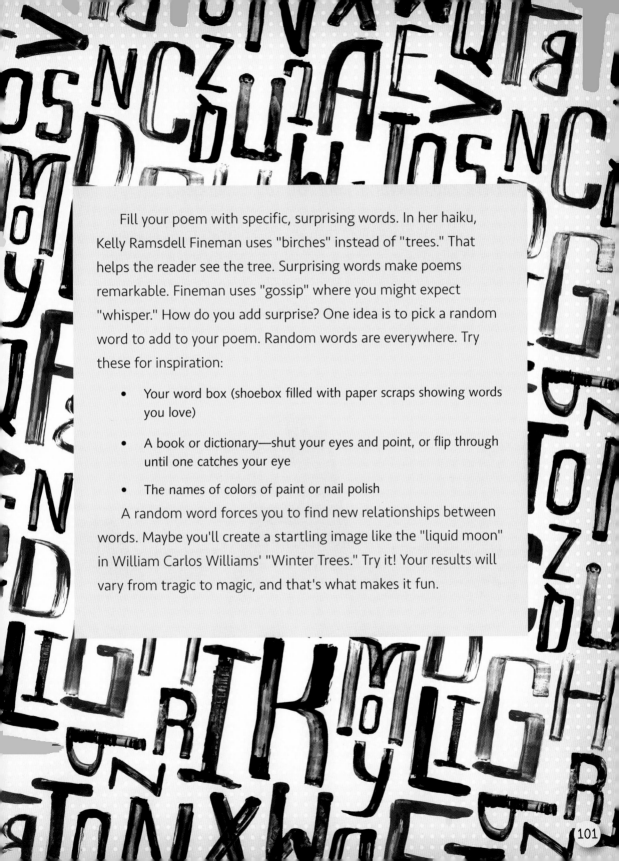

Fill your poem with specific, surprising words. In her haiku, Kelly Ramsdell Fineman uses "birches" instead of "trees." That helps the reader see the tree. Surprising words make poems remarkable. Fineman uses "gossip" where you might expect "whisper." How do you add surprise? One idea is to pick a random word to add to your poem. Random words are everywhere. Try these for inspiration:

- Your word box (shoebox filled with paper scraps showing words you love)

- A book or dictionary—shut your eyes and point, or flip through until one catches your eye

- The names of colors of paint or nail polish

A random word forces you to find new relationships between words. Maybe you'll create a startling image like the "liquid moon" in William Carlos Williams' "Winter Trees." Try it! Your results will vary from tragic to magic, and that's what makes it fun.

# Read Aloud

## (Where People Won't Look at You Strangely)

Poetry is read aloud more than any other literary form. Reading your work aloud as you revise is critical. Your poetry should flow—it should be easy to say out loud, without stumbling over words or phrases. It should sound good and be fun to say.

So shut your door and read your lines aloud as you try out different words. Choose words that sound good and add musicality to your poem.

# Revising for Meaning

## (Did You Say What You Meant to Say?)

Poets say things in new and interesting ways. That's part of poetry's magic. But you also want your meaning to be clear. There's only one way to make sure your poem says what you want it to: share it with some trusted friends. Ask them, "What happens in this poem?" Or "What is this poem about?" If their answer isn't what you expect, you can work on your poem to make it clearer.

It can be hard to hear that part of your poem isn't quite working. Just remember that they are not telling you that your poem isn't good. They're just asking questions or pointing out trouble spots in your writing. It's not personal. Listen. Then work on other projects for a little while. Later, reread your poem. Do their comments ring true now? Often you'll see things you hadn't noticed before and can work to make your poem even better.

## SHARING YOUR WORK

# Shout It Out or Keep It Secret

Sharing a poem is kind of like cutting a piece of your heart out and projecting it on a big screen. Is it terrifying? Sometimes, but you are sharing something important—something that can only come from you. That can be powerful.

If you're nervous, start small. Give a copy of a poem to one person. Is your best friend having a rough day? Slip a funny verse story into her locker. Seeing how your writing affects other people is amazing. Their reactions can motivate you to write more, which will help you become an even better poet.

What if you're really private? Or your poems are too personal to share? That's totally fine. Writing poetry can help you sort through your feelings and process big things in your life. Your work is as valid and important to you as the poems of someone who can't wait to read her poems to the whole school.

If you can, take the leap. Text your poem. Tweet it, message it, share it! And share yourself. If you can't or don't want to, know that your poems are still a gift, even if they're a gift for only you.

# VOICE

Expressing unspoken thoughts
and burning desire,
a voice that is not part of the narrative
pauses for a breath;
the essential commands
and
extreme situations
still seem confusing.
Don't get discouraged.
Slow down,
evaluate your work,
and take your time
through talent,
steely focus,
and faith
to change the world.

–Matt Forrest Esenwine, all rights reserved

# Publish Your Poems

## (When You Want to Make It Official)

Maybe you're hoping to do something more official, such as publish your poems. You have a couple of options—self-publishing (meaning you publish them yourself) or submitting to a magazine or newspaper that publishes poetry.

Self-publishing poetry is pretty easy in this high-tech world. If you have access to a computer and printer, you're set. Choose your best work, ask a friend who's good at grammar to proofread it, and add some nice design touches. Then, print out 20 copies of your poetry collection to share with family and friends.

You can also explore outside publishing possibilities. If you search online for "teens" and "poetry contest," or for "teen poetry submissions," you'll find contests and magazines that publish teens' poems, either in print or online. Ask a parent or teacher to make sure the contest is legit. You shouldn't have to pay an entry fee or pay for a copy of a magazine or book in which your poem is published.

Here are a few tips for submitting your work:

- Send only your best poems.

- Include your name and contact information.

- Read the directions carefully and follow them to a T.

- Once you send off your work, start writing something new!

Hopefully, you feel ready to try new topics, new forms, and new approaches. When you look back over poems you've written, you'll probably find some that are ok, some that are embarrassingly bad, and one or two you absolutely love. That's awesome! It's like soccer. It takes a thousand drills to create one game-winning goal. So get out there and keep writing!

# Chapter 3

# Writing Amazing Drama

Write drama and your words will literally leap off the page. Where do they land? On stage, of course! Writing drama means writing plays. Unlike books, short stories, or poems, plays are meant to be performed. But, as with other forms of writing, plays have a beginning, middle, and end. They include a conflict, or problem your hero must overcome. Plays also include a climax, which is the crucial point in the drama. And they end with a resolution. At that point, the problem is solved.

Plays are written in the form of a script. A script includes a cast of characters and stage directions, so performers know where and how to move. It also includes the setting where the action takes place. Most importantly, scripts are made up of dialogue. In a play, the story is told through the words characters speak to each other. Sometimes, characters in plays even speak—out loud—to themselves.

Some plays are full length, which means they have more than one act. Each act has a number of scenes. Generally, full-length plays have subplots as well as the main conflict. In *Hamlet*, by classic British playwright William Shakespeare, for example, the main story concerns Hamlet's need to avenge his murdered father. Among the subplots, though, are Ophelia's unrequited love for Hamlet, and the recruitment of two men to spy on him. That particular subplot resulted in a whole new play, *Rosencrantz and Guildernstern Are Dead*, by modern playwright Tom Stoppard.

Many playwrights start out writing one-act plays. These generally have a simpler, more direct story line for audiences to follow. As the short story is to the novel, so the one-act is to the full-length play. It's up to you to decide how long your play will be. In fact, as a playwright, you get to make every creative decision.

**In Tom Stoppard's play, Rosencrantz and Guildernstern travel to England in a barrel to deliver a message from the king.**

# START WTIH AN IDEA

## Base It on Real Life

To write a play, you need an original idea for your story. Seeing and reading plays (or seeing movies based on plays), is a great way to get inspired. Hit the library for plays by a variety of playwrights. Take note of what you like and dislike about different storylines.

For a selection of plays with a common link, try reading these.

- Neil Simon's *The Odd Couple* is about friends with clashing personality traits who share an apartment.

- Lorraine Hansberry's *A Raisin in the Sun* focuses on an African-American family trying to combat racism.

- Tennessee Williams' *The Glass Menagerie* is about a young man who is unable to live on his own because he must support his mother and sister.

- Brian Friel's *Dancing at Lughnasa* is a memory play, told by an adult narrator, about a summer spent with this aunts when he was a boy.

These plays cover very different subject matter. But they have two important things in common. All are based in part on real-life events the playwrights—or people they knew—experienced. At the same time, each play creates fiction from facts, using real life simply as the basis of an invented story.

**In the 2007 London production of *The Glass Menagerie*, Jessica Lange's costar was Ed Stoppard, son of the famous playwright.**

Famous playwrights aren't the only ones who have interesting experiences (or know others with great stories to tell). You can write a play based on events from your own life too.

Do you draw a blank trying to think of real-life experiences that could be dramatic? Try asking yourself specific questions like the ones below and then jotting down the answers. Have you ever:

- lost or damaged something that didn't belong to you? What was the owner's reaction? How did you handle the situation?

- laughed uncontrollably when you were supposed to be quiet? Did you get in trouble? What finally made you stop?

- told a lie? Why did you tell it? Did you get caught?

- had an embarrassing moment? What happened? Who was watching? How did you finally live it down?

- made a bad decision? Did it affect anyone else? What did you do next?

When you brainstorm ideas based on real life, write a page or a few paragraphs describing entire experiences from beginning to end. That way you'll have whole stories to work with later. You can come back to them and make creative changes to write a play that works dramatically. Remember: no need to stick to the facts. You're writing fiction. The facts serve as a springboard.

# Ripped from the Headlines

You may also be inspired by events that have nothing to do with your own life or anyone you know personally. Many playwrights draw stories from historical or current events. *Moments with Dr. King*, by Eric Falkenstein, for example, is about the Rev. Dr. Martin Luther King Jr. It focuses on the civil rights movement, a time of great change in American history.

*Grounded*, by George Brant, tells the more modern story of a female fighter pilot who is reassigned to operate drones. Brant became interested in his topic after reading an article in the *Columbia Journalism Review*. *Democracy*, by Michael Frayn, tells the tale of a German chancellor who had to expose a spy working in his own government.

Flip through newspapers and magazines. Search the Internet. Watch documentaries. Read history books. There's no end to the number of historical and current events you could write a play about. If you want to write a play that includes facts as well as fiction, dig in and do more research on your topic. In a historical play, you want to stay as true to the facts as possible. Even so, you can use the form to explore the motivations and feelings of your hero.

# Getting to Know: Shakespeare

William Shakespeare (1546-1616) lived in England. He is widely regarded as the greatest playwright in history. His plays, which include comedies, tragedies, and history plays, are still performed regularly worldwide. His history plays include *Henry VI Parts 1, 2, & 3 (three plays)*, *Richard III*, *Richard II*, *Henry IV Parts 1 & 2 (two plays)*, and *Henry V*. He consulted *The Chronicles of England, Scotland and Ireland*, by Raphael Holinshed and other works to research historical events. When he wrote, he combined what he'd learned with fictional details.

**William Shakespeare**

Shakespeare's plays live on—as in this production of *Richard III* starring Kevin Spacey.

At the end of *Richard III*, Shakespeare imagines a scene in which ghosts visit King Richard III and warn he'll die the next day. Note the way the script is set up. Each character's name is in bold and all caps. Anything that is not dialogue (setting, movement) is set in italics and parentheses, and space is left between each speaker.

*Enter the Ghost of LADY ANNE*

**Ghost of LADY ANNE** *(To KING RICHARD III):*

Richard, thy wife, that wretched Anne thy wife,

That never slept a quiet hour with thee,

Now fills thy sleep with perturbations

To-morrow in the battle think on me,

And fall thy edgeless sword: despair, and die!

*(To RICHMOND)*

Thou quiet soul, sleep thou a quiet sleep

Dream of success and happy victory!

Thy adversary's wife doth pray for thee.

*(Enter the Ghost of BUCKINGHAM)*

**Ghost of BUCKINGHAM** *(To KING RICHARD III):*

The last was I that helped thee to the crown;

The last was I that felt thy tyranny:

O, in the battle think on Buckingham,

And die in terror of thy guiltiness!

Dream on, dream on, of bloody deeds and death:

Fainting, despair; despairing, yield thy breath!

*(To RICHMOND)*

I died for hope ere I could lend thee aid:

But cheer thy heart, and be thou not dismay'd:

God and good angel fight on Richmond's side;

And Richard falls in height of all his pride.

*(The Ghosts vanish)*

*(KING RICHARD III starts out of his dream)*

# Consider Your Audience

Why choose one story over another? The playwright most likely feels strongly about something that happened in his or her life. Or he or she has a passionate interest in the topic he or she has chosen. When you write drama, you know you're not just writing for readers. You're also writing for an audience that will see your story acted out. It helps some playwrights to consider who that audience is going to be.

Wendy Wasserstein was inspired when she noticed that women never seemed to be the heroes of plays, and were usually shown as desperate or crazy. She wanted to see stories about women that were true to life and portrayed them as whole human beings. That's how she became an award-winning playwright. Like Wasserstein, you can write a play that focuses on your personal interests and also informs, entertains, and inspires your audience.

**GREENWICH THEATRE**

# THE HEIDI CHRONICLES
## BY WENDY WASSERSTEIN

Wasserstein wrote many groundbreaking plays, such as *The Heidi Chronicles*.

**22 AUGUST TO 5 OCTOBER 1996**

# YOUR TURN

People are often drawn to plays that show characters like themselves in situations they've experienced. But remember, a powerful story can attract wider audiences too. You can start with even the simplest idea.

Grab your notebook and jot down one-sentence or two-sentence opinions on issues that move you. Some choices might be bullying, dating, or curfews, but don't feel limited to those. Next, play the role of the audience. Single out the issue you most want to dramatize and consider why you might want to see a play about it. Is it a topic you've never seen on stage before? Do you have questions about it? Do you have more you'd like to learn or say about it?

If you feel that way, other people probably do too. You could write a play that answers your questions, lets you speak your mind, and speaks to others too.

# Tennessee Williams

Born in 1911, Tennessee Williams experienced many difficulties throughout his life. Growing up, he witnessed his parents' troubled marriage. His sister was mentally ill. The family moved often, and each time, young Williams had trouble fitting in with his new classmates.

Williams' father forced him to quit college and work at a shoe factory. He suffered a nervous breakdown before finally returning to school. As an adult, Williams struggled with depression.

Throughout his life, Williams used his experiences to write successful plays that would later become classics. When he wrote *The Glass Menagerie*, he created the character of Amanda based on his own mother. When he wrote *Cat on a Hot Tin Roof*, his father was the model for Big Daddy. His experiences living in New Orleans helped him write *A Streetcar Named Desire*.

By the time of his death, in 1983, Williams was the respected author of many published works, including 25 full-length plays, more than 71 one-act plays, and five screenplays.

In 2009 Cate Blanchett, left, played the role of Blanche DuBois in *A Streetcar Named Desire*. The troubled DuBois famously "depended on the kindness of strangers."

# Heighten the Drama

When you write drama, you need to make sure the plot of your play includes a conflict that will engage an audience. In George Bernard Shaw's *Pygmalion*, the conflict kicks off when one character (the Note Taker) decides he can transform another (the Flower Girl). The task isn't as simple as he thinks, and it also creates unanticipated consequences. (You might recognize this as the basis for the later musical, *My Fair Lady*. Both the musical and a film version of *Pygmalion* can probably be found in your local library.)

In the beginning of *Pygmalion*, the Flower Girl's ambition is to own her own flower shop. Later in this scene, the Note Taker first comes upon her. He makes a bet that he can improve her speech and pass her off as a duchess.

# Getting to Know: George Bernard Shaw

**THE FLOWER GIRL** *(with feeble defiance):* I've a right to be here if I like, same as you.

**THE NOTE TAKER:** A woman who utters such depressing and disgusting sounds has no right to be anywhere—no right to live. Remember that you are a human being with a soul and the divine gift of articulate speech: that your native language is the language of Shakespear[e] and Milton and The Bible; and don't sit there crooning like a bilious pigeon.

**THE FLOWER GIRL** *(quite overwhelmed, and looking up at him in mingled wonder and deprecation without daring to raise her head):* Ah-ah-ah-ow-ow-ow-oo!

**THE NOTE TAKER** *(whipping out his book):* Heavens! What a sound! *(He writes; then holds out the book and reads, reproducing her vowels exactly)* Ah-ah-ah-ow-ow-ow-oo!

**THE FLOWER GIRL** *(tickled by the performance, and laughing in spite of herself):* Garn!

**THE NOTE TAKER:** You see this creature with her kerbstone English: the English that will keep her in the gutter to the end of her days. Well, sir, in three months I could pass that girl off as a duchess at an ambassador's garden party. I could even get her a place as lady's maid or shop assistant, which requires better English.

To create a conflict in your own play, make your hero really want something—then don't let the hero get it too easily. Put a few obstacles in his or her way. Add some more. Finally, create a situation that will convince your audience the character may *never* get what he or she wants.

That's called raising the stakes. And the more your hero struggles, the better. His or her struggle is what keeps audience members on the edge of their seats.

A conflict isn't a conflict unless your hero really cares about it. And he or she won't care unless the rewards for overcoming it (and the consequences for failing) are huge!

As the playwright, it's your job to make your conflict, no matter how minor, feel like life or death for your hero—and your audience. What will your hero win if he or she solves her problem? What will he or she lose if the problem isn't solved?

Use this exercise as a way to help you figure out how to raise the stakes. List five terrible things that might happen in the following situations. Make sure they're consequences you could show to an audience. Let your imagination go wild! Here are some examples of what might happen:

- Your hero loses a battle.
- Your hero fails a test.
- Your hero loses her babysitting job.
- Your hero crashes his car.

# Problem Solved!

When the conflict is at its worst for your hero, your play has reached its climax. Next you must find a way to wrap it up. The resolution, or denouement, marks the point at which the central problem is solved: the Flower Girl goes to the ball and is mistaken for royalty. Hamlet kills the man who killed his father. Sometimes there is a final scene that shows what happens after the dust of the climax has settled.

In this scene, the Flower Girl is dressed in a ballroom gown, and looks like royalty.

The denouement may even inspire another play. Shakespeare's *Henry IV, Part 1* led to *Henry IV, Part 2*, as well as *The Merry Wives of Windsor*. Many contemporary playwrights continue their characters' lives in sequels or trilogies that follow them through time and other events.

August Wilson even wrote a series of 10 plays, *The Pittsburgh Cycle*, depicting African-American life throughout the twentieth century.

*Fences*, the sixth play in *The Pittsburgh Cycle*

Got a storyline in mind? Figured out your conflict and resolution? It's a good idea to create a system that will keep you on track while you're writing your script. Here's one way to stay organized.

1. Write out the plot for your play from start to finish in a notebook or on your laptop. Don't worry about style, character development, stage directions, or dialogue for now.

2. Read over your story and notice points where things change. Mark spots where characters refocus their attention, shifting from one issue to another. Also mark places in the plot where the setting changes.

3. Copy your story onto index cards, using a new one for each moment of change you marked. Think of these as separate scenes in your script.

4. When you're finished, create three cards labeled Beginning, Middle, and End. Stack the cards according to where they belong in your story.

5. Now, you have a collection of scenes that you can start organizing into a finished play.

# Organize, Then Reorganize

Suppose you have a story idea that seems full of suspense. But when you write it out, the script falls flat. That doesn't necessarily mean you should scrap your idea. It could just mean you need to reorganize your material.

Telling your story in chronological order, from beginning to end, may not be the best way to go. Look for the crucial conflict in your plot. Is it buried somewhere in the middle of the story? Move it closer to the start of your script to draw the audience in ... but draw them in slowly. The conflict should build and build until it begs for resolution.

Writers often work from the beginning to end of the story. As they continue writing, they read the early scenes over and over. They tweak and edit them. By the time they've reached the end of the script, the beginning is highly polished. The end, however, hasn't received nearly as much attention. It simply hasn't been around as long.

You can create a highly polished ending to your play by writing those later scenes first. This strategy will also give your script a clear direction. You'll know right from the start where your plot is headed.

Try writing the last scene of the play you have in your head and see how that feels. If you're not sure how the play should end, first write an outline. Once you have the outline in front of you, write out the last scene.

# Leave 'Em Laughing— or Crying

How do you want your audience to feel when your play is over? Happy? Sad? Surprised? Outraged? The range of emotions you might inspire is endless. Just remember to make it believable. Certain types of endings leave an audience feeling cheated. Like these:

- It was all a dream.

- Characters have sudden and dramatic personality changes.

- Unbelievable coincidences occur to resolve problems.

- People die for no apparent reason.

- Magical elements are brought into an otherwise realistic story.

Even a play set in an imaginary world populated by mythical creatures, robots, or aliens has to make sense. Plays about nonhuman characters usually accomplish this by telling stories about very human problems. *Animal Farm*, which has been staged as a play based on the George Orwell novel, is about a group of farm animals. It's also about power, inequality, and politics. The animals stand in for humans to help Orwell more clearly make his point about the corruption of power.

**YOUR TURN**

Ready to wrap up your story? To make sure the very last scene of your script works, try this two-step process.

First, answer these questions:

1. Will your characters continue to know one another?

2. Will they stay in the same location or continue their lives somewhere else?

3. What will happen to the world around them?

4. Do your characters have specific plans for the future?

5. Are your characters likely to succeed or fail in the future?

6. How have their experiences in the play changed their lives?

Next, try writing the last scene as the start of a new script, showing the audience the beginning of your characters' next story. You may get ideas about how to finish up. Or you may even be inspired to write a sequel.

# BRING CHARACTER TO LIFE

Even the most exciting play in the world needs more than an engaging plot. It needs a strong main character to capture and keep the audience's attention. If people care about your main character, they'll care about what happens in your play.

Most plays have a cast of several characters. Even one-person shows may include several characters. In *Bridge and Tunnel*, for example, playwright and actor Sarah Jones plays more than a dozen multicultural men, women, and children who have immigrated to New York.

# Characters in a play typically include the following:

**Protagonist**—a main character, the hero of the story

**Antagonist**—a main character (villain) who causes problems for the protagonist

**Confidante**—a friend the main character confides in

**Foil**—a character with traits that highlight a main character through contrast

**Static characters**—characters who do not change at all as the story develops

**Dynamic characters**—characters who are changed by the story

**Round characters**—characters with many sides to their personalities

**Flat characters**—characters who only show one personality trait

Can you identify these character types in plays you've read or seen?

Character types don't have to remain separate. They can overlap. A confidante could also be a foil, for example. A villain could be a round character. Create a typical villain, set on destroying the world. Follow these steps to understand the character better and write him or her more realistically.

1. Consider what made this character become a villain. Write a paragraph or two about the character's background.

2. Brainstorm humorous habits that might balance out the character's evil personality. Maybe he or she sucks his or her thumb or sleeps with a teddy bear.

3. List positive qualities your villain could possess. Get ideas from your favorite real-life and fictional villains.

4. Brainstorm your villain's worst fear. Consider what's scary to a young child, an astronaut, a cat, or a criminal. The fear you give your villain could be anything at all.

5. Give your villain something or someone to love. It could be something normal or something completely strange. There's no right or wrong answer when you create characters. It's all up to you.

# Write Who You Know

Have you ever heard the expression, "Write what you know"? Really understanding a subject makes it easier to write about. From the start, you have plenty to say.

The same is true when you're developing characters. When you write who you know, you can base characters on real people. They offer lots of material to work with when you place them into your plot.

Many famous playwrights borrow personality traits from people they or their friends know when creating characters. Neil Simon modeled his characters in *The Odd Couple* after his brother and a talent agent he knew. John Guare based the teen con man in *Six Degrees of Separation* on a story his friend told him about hosting a similar character. Sarah Ruhl's *The Oldest Boy* is based on characters in a true story her children's nanny told her.

*Six Degrees of Separation* is a play about a young man who cons his way into the life of a wealthy couple. The story is based on real life.

Think of all the people in your life. Some you know well, such as your family, friends, teachers, and coaches. Others you may not know well, such as your dentist, doctor, bus driver, or cafeteria server. Whether you're close or not isn't really important. What is important is to observe and listen to the people with whom you interact. You'll notice that they all speak differently and have different identifying movements. One person may brush her hair back from her face when she's nervous, where another might clear his throat when he's going to tell a lie.

To get started, pick a few real people and fill in the following details. When you create fictional characters for your play, you can borrow, mix, and match their traits. The chart shows a few examples, but go wild and create your own.

| | |
|---|---|
| Appearance | tall, short, messy, distinguished |
| Age | |
| Job/Daily activities | |
| Hobbies | |
| Likes | |
| Dislikes | |
| Family | |
| Friends | |
| How he/she moves | clumsy, graceful |
| Things he/she says | tells jokes, says "like" after every other word |

## PLAYWRIGHT PROFILE:

### Lorraine Hansberry

Lorraine Hansberry's first play, *A Raisin in the Sun*, was unusual in 1959 for its realistic portrayal of a working-class African-American family. When it debuted, it was the first play written by an African-American woman ever to be produced on Broadway. Hansberry was 29 years old. She was also the first African-American playwright to win a New York Critics' Circle Award for Best Play of the Year.

Hansberry began her career as a receptionist, typist, and editorial assistant, as well as writing news articles and editorials for a New York newspaper called *Freedom*. She also held part-time jobs as a waitress and cashier. When she started writing *A Raisin in the Sun*, she drew from her own life experiences. Though her family didn't struggle financially when she was young, she knew people who did. *Raisin*'s plot was rooted in her life. When her father bought a house in a white neighborhood, those neighbors went to court to force them out. They did not succeed.

Hansberry died of cancer at age 34 in 1965. With *A Raisin in the Sun*, she left behind a legacy that exposed racial tensions and spoke to families of all races struggling in America and around the world. The dream of owning a house is universal.

# DELIVER STRONG DIALOGUE

In a play dialogue does most of the work. Through dialogue, your audience will get to know your characters and learn what they want. Dialogue reveals the conflicts characters face. It also sets the scene and advances the plot of your play. While doing all of that, it has to sound natural too. It wouldn't work, for example, to have one character talk in lengthy paragraphs about what led to the current moment or what happened in the past while everyone else in the play stands around listening. If you want to talk about the past, you have to show the past.

Arthur Miller did so in *Death of a Salesman*. The set and costumes helped him portray the salesman's family in both the past and the present. Another method would be to have your characters speak all at once. They could interrupt one another, as you and your siblings might when you talk. But remember: talking about the past has to relate to the play's present conflict.

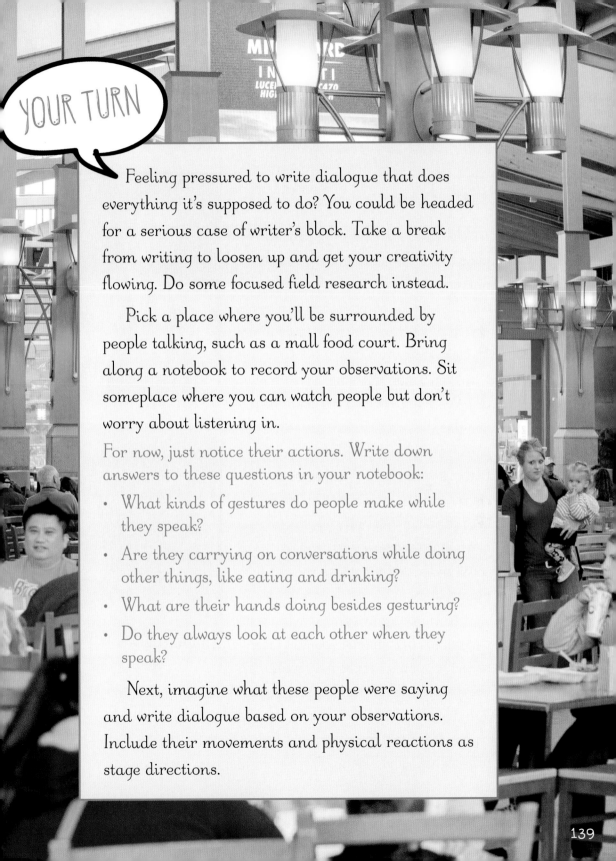

**YOUR TURN**

Feeling pressured to write dialogue that does everything it's supposed to do? You could be headed for a serious case of writer's block. Take a break from writing to loosen up and get your creativity flowing. Do some focused field research instead.

Pick a place where you'll be surrounded by people talking, such as a mall food court. Bring along a notebook to record your observations. Sit someplace where you can watch people but don't worry about listening in.

For now, just notice their actions. Write down answers to these questions in your notebook:

- What kinds of gestures do people make while they speak?
- Are they carrying on conversations while doing other things, like eating and drinking?
- What are their hands doing besides gesturing?
- Do they always look at each other when they speak?

Next, imagine what these people were saying and write dialogue based on your observations. Include their movements and physical reactions as stage directions.

## PLAYWRIGHT PROFILE:

### Neil Simon

**Neil Simon**

Neil Simon is famous for penning plays full of flawed characters whose lives and stories mix comedy and drama. He is the author of more than 30 plays as well as more than 30 screenplays for film and television.

When Simon is writing, he reads his dialogue aloud. Hearing the words helps him find the rhythm of the speech. It gives him a chance to rewrite dialogue that may be difficult for an actor to deliver. He also imagines himself as each character in his play. That helps him understand how they need to speak and act differently, to show their personalities.

"When you write a play, maybe even a novel, you become everybody. It may seem like I only write the lines spoken by the character who is like Neil Simon, but in *Lost in Yonkers* I'm also the grandmother—and Bella," he says. "And to do that you have to become that person. That's the adventure, the joy, the release that allows you to escape from your own boundaries."

How can you tell if you're writing good dialogue or bad dialogue? Check this step-by-step checklist.

1. Read your dialogue aloud. Make sure you haven't accidentally created any tongue twisters that would be difficult for an actor to say. If you did, then rewrite!

2. Beware of lines that are too realistic. In life people are always saying "Hello" and "Good-bye." Sometimes you have to use those words, but they rarely create good drama. The best writing? Rewriting. Replace dialogue if it doesn't move the plot or conflict along.

Let characters speak for themselves. In other words, they should sound like individuals. If two characters sound too similar, rewrite one character's dialogue with more personality. Add style, such as more slang, a catchphrase, or an accent, for example.

# The Same ... But Different

Does your play have a cast of several characters? How different are they from one another? A play about a school might include several high school student characters. A play about a family could include several sibling characters who are close in age. It's fine to write characters with similar lives and experiences. However, each should be unique enough to earn a place in your play.

Part of how you show that uniqueness is through their patterns of speech and conversations with one another. One might use specific expressions, such as "like" or "LOL" a lot. Another might make frequent jokes or speak sarcastically. Characters can also show their individuality in the way they move and behave. Your stage directions should indicate how characters react physically to other characters as well as the story. You can make two characters react very differently to the same news, for example. One might smile and shout "hurrah" when they hear their cousin Susan is coming to visit, while another might start screaming, saying "I can't stand her."

If a character in your play doesn't stand out from the others, or advance the plot or conflict, ask yourself if he is needed. Eliminate characters that serve no purpose. You'll know a character belongs when he or she acts like a real person, with his or her own style of speech and mannerisms—and goals.  Remember: each and every character wants something, just as every person does in real life.

143

## YOUR TURN

Making characters come alive through their dialogue is a challenge. But you don't have to start from scratch, inventing every sentence in your imagination. Steal some lines of dialogue from real life. Think of them as starter sentences and jot them down in your notebook.

Use those starter sentences to practice writing dialogue and stage directions for different types of characters. Try writing eight lines of dialogue back and forth between two characters based on the same starter sentences. Imagine your characters as:

mother and daughter

father and son

husband and wife

teacher and student

boss and worker

brother and sister

# Get Real!

Dialogue isn't about making idle conversation. People in a play say what they say because it's important to the plot and character development. Often, though, they speak about issues indirectly. For example, in Oscar Wilde's comedy, *The Importance of Being Earnest*, Cecily has romantic feelings for Algernon, whom she believes is exciting rather than sensible. Wilde might have chosen to have her come right out and say, "I like you, Algernon, because I've heard about you and know you are more exciting than other men."

Instead, he writes the dialogue so Cecily sends the same message without saying that straight out.

## Getting to Know: Oscar Wilde

**ALGERNON** You are the prettiest girl I ever saw.

**CECILY** Miss Prism says that all good looks are a snare.

**ALGERNON** They are a snare that every sensible man would like to be caught in.

**CECILY** Oh, I don't think I would care to catch a sensible man. I shouldn't know what to talk to him about.

# UPGRADE YOUR WORK

At last your play is finished! But is it really? Probably not. Upping the stakes doesn't apply only to your plot. It also applies to your work as a writer. Good writing means lots of revising and rewriting. It means challenging yourself to make your play even better.

When you revise, you need to figure out which scenes should be slashed and which sections of the plot need further development. You may want to do away with certain characters or combine two or more into one.

Adding, eliminating, or combining elements of your play doesn't mean that what you've written isn't good. Revising is just a part of the writing process. Reading your work aloud is one way to determine which parts of your play need revision. But remember, playwrights don't just read their plays aloud when they're done. They have actors perform their plays.

**YOUR TURN**

Don't be shy about sharing your work once you have a finished draft. It's time for a test of what's working and what's not. To truly complete a play you need to bring others into your writing process.

Gather a group of friends together for what's called a table read. Give them each a copy of your script. Assign them each a character and have them read your play out loud. They don't need to follow stage directions, but you should have someone read them. (If no one is available, you can do that yourself.) As they read, observe, and take notes with a printed copy of your play in hand.

Pay special attention to any difficulties your actors experience. If they trip over their words, mark that spot in the script. Do the same if anyone expresses confusion about what's happening in the play. You may need to add dialogue or an extra scene or change the stage direction.

While you're likely to uncover problems in your play, give yourself some credit, too. Mark the script whenever you notice anything that really works. And write down any positive feedback your actors give you.

Later, you can go through the script and address problem areas. Those positive notes will help you feel less overwhelmed. So will remembering that revision isn't a race to the finish. Just take it one note at a time. One advantage playwrights have over other writers is that they can immediately see and hear how their ideas sound. When you write a story or a novel or poem, you only know if something works if someone buys it.

## PLAYWRIGHT PROFILE:

### Wendy Wasserstein

Wendy Wasserstein wrote many plays about strong female characters. In 1989, she won two major awards for *The Heidi Chronicles*. One was a Pulitzer Prize for Drama. The other was a Tony Award for Best Play—and she was the first woman ever to win it. What were some secrets to her success?

When Wasserstein started writing a play, she didn't make an outline. She liked to focus on dialogue instead and just get her characters talking. Later she would revise and create new drafts of the same play. She wrote six drafts of her play *Old Money* before she felt satisfied with her work.

Wasserstein was a private person who enjoyed writing and working alone. But she also liked giving her plays to actors who could help her discover what kind of revisions were needed. She felt that process made her work even better.

"I am a playwright, and I have the ability to see my work come alive … I can sit alone in a room and make things up, and then I can sit in a rehearsal room and hear it, talk to others, and fix it," she said in an interview. "I like being in rehearsal, I like that process, and I've always said I want to keep writing plays, I want to get better at it." Sadly, Wasserstein died at age 55 in 2006.

YOUR TURN

Revising is a normal part of the writing process, but that doesn't mean it's easy, even for professional playwrights. Here's one way to keep your focus: work to improve your play scene by scene.

Think of each scene in your play as a mini-story within the overall plot. Each should have its own beginning, middle, and end. You'll need both dialogue and stage directions within each scene too.

When you're at the revision stage, pay close attention to just one scene at a time. Sharpen your focus by zooming in on each element the scene needs. Work to improve the scene's beginning, middle, end, dialogue, and stage directions. For example, you could pump up the drama or make dialogue more compelling. You might add stage directions that are clearer or add drama to the scene.

# Working the Workshops

Professional playwrights do more than write and revise. They do more than test their work with a table read. In fact, they often workshop their plays extensively. That means producing the play several different times before putting on a real performance. In these workshop performances, they keep costs down and don't bother with costumes and scenery. The point is to learn more about how the script is or isn't working.

It's never easy to take criticism or find out your play needs more revisions. But try to be open to the ideas of others without taking their comments too personally. Remember, no one who writes drama gets it right the first time. Even famous playwrights rewrite and revise to make their work even better.

A staged reading can help you gather even more information about how to improve your play. Ask the head of your school's drama department or community theater for help organizing. To make your case, point out that you don't need costumes or scenery. You'll just need a performance space and a dedicated cast of actors. They won't have to memorize the script. But they will need to get to know it, so they can follow stage directions.

With some help, you may even be able to invite a small audience. They can offer useful feedback after a staged reading. Write down their ideas to consider later on.

When you sit down to revise, think about how the feedback you've received might change your play. Remember, as the playwright, you have creative control over your work. Decide for yourself which changes would make your play better and which you'd rather not make at all.

# IT'S WRITTEN! NOW WHAT?

Once you've written a play, be proud! It may not be perfect. But, according to at least one accomplished playwright, that's not the point. Lillian Hellman tried to revise the ending to her play *The Children's Hour* for a year without success. "I finally came to the conclusion that you might as well accept what's bad about your work along with what's good," she later wrote. "Maybe they are one and the same. To try to make it perfect is often to muck it up."

You may want to try and stage a full production of your play, complete with actors, costumes, scenery, and an audience. Or you might not. Either way, you've done something amazing. You've imagined a story and characters, and you've brought them to life through your script. You've earned the right to consider yourself a true writer of drama.

# Chapter 4

# Writing Fearless Nonfiction

Most of the time, we see the world as if we're looking out the windshield of a moving car. A drive to the store blurs by: tree, house, car, sidewalk, car, car, curb. But what if you stopped and really looked at one of those cars? You'd see bumper stickers, dents, and scratches. You'd see a puddle of coffee on the dashboard. It drips onto a stack of handwritten papers ... a letter? What kind of letter? One detail leads to another. Soon they start to tell a story.

Details are the building blocks of nonfiction. They make your writing vivid, believable, and interesting. A fiction writer invents details. Your job is to notice them and choose the best ones to tell your story.

"Instructions for living a life:
Pay attention.
Be astonished.
Tell about it."

-Mary Oliver, American poet and essayist

# Interesting, Odd, Beautiful

Imagine walking down a rocky beach. Your eyes scan hundreds of gray pebbles and broken shells. You pass over these ordinary pieces in search of a real beauty—sea-polished glass or a multicolored rock.

When you are writing nonfiction, selecting details is a lot like picking up treasures on the beach. There are many possible details you could add to your writing to paint a picture in your readers' minds. On the beach, you stay open to any discovery but pocket only those prizes that are most interesting, odd, or beautiful.

Similarly, on the page, you want to include the very best details. Like beach treasures, they may take a little more time to collect, but the result is a rich, one-of-a-kind description that highlights your unique view on the world.

## YOUR TURN

What interesting, odd, or beautiful details can you observe in this picture? Write a paragraph or two describing what you see, including five details that other people might not notice without your help.

Bonus challenge: Try this exercise again, but this time choose a picture you know well. You'll need to be extra observant to find new, interesting details in a photo you've seen many times.

# The Telling Detail

So you're writing about your latest crush, Josh. You love how awkward he is. It's part of his charm! But how do you put his unique qualities into words?

Think of everything you could describe about Josh. You could mention his style-less style, his scuffed shoes, his free-falling hair, the angles of his face, his voice, and more. But wait—these details might seem fascinating to you, but won't they put readers to sleep? Do your readers a favor! Instead of cataloging every single detail you notice about Josh, choose just one or two choice descriptions, or telling details.

Telling details do double duty. They describe, but they also suggest. They point to a deeper meaning beyond what's at hand. Telling details are precise, vivid, and memorable.

So tell about the teeth marks in Josh's glasses. Tell about how he picks at his calloused palms while he talks. Why does he chew on his glasses? What made his hands calloused? A telling detail prompts the reader's curiosity and makes them want to know more.

> "You do not have to explain every single drop of water contained in a rain barrel. You have to explain one drop—$H_2O$. The reader will get it."
>
> -George Singleton, American author

Go to a public place and observe five people. Write down three interesting details about each one. Then write down what each detail might suggest about the person. Take a second look at the man in a shirt and tie with sweat dripping down his face. Was he just working out? Or maybe he has received terrible news. Notice the woman with earrings that are just slightly mismatched. Is she colorblind, absentminded, or just really busy? What about the teenage boy texting without looking down at his phone?

After you're done making observations, choose your most telling detail for each person. What made it stand out from the others?

# Gather and Cut

First you gather up tons of observations, then you take most of them away. That's how nonfiction writers generate the best details. It's a lot of work. Good thing it's also tons of fun.

Think of a memorable meal you've had with someone. Next, expand the sentence, "We ate together" with as many details as you can. Really go for it, so your paragraph looks something like this:

On a misty July morning, while the rain evaporated, molecule by molecule, into a blue sky of daydreams, I followed you to a thorny patch of raspberries. "C'mon!" you yelled back to me. The humid air rubbed against our skin like a purring cat. Our feet sank and popped with each muddy step. Bending, we shook the soft, ripe, pink berries into our open mouths. "Mmmmmmmm," we chorused. "So good!" The berries practically sprang from their branches. We squatted in the dirt like toddlers. We crushed the raspberries with our tongues, letting the sweet juice spill down our throats like prehistoric animals. Some fell onto our faces, leaving pink stains on our cheeks. You looked like you'd been laughing raspberry tears. Completely satisfied, we traced our muddy footsteps back. Dirt stains crawled from our ankles to our elbows, while thin, red scratches played tic-tac-toe over our bare shins. Our cheeks stayed pink for days.

Now, go through your description and circle the best details. Cross out anything vague, repetitive, or unnecessary. Edit your paragraph down by half or more:

Under a blue sky of daydreams, I followed you to a raspberry patch. Our feet sank and popped with each muddy step. We squatted under thorny branches, shaking berries into our open mouths. We crushed them with our tongues like prehistoric animals. Dirt crawled from our ankles to our elbows, while scratches played tic-tac-toe on our shins. Our cheeks stayed pink for days.

Do you see how this edit focuses on imagery of kids playing? Without extra details, the messy fun of the meal shines through.

## AUTHOR PROFILE:

### Paul Zindel

YA author Paul Zindel wrote an acclaimed memoir about his troubled years growing up in Staten Island, New York, in the 1940s. *The Pigman & Me* focuses on a friendship between young Paul and a grandfatherly Italian man, Nonno Frankie, who showed a remarkable zest for life.

Paul met Nonno Frankie in the shared backyard of his family house. Through telling detail, Paul vividly shows the old man's playful spirit:

"He stood up, sniffed at the earth in his hands, then breathed in deeply like he was sampling a French perfume. He began checking out every square inch of the backyard. His billowing plaid shirt flickered against his belly, and he wore brown baggy pants like a clown's."

# STORYTELLER'S TRICKS

Nonfiction storytellers try to make their stories as vivid in their readers' minds as in their own minds. Some people are natural storytellers. They have the audience on a thread without even knowing what they are doing. If it doesn't come naturally, no need to stress. Some tried and true tricks can help bring out the captivating storyteller in everyone.

# Visualize!

Imagine your friend Madison is telling you a true story from her life. She sends you this text:

Got high score in history.
Mr. Swan so embarrassing about it!

Ho-hum. You had to be there, right?

But what if Madison rewrote her text as a scene that brought the event to life?

"Ladies and gentlemen, may I have your attention?" Mr. Swan boomed out during sixth-period history. "I have an announcement regarding your fellow scholar, Madison Monroe!" He peered down at me over the top of his little round glasses. He was holding a rolled-up paper in his hand. He waved it over my head like my fairy godfather.

"Drumroll, ple-eeee-ase!" he sang out.

My classmates attacked their desks with pencils, while I slumped deeper in my seat.

Mr. Swan's eyes twinkled at me, and I thought to myself how much he looked like Santa. With a flick of his wrist, he unfurled his mysterious scroll.

"Ninety-nine!" Mr. Swan read aloud the neon pink numbers on the top of the page. "The highest grade on last week's test!" His cheeks turned merry and bright. "Congratulations!" he grabbed my hand and shook my arm. "Ms. Monroe, would you like to share a few words with your classmates?"

"Um, thank you? Really, thanks so much," I murmured, hoping to turn invisible. "I'm speechless."

Madison's new story is an example of narrative nonfiction. She's using storytelling tricks such as dialogue to show the quirkiness of Mr. Swan's personality. His actions—the way he waves the scroll like a fairy godfather—add to his characterization. She gives a sense of her own point of view—what she was thinking and feeling during the event. Madison's text reported the event, but her scene shows what happened, as if we are seeing it in a movie.

"Let the world burn through you. Throw the prism light, white hot, on paper."

—*Ray Bradbury, author of*
*The Martian Chronicles*

## FROM SENTENCE TO SCENE

Now you try to craft a scene between you and one other main character. Think of a time someone embarrassed you, or made you angry, sad, or happy. Write down what happened in one or two sentences:

Miranda said she's not my friend anymore.
Henry invited me to sit with him at lunch.
My mom hugged me in front of my friends.

Next close your eyes and try to remember everything you can about the event. What did the two of you say? Where were you? What were the other person's expressions and gestures? What were you thinking and feeling during the conversation?

Turn your sentence into a scene with dialogue, action, and your point of view. Make it so vivid that you'll be able to live the event all over again.

Bonus challenge: Write the scene again, but flip the point of view. The other character is now the "I." See the story through their eyes instead of yours. Stretch your imagination and put yourself in their shoes.

# Eavesdropping for Dialogue

Are you nosy? Do you have an "ear" for details? Good! That will help you write better nonfiction dialogue. The best written speech sounds natural, which can be hard to pull off. You have to train your ears by listening—really listening—to how people talk.

Good nonfiction writers notice what people say and how they say it. Do most people speak in complete sentences or fragments? Do they interrupt? How do people talk differently to children, to their friends, to strangers? What makes someone sound odd, excited, sad, or thoughtful?

Make a habit of eavesdropping on people in public places. Write down what you hear. (If your head is in a notebook, no one will suspect you're listening in!) Notice their gestures, expressions, and habits. Don't worry about getting everything down exactly. You can fill in the details later.

Once you've collected a dozen or so conversations, pick your favorite. Turn it into a scene by choosing just the most interesting bits of dialogue. Break up the speech with actions and telling details to make your scene even more vivid.

# Writing Memoir

Memoir comes from the French word for memory, *mémoire*. A memoir is a true story, told in the first person "I," based on the writer's own memory. Memoir writers care about the facts and believe deeply in the truth of what they are writing. Often they base their work on diaries, or they do extensive research to back up their memories.

Unlike an autobiography, a memoir does not document a person's entire life. It focuses on just a slice—a specific challenge or times of change. How the author remembers his or her past is just as important as what happened. Memoir writers look in the shadows and corners of their lives to reveal truths that are both surprising and familiar. The process can be awkward, uncomfortable, or downright frightening.

Another challenge is that memories aren't always 100 percent accurate. Sometimes there's no way to verify the facts. For example, a memoir writer may describe her ruined party dress as black satin because that's how she remembered it. Perhaps the dress was actually deep purple, but if there's no way to know for sure, the best the writer can do is be true to her memory.

"I write as a witness to what I have seen. I write as a witness to what I imagine."

-Terry Tempest Williams, American author

## AUTHOR PROFILE:

### Malala Yousafzai

On October 9, 2012, Malala Yousafzai was riding home from her school in northwest Pakistan when two armed men stormed the bus. "Who is Malala?" they asked. Though just a teenager, Malala was well known in Pakistan and, increasingly, around the world. She was an outspoken advocate for girls' education, a right that was threatened by Taliban terrorists. As a result of her activism, a Taliban gunman shot her in the head. After many months, Malala recovered and continued her work as an activist. In 2014, at age 17, she became the youngest person ever to receive a Nobel Peace Prize. She also published the YA version of her bestselling memoir, *I Am Malala: How One Girl Stood Up for Education and Changed the World.*

"Yes, the Taliban have shot me," Malala wrote. "But they can only shoot a body. They cannot shoot my dreams."

Malala ends her inspiring story with her dreams for the future: "Peace in every home, every street, every village, every country—that is my dream. Education for every boy and every girl in the world. To sit down on a chair and read my books with all my friends at school is my right. To see each and every human being with a smile of true happiness is my wish."

YOUR TURN

What is your dream? Write a paragraph about a dream you would be willing to put yourself in danger to achieve.

# I Like to Move It, Move It!

A bowl of chocolates reminds you of getting sick on Halloween, right on your tap shoes. That makes you think of last year's recital, and that in turn reminds you of that song you danced to, about the moon ...

Let's face it—our memories don't always occur in order, and neither do memoirs, necessarily. They can be strange and wandering, just like memory itself.

It's OK to let memories flow organically. Arranging events in the order they happened is a predictable story plot. Why not try mixing up things a little to keep your reader guessing?

Putting two non-chronological events side-by-side can highlight differences between them. On the other hand, it can also draw out the similarities between two scenes. The organization of your nonfiction can also help readers draw conclusions they may not have thought of otherwise.

So how do you do it? Well, you might write one chunk of memoir at a time, piece by piece, in the order in which they occur to you. Once the whole story is written, take a second look and rearrange as needed. Or you might write everything chronologically, then rearrange things afterward. Whatever works best for you is the best practice to follow.

Write your own experimental memoir on four index cards, writing just a few sentences on each card.

Card 1: Think of a smell from your past. Is it sour, sweet, sharp, or fresh? It might be from a day outside, a favorite food, or a time when you were sick. Describe the smell and what it reminds you of.

Card 2: Describe the eyes of someone you love: "My grandma's eyes are gray and watery. Wrinkles fan out from the corners. They squint into slits when she laughs."

Card 3: Write a remark that you hear all the time, either at school or in your family. It can be anything. "No dessert until you've eaten your veggies." "Goodnight, my angel." Or, "Be a good example for your brother."

Card 4: Think back on an important first in your life. It might be your first day of school, the first time you flew on an airplane, or the first time you met your best friend. Quickly list 10 nouns (specific physical things or people) about that memory. Your first time at the beach might begin like this: sunscreen, sandy footprints, Mom's sunglasses, tears, Port-A-Potty, salty waves ...

Shuffle your cards, and write a title for each one. Read your memoir out loud, including the titles. You've created a nonfiction word collage. What interesting connections and comparisons do you notice?

# Secrets and Consideration

Memoirs are our stories about our lives, told just as we remember them. A host of other characters—family members, friends, teachers, neighbors, and more—appear in memoirs. Why is this important, you ask? If you portray a someone in a negative way in your memoir, he or she may feel upset if you share the story with others. Also, some people are very private. Revealing details of their lives may make them uncomfortable.

It's smart to think about who will be reading or hearing your work. If you write that your brother can't add up to five, and he's older than five—he may be very upset. If you write about a teacher you had a crush on in third grade and it's published in the school literary journal, that might embarrass you. Or him.

A good rule of thumb is not to publish or share writing that makes anyone look bad. Does that mean you should stop writing blazingly honest material? Not at all. You have every right to express yourself in your writing. The key is to be sure you distinguish between the writing you will share with others and the writing that is done for your personal experience and benefit—in your diary. Tell your story, but be considerate, honest, and fair.

HONESTY

## AUTHOR PROFILE:

### Jack Gantos

> "I have learned this: it is not what one does that is wrong, but what one becomes as a consequence of it."
>
> Oscar Wilde, 19th century playwright

Jack Gantos chose this famous quote by Oscar Wilde to set the stage for his memoir, *Hole in My Life*. The best-selling young adult author recounts how, as a desperate teenager, he took a job smuggling drugs that landed him in prison. His life as a writer began there as he scribbled a secret diary between the lines of a prison library book.

In high school Jack had searched endlessly for "juicy" subjects to fill his journal. But he lacked the confidence and patience to see the opportunities right in front of him. "In prison I got a second chance to realize I did have something to write about."

> "If I don't write to empty my mind, I go mad."
>
> -19th-century poet Lord Byron

# PROSE WITH A PURPOSE

Want to sell something online? Invite a friend to a party? Explain how to craft a Duct Tape wallet, review a book you love, or convince your classmates to elect your best friend for student council? Count on nonfiction when you have a job to do, such as guide, explain, advise, or make a point.

"Don't try to figure out what other people want to hear from you; figure out what you have to say. It's the one and only thing you have to offer."

-Barbara Kingsolver, American novelist, essayist, and poet

# Getting to Know: Sojourner Truth

"Ain't I a woman?"

You may have heard of Sojourner Truth in history class. A former slave, Sojourner was an important voice in the abolitionist movement and a fierce advocate for women's rights. Sojourner never learned to read or write, but she showed a remarkable flair for words. In 1851, she delivered a speech at the Women's Convention in Akron, Ohio, that she made up on the spot. As men in the audience heckled and jeered, Sojourner made the point that women were equal to men, using her own experiences as a slave to prove her point.

> That man over there says that women need to be helped into carriages, and lifted over ditches, and to have the best place everywhere. Nobody ever helps me into carriages, or over mud-puddles, or gives me any best place! And ain't I a woman? Look at me! Look at my arm! I have ploughed and planted, and gathered into barns, and no man could head me! And ain't I a woman? I could work as much and eat as much as a man—when I could get it—and bear the lash as well! And ain't I a woman? I have borne thirteen children, and seen most all sold off to slavery, and when I cried out with my mother's grief, none but Jesus heard me! And ain't I a woman?

I Sell the Shadow to Support the Substance.

SOJOURNER TRUTH.

## YOUR TURN

"Ain't I a woman?" is an example of a rhetorical question. Sojourner wasn't expecting an answer—she repeated the question to make a point. Write your own speech that makes a point by using a repeating rhetorical question.

First, choose an issue you care about. It could be a social issue such as the environment, women's rights, or homelessness. Or write about something that affects you personally, such as a school policy or a family rule.

Second, find a rhetorical question. Choose from this list, or make up your own:

Why not?
Who says so?
Why can't we change?
How much longer?
Since when?

# David Macaulay

David Macaulay is a children's book author and illustrator who follows his curiosity wherever it takes him. He creates lavishly illustrated books that explain how things work, from an old cathedral to modern technology. His three goals for every book are that they be clear, accurate, and engaging.

Macaulay knows very little about a subject when he begins. *The Way We Work*, about the human body, was no exception. Macaulay spent six years on the book, filling up 10 books of notes along the way. He took anatomy courses and observed live surgeries. He felt and sketched real organs in a lab.

Pick an organ that you know practically nothing about—maybe your spleen, gall bladder, or pancreas. Find out how it works. Write a paragraph explaining how it works. Draw pictures with labels and arrows, just for fun.

# Sell It

Writers have a way with words. Nonfiction writers can use their skills in very practical ways. For example, if you were to write an online ad selling something you own, your writing skills would help you to get a great response.

When writing persuasive text, whether it's an essay or an ad, first ask yourself what would be the strongest, most enticing ways to make your point. Brainstorm at least five strong points, then pick your favorite and make that the focus of your headline. After you grab the reader's attention with a killer headline, follow it up with specific details in the body of the ad. When you can flex your writing skills in a practical way, you'll have buyers begging for your hand-me-downs!

## CUTE-AS-A-BUNNY WINTER HAT

White knit hat with bunny ears, purchased last fall from a street vendor in Uptown. So soft you'll want to hug it. Silky pink lining keeps it 100 percent itch-free. Ears tie under the chin for extra-chilly emergencies. Kept me warm when bus was 30 minutes late last January! $45, or highest bidder. Cash only, please.

Think of your teacher's rules at school. Perhaps they include such things as:

Pay attention.

Be organized.

Do your homework.

Those rules are tried-and-true for succeeding in school. But what about the other rules? The little-known rules that only the kids at your school know?

Don't eat the cottage cheese in the salad bar.

You can take your shoes off in Ms. Walker's class.

Avoid the second-floor water fountain—it sprays your feet.

Imagine that you are helping a new transfer student at your school get adjusted. What 10 things will he or she need to know to feel like part of the group? Write a guide to your school's special rules.

# Be Convincing

Are you persuaded that these meals were awful by this description?

"The daily lunches at my elementary school's cafeteria were easily the most vile meals I've ever experienced. My unlucky classmates and I were often the recipients of overcooked goulash, an acidic tomato-and-pasta disaster baked into a putty-like form. Gravy on bread was another doozy. The slimy, yellowish-gray gravy was ladled onto a piece of white bread. Even the macaroni and cheese was off-colored. It  tasted like the first ingredient might just be glue. Even the smell of the cafeteria was enough to unsettle my otherwise rumbling tummy."

Are there meals you dread? Movies you'd just as soon skip to do homework? Or what about things you love?

YOUR TURN

Writing a review can be a great way to practice writing creative descriptions. Write a review of your own. When you've finished, go back and circle your favorite descriptions and phrases. Why are they your favorites? Keep the review as possible material for later work.

# VOICE EXPERIMENTS

Compare these three descriptions:

All day long, snowflakes fell from the gray sky.

The snow fell and it fell and it fell. Icy flakes from a dishwater sky.

The snowflakes swirled and swooped like dancers. Their stage was the winter sky.

These three descriptions basically say the same thing, right? It snowed a lot. But each one feels so different. Each has its own voice that conveys a distinct tone.

In these examples, notice how much the mood shifted by changing word choice, sentence structure, and images. "Winter sky" sounds lovely, while "dishwater sky" feels depressing. Rhythms and sounds affect voice, too. "Snowflakes swirl and swoop" sounds playful and light. "The snow fell and it fell and it fell" sounds dreary and monotonous.

You can make your voice stark, serious, strange, sarcastic, angry, aloof, funny, over-the-top, and so much more. In nonfiction, the reader understands that the voice comes from you, the author, not any other character. Your voice is a window into your true thoughts and feelings.

# 1, 2, 3, Change It!

How do you develop your voice as a writer? Read like crazy. Read your favorite passages aloud. Look closely at the word choice and sentence structures. Let the music of the language train your ear. Read aloud if that helps.

Experiment, experiment, experiment! Don't ever be afraid to change your words. Just hold on to your drafts, so you can always change your words back.

Choose a paragraph from your diary, a school essay, an e-mail, or any piece of nonfiction you have written. Rewrite it to change the voice. Remember—change only words, rhythms, and images. The content stays the same. Pick three voices from this list and go:

- childish
- stuffy
- depressing
- annoying
- excited
- creepy
- devastated
- half-asleep
- emotional

You're not done yet. Rewrite your original paragraph three times. Don't worry about whether it's good—just change as much as you can. In the first draft, change your sentence structures. Break up sentences and combine them. Move words and clauses around. "He danced and laughed" becomes "He laughed and danced."

In your second draft, swap out as many words as you can. "He danced and laughed" becomes "He twirled and giggled."

Third, add in as many images as you can squeeze in there. "He danced like a kid on a pogo stick." "His head flew back as he laughed."

Review your results. How did your changes affect the tone of the paragraph? What changes would you keep, and what would you change back?

# Break the Rules

Your teachers have instructed you in the rules of writing: Don't use sentence fragments. Avoid run-on sentences. Vary your sentence structures. Those trusty rules will steer your right for most of your writing. But sometimes, creative writers break rules for special occasions.

In the essay "Pop Art," Brian Doyle, an award-winning Canadian children's author, describes what he's learned about his three children:

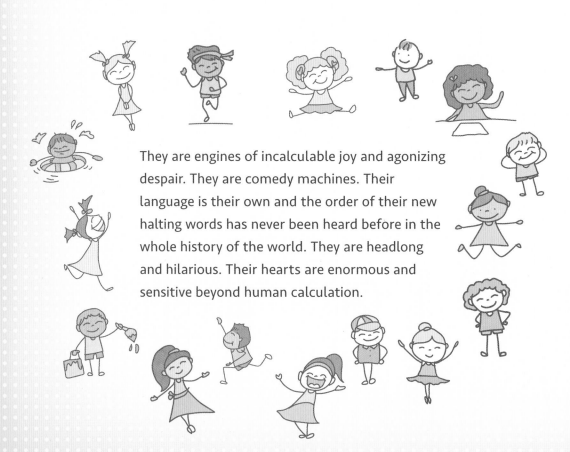

They are engines of incalculable joy and agonizing despair. They are comedy machines. Their language is their own and the order of their new halting words has never been heard before in the whole history of the world. They are headlong and hilarious. Their hearts are enormous and sensitive beyond human calculation.

**YOUR TURN**

Think of somebody who intrigues you. It could be a teacher, coach, relative, famous person, or friend. Make a list of everything you've learned about him or her. Write your notes into a paragraph with sentences that all start with she/her or he/him.

Bonus Challenge: Use sentence fragments to write about a dream you can only half-remember or a time when your thoughts were racing. Use run-on sentences to write about something that's really messy, like your room or a friend's locker.

# Hook 'Em!

Which of these essays about cats would you rather read—sample A or sample B?

A. Cats are such amazing animals. They're so different from dogs. They're different from what you'd expect. You'll be really surprised when you read about these cat facts ...

B. True or false?
A cat can jump up to six times the length of its body.
A cat can make 100 different sounds, while dogs make only 10.
Cats sweat through their feet.
The answers are true, true, and true. Read on, and learn what makes cats so amazing.

OK, that was easy. You picked Sample B, right? The author of that essay used a hook in her introduction to grab your interest and make you want to read more. In this case, she used startling information to hook you. That's just one successful strategy. Here are some others ways to hook a reader:

## START WITH A STORY

My cat Doodle once got me kicked out of school. True story. He climbed into my backpack and fell asleep. When I unzipped my bag in homeroom, out jumped a spitting, hissing, furry monster. Doodle sprang off my desk and jumped, at least six times the length of his body. He landed right in Ms. Laugerman's lap.

## START WITH A QUOTE

"Not all those who wander are lost." When J.R.R. Tolkien wrote that famous line, I think he had a cat in mind. Cats are survival machines who claim their homes wherever they feel like it.

## ASK QUESTIONS

What would you do if you could jump six times the length of your body? What if you could see seven times better in the dark? What if you ears could rotate 180 degrees? You'd be a cat.

**YOUR TURN**

Write your own essay about an animal that fascinates you. Hook your reader with startling information, a story, a quote, or questions. Hint: You may find it easier to write the body of your essay first, and then write the hook afterward.

Bonus challenge: Take an essay that you've already written and write a new hook.

# JUMP STARTS!

It's happened to every writer. You have
an idea about something you want to
write about. But when you sit down to do
it, words don't come. Or if they do come,
you delete them right away. Either way,
you're facing a blank screen.

Maybe you're having trouble figuring out your idea and it's keeping you from writing. Here are some ways to help you get there—and block writer's block!

"Just Five Minutes." You can do anything for five minutes, right? Set the timer and write without stopping.

Write about Writing. So you're having trouble writing about your idea. How do you feel about that? Why do you think that is? Write about what's happening in your mind this very second.

Elevator Pitch. Maybe you need to clarify exactly what your idea is about. Imagine you have two minutes to describe your idea to a person next to you in an elevator. Go ahead—talk to yourself. Or call up a friend and make your pitch.

It's Like This. Here's another way to clarify your idea. Make it into a comparison. What is your subject like? For example: "My sister is like a queen bee." Or, "Learning to swim is like trying do jumping jacks with ropes tied to your arms and legs." Or, "That movie was like falling asleep on a summer day." How many different comparisons can you come up with?

## AUTHOR PROFILE:

### Ashley Rhodes-Courter

"I have had more than a dozen so-called mothers in my life," Ashley Rhodes-Courter begins her memoir, *Three Little Words.* Ashley was just 22 years old when her true story of life in Florida's foster care system hit the *New York Times* bestseller list. From ages 3 to 12, Ashley was shuttled between 9 schools and 14 foster families. At one point, she lived in a two-bedroom trailer with 16 other children. Almost one-quarter of her foster parents were or became convicted felons.

Ashley recounts vivid scenes from her very early childhood. To do so, she conducted extensive research. She reviewed her government records and sifted through photos. She traveled back to her former foster homes and interviewed past contacts.

Think back to one of your earliest memories. Write about it in a scene with dialogue and action. Interview family members and look through old photos to bring it to life.

# List Away

One of the best ways to get your pen scratching is simply to make a list. List three fun things you did today. List your favorite movies, books, and games. What are the five foods that make you gag? Six things you secretly like but would never admit? Eight songs you wish you could erase from your head?

### Five Funny Things I Believed When I Was Little:

1. The moon followed me wherever I went.

2. Squirrels would crawl on me if I pretended I was a tree.

3. A graham cracker made a good bookmark.

4. My dog was related to me.

5. Marshmallows were berries that grew on marshmallow bushes.

## YOUR TURN

Make a list of things you'd like to write about. When you are stumped about what to write, revisit your list to get the creative juices flowing. Simpy pick your favorite, and write away!

Bonus challenge: Illustrate your list with old photos, clip art, or free images from the web.

"If it sounds like writing, I rewrite it. Or, if proper usage gets in the way, it may have to go. I can't allow what we learned in English composition to disrupt the sound and rhythm of the narrative."

-Elmore Leonard, American novelist and screenwriter

"If they give you ruled paper, write the other way."

-Juan Ramón Jiménez, Nobel-prize winning Spanish poet

# The Short Memoir and Flash Nonfiction

## Six-Word Memoir

"If you had exactly six words to describe your life, what would they be?"

For more than six years, the editors of the Six-Word Memoir Project have been asking people that question. In several print and online collections, people from all around the world have written and shared their entire lives in six words. Whether silly, sad, or poignant, a six-word memoir can be a challenge to write.

HERE ARE SOME REAL SIX-WORD MEMOIRS FROM KIDS
IN MIDDLE SCHOOL:

Fit in or be tossed out.

Not as strong as I pretend.

Drawing is my airplane to imagination.

I can't survive without ice cream.

Quiet, shy, give me a try.

# Writing Flash Nonfiction

It's like nonfiction, but bite size! Writing flash nonfiction is often tricky, especially for people who love to write. Even though you are usually advised to write more, for this exercise, limit your entire nonfiction story to 10 to 12 sentences.

The challenge of presenting a poignant event in so few sentences can push your writing and revision skills to a new level. Flash writing forces you to use crisp, precise language with no thoughtless repetition. When you have a strict limit, each word becomes more important. Choosing the best, freshest words possible is half the battle. Choosing a good topic is the other, so brainstorm a list of ideas first. Then, choose your favorite topic and give it a try.

# Works Cited

**Ambrose Bierce**, *Devil's Dictionary*
https://www.gutenberg.org/files/972/972-h/972-h.htm

**Bradbury, Ray.** *Bradbury Stories: 100 of His Most Celebrated Tales.* New York: William Morrow, 2003.

**Christie, Agatha, and Charles Todd.** *Hercule Poirot: The Complete Short Stories.* New York: William Morrow, 2013.

**Dickens, Charles, and Mark Peppe.** *A Christmas Carol.* [New] ed. London: Puffin, 2008.

"Conversations with **Lillian Hellman,**" by Lillian Hellman, University Press of Mississippi, 1986, Page 131. https://books.google.com/books?id=k eOUXb5gxQsC&pg=PA130&lpg=PA130&dq=lillia

**Irving, Washington.** *The Legend of Sleepy Hollow and Other Stories.* Mineola, N.Y.: Dover, 2008.

**Kipling, Rudyard.** *A Collection of Rudyard Kipling's Just So Stories.* Cambridge, MA: Candlewick Press, 2004.

**London, Jack, and Robert Court.** *Jack London: Collected Short Stories.* Mankato, Minn.: Peterson Pub., 2002.

**Poe, Edgar Allan, and Neil Gaiman.** *Selected Poems & Tales.* New York: Barnes & Noble, 2004.

**Six-Word Memoir Project**
All entries from: http://www.sixwordmemoirs.com/schools/index.php

"**Neil Simon**, The Art of Theater No. 10," Interviewed by James Lipton. The Paris Review, 1994. http://www.theparisreview.org/interviews/1994/the-art-of-theater-no-10-neil-simon

**Sojourner Truth**, *Ain't I a Woman?*
http://www.nps.gov/wori/learn/historyculture/sojourner-truth.htm

**Twain, Mark.** *The Complete Short Stories.* New York: Alfred A. Knopf, 2012.

"**Wendy Wasserstein**," by A.M. Homes, Bomb, Spring 2001. http://bombmagazine.org/article/2399/wendy-wasserstein

# Index

# About the Authors

Laura Purdie Salas has been writing poetry for more than 15 years. Her how-to book, *Picture Yourself Writing Poetry*, was on the International Reading Association's 2012 Teachers' Choice List. She has won a Eureka Gold Medal, NCTE Notable, and Minnesota Book Award for her collection, *BookSpeak! Poems About Books*. Laura lives in Minneapolis, Minnesota.

Nadia Higgins is the author of more than 80 nonfiction books for children and young adults, and she has personally used several of the tips and tricks in this book many times over. One of her favorite parts of being a nonfiction writer is figuring out how to organize all her facts in surprising or interesting ways. A die-hard researcher, Ms. Higgins has written about everything from ants to popsicles to zombies. She lives in Minneapolis, Minnesota, with her family.

# About the Authors

Rebecca Langston-George is the author of several books including *Choice Words: A Crash Course in Language Arts*; *A Primary Source History of the Dust Bowl;* and *For the Right to Learn: The Malala Yousafzai Story.* She's a middle school language arts teacher and the Assistant Regional Advisor for the Society of Children's Writers and Illustrators in Central-Coastal California.

Heather E. Schwartz is the author of more than 45 nonfiction children's books. Her book, *Girls Rebel: Amazing Tales of Women Who Broke the Mold!*, published by Capstone Press, won a Eureka! Gold Award from the California Reading Association in 2013. Heather performs with the improv troupe Dollars to Donuts in upstate New York.

**Published by Capstone Young Readers,**
1710 Roe Crest Drive, North Mankato, Minnesota 56003
www.capstoneyoungreaders.com

Copyright © 2016 by Capstone Young Readers. All rights reserved. No part of this publication may be reproduced in whole or in part, or stored in a retrieval system, or transmitted in any form or by any means, electronic, mechanical, photocopying, recording, or otherwise, without written permission of the publisher.

Library-in-Cataloging data is available through the Library of Congress.

**Editorial Credits**

Michelle Bisson, editor; Veronica Scott/Lori Barbeau, designer; Morgan Walters, media researcher; Katy LaVigne, production specialist

**Photo Credits**

Alamy: flab, 128, Geraint Lewis, bottom left 124, 135, sjtheatre, 117; AP Images: Tina Fineberg, 60; Capstone Studio: Karon Dubke, (book) bottom 33; Corbis: Jeffrey Coolidge, (locker) bottom right 193, Rick Friedman, 178, Roger Ressmeyer, 164; Getty Images: Ilya Dreyvitser/Stringer, (nikki) top 95, Popperfoto, (Agatha) top 43, Ron Galella, 151, The Washington Post, 119, Universal History Archive, (shakespeare) right 114; iStockphoto: ferrantraite, 154-155; Library of Congress: Gladstone Collection of African American Photographs, (Sojourner) middle 181; Newscom: Alastair Muir/REX, 109, 111, CB2/ZOB, (witch) 132-133, Everett Collection, 137, EVI FILAKTOU, (kevin) left 114, ITV/REX, 121, Ray Tang/REX, top right 124, ZUMA Press, 199; Shutterstock: 0mela, 198, 29september, 75, 33333, (marshmallows) top left 200, 360b, 156, Africa Studio, 29, africa924, (house) top left 9, Aleks Melnik, (film strip) bottom left 20, Aless, 49, 126, Alice Franz, 42, Aliona Manakova, (stickies) design element throughout, alongzo, 182, amiloslava, (writing) background 165, anawat sudchanham, 157, Annette Shaff, (chiuahua) bottom left 13, Anuka, 74, Areipa.lt, (milkyway) background 15, 16, Artex67, 104, 120, 152, 187, Artography, (stone) background 35, Artulina, 153, Asier Romero, (girl) bottom right 181, Atelier Sommerland, (woman) 16, AtthameeNi, 192, AVA Bitter, 130, BackgroundStore, (gold) top right 9, Baronb, (sheep) top 12, blue67design, 18, 134, 205, bluelela, 52, Canadapanda, (mall) middle 27, Candus Camera, 203, Carolyn Franks, 131, Cat Rocketship, 92, Christian Bertrand, (dancers) 148, 149, 150, chronicler, 28, 30, (man) bottom left 37, 141, chuhail, (book) bottom left 37, (magnify glass) bottom left 43, Cienpies Design, 17, Claire McAdams, 174, CREATISTA, 169, Creative Travel Projects, (lake) bottom right 9, Daniel MR, (postits) throughout 12, 13, dimitris_k, 158, duncan1890, 41, East, 160, EkaterinaP, (raspberry) background 163, Elise Gravel, Cover, Elizaveta Ruzanova, 191, enciktat, (women) top 177, Eric Isselee, (bulldog) bottom 11, evarin20, 194, Everett Collection, 140, Everett Historical, 53, Farferros, 5, Gil C, (alien) bottom 14, hammett79, (zebra) middle left 13, Iancu Cristian, 26, Igor Zakowski, 48, isaxar, 77, 197, Ivan Kruk, 176, ivangraphics, (robot) 15, Iya Khrakovsky, 107, janecat, (pigs) top left 13, Jearu, (lemur) middle right 13, Jennie Book, (ray) top right 14, Jessmine, 143, jumpingsack, 81, KAMONRAT, (tiger) bottom left 12, kasha_malasha, 101, Kathrine Martin, 139, KERIM, 23, Kira Culufin, 106, Kobby Dagan, (band) top 27, KUCO, 59, Le Do, 91, Leah-Anne Thompson, 8, Legend-tp, 86, Lena Pan, 184, lineartestpilot, 44, lolya1988, (leaves) background 67, Louella938, (crackers) middle right 200, Luis Molinero, 190, Maciej Sojka, 159, Macrovector, 45, makar, 68, MANDY GODBEHEAR, (headphones) bottom left 32, (painting) middle 32, (reading) top 32, (sleeping) bottom right 32, marchello, (polar bear) bottom right 12, Maridav, 170, Marina Giniatulina, 97, Marina Zezelina, (winter) 188-189, Markovka, (sea life) background 64-65, maverick_infanta, (animals) 196, mayrum, 7, meanep, (bamboo) bottom left 9, Michael Pettigrew, (child) bottom right 200, Michele Paccione, (cat) middle 67, miya227, 54, mlorenz, (owl) middle 12, Mrs. Opossum, 79, Nadalina, 4, (words) background 147, Natalia Hubbert, 87, Natalia Skripko, 24, natalia_maroz, 88-89, 96, Nazar Yosyfiv, 57, 71, Nelosa, (word) bottom 177, New York Daily News Archive, (walter) top 33, Nicram Sabod, (seal) bottom right 13, Nikiteev_Konstantin, (light bulb) top 37, Nomad_Soul, (moon) top right 200, npine, 94, Ohmega1982, (hand) 165, Oleksandr Kostiuchenko, 162, Oleksiy Mark, (newspaper) top 10, (globe) bottom 10, Ollyy, 63, Paisit Teeraphatsakool, 136, Phil McDonald, 66, Pim, 20, Piotr Marcinski, (hand) right 163, 167, Piti Tan, 161, Pshenina_m, 72, racorn, (girl) 147, Raisman, 201, Rawpixel, 34, (speech bubbles) bottom 35, 179, Robert Adrian Hillman, (words) background 11, Ron Leishman, 186, SAHACHAT SANEHA, (lobster) top left 13, sarsmis, 69, savitskaya iryna, 171, sbego, 185, schatzy, 82, Sergey Nivens, 55, Sergey Peterman, 85, softRobot, 36, Steve Cukrov, 73, Stmool, 100, Sunny studio, (squirrel) bottom left 200, szefei, (woman) bottom left 38, szefei, 46, Tati Nova photo Mexico, (woman) top 193, Tatiana Kholina, 173, Taweepat, (notebook) bottom 95, topform, backgroun 40, Tropinina Olga, (landscape) background 38, 39, v.s.anandhakrishna, 51, Valery Sidelnykov, 102, xpixel, 108, Yu Zhang, 61, zhuk.alyona, 58, 62, Zita, 103; Wikimedia: Brittany.lynk/Sonya Sones, 93, Deerstop, 83, Jennifer Hauck, 183, Russell Watkins, 172, Slp1, 70

Printed in China.
072015     008868RRDF15